Houghton Mifflin Science
DISCOVERYWORKS

 HOUGHTON MIFFLIN

Boston • Atlanta • Dallas • Denver • Geneva, Illinois • Palo Alto • Princeton

Authors

William Badders
Elementary Science Teacher
Cleveland Public Schools
Cleveland, OH

Lowell J. Bethel
Professor of Science Education
The University of Texas at Austin
Austin, TX

Victoria Fu
Professor of Child Development
and Early Childhood Education
Virginia Polytechnic Institute and
State University
Blacksburg, VA

Donald Peck
Director (retired)
The Center for Elementary Science
Fairleigh Dickinson University
Madison, NJ

Carolyn Sumners
Director of Astronomy and Physical Sciences
Houston Museum of Natural Science
Houston, TX

Catherine Valentino
Author-in-Residence, Houghton Mifflin
West Kingston, RI

Acknowledgements appear on page H36, which
constitutes an extension of this copyright page.

Printed in the U. S. A.

ISBN 0-618-00829-2

5 6 7 8 9 10 RRD 08 07 06 05 04 03 02 01

CONTENTS

Populations and Ecosystems

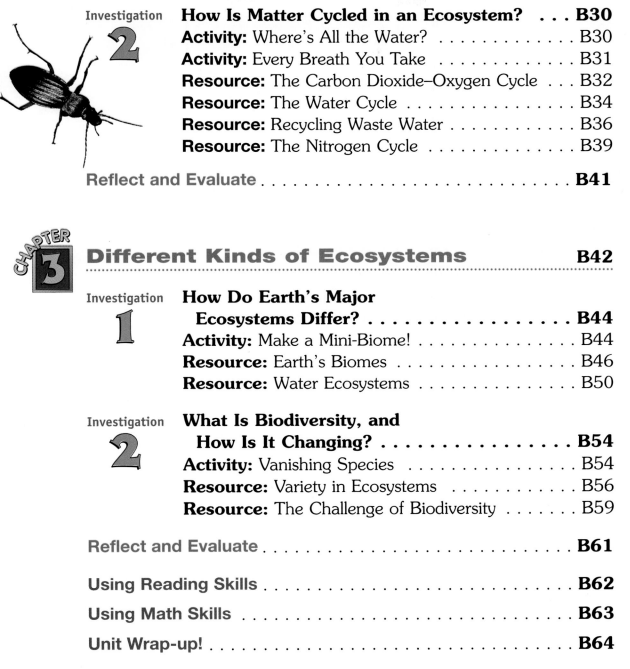

CHAPTER 3

Different Kinds of Ecosystems B42

The Solid Earth

THINK LIKE A SCIENTIST

Rocks C34

Earth's Structures C64

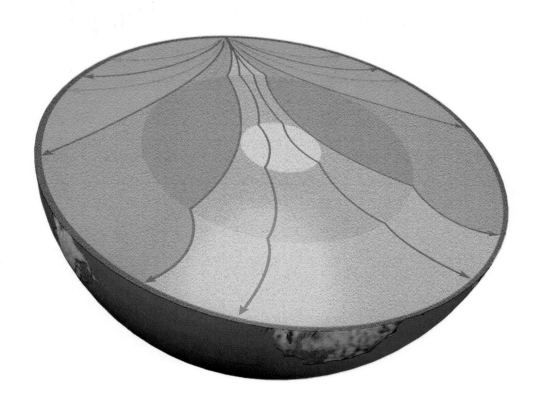

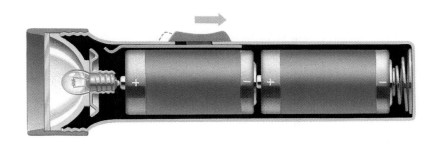

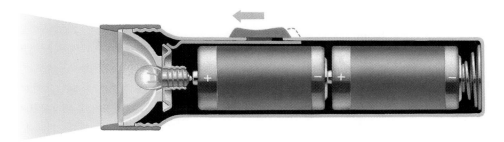

Electricity at Work D54

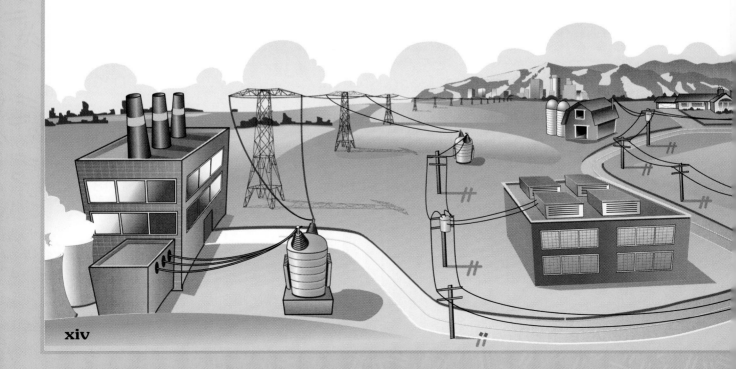

Science and Math Toolbox

THINK
LIKE A SCIENTIST

HOW TO THINK LIKE A SCIENTIST

Make Observations

To think like a scientist, learn as much as you can by observing things around you. Everything you hear, smell, taste, touch, and see is a clue about how the world works. As you test your ideas, you'll continue to make careful observations.

Ask a Question

Look for patterns. You'll get ideas. For example, you know that there are more hours of daylight in summer than there are in winter. Ask questions such as this.

How does the time that the Sun sets change from day to day?

Make a Hypothesis

If you have an idea about why something happens, make an educated guess, or hypothesis, that you can test. For example, suppose that your hypothesis about sunset time is that it changes by one minute each day.

Make Observations

Make Observations

Plan and Do a Test

Plan how to test your hypothesis. Your plan would need to consider some of these problems.

How will you measure the time that the Sun sets?

Will you measure the time every day? For how long?

Then test your hypothesis.

Record and Analyze

When you test your idea, you need to observe carefully and record, or write down, everything that happens. When you finish collecting data, you may need to do some calculations with it. For example, you might calculate how much the sunset time changes in a week.

Make Observations

Draw Conclusions

Whatever happens in a test, think about all the reasons for your results. Sometimes this thinking leads to a new hypothesis. If the time of the sunset changes by one minute each day, think about what else the data shows you. Can you predict the time that the Sun will set one month from now?

Make Observations

Now read "Off to the Races" to see scientific thinking in action.

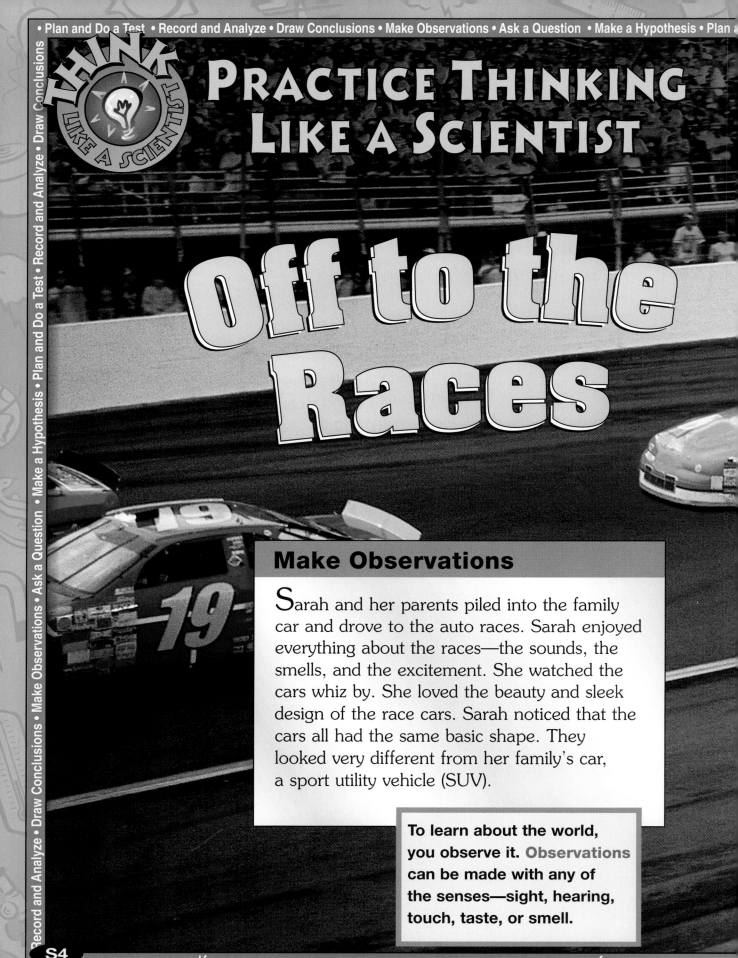

THINK LIKE A SCIENTIST

PRACTICE THINKING LIKE A SCIENTIST

Off to the Races

Make Observations

Sarah and her parents piled into the family car and drove to the auto races. Sarah enjoyed everything about the races—the sounds, the smells, and the excitement. She watched the cars whiz by. She loved the beauty and sleek design of the race cars. Sarah noticed that the cars all had the same basic shape. They looked very different from her family's car, a sport utility vehicle (SUV).

To learn about the world, you observe it. **Observations** can be made with any of the senses—sight, hearing, touch, taste, or smell.

a Test • Record and Analyze • Draw Conclusions • Make Observations • Ask a Question • Make a Hypothesis • Plan and Do a Test

Ask a Question • Make a Hypothesis • Plan and Do a Test • Record and Analyze • Draw Conclu

Ask a Question

First Sarah thought about the shape of race cars. Then she thought about the different shapes of family cars. She wondered why some cars were faster than others. "Suppose two cars weighed the same and had the same kind of engine. Would their shapes affect how fast they could go?" wondered Sarah. Sarah asked a question that she wanted to answer.

How does a car's shape affect its speed?

Sarah decided to try to answer the question as part of a school science project. She had an idea about what the answer might be.

Scientific investigations usually begin with ideas that you're not sure about. Such ideas can help you ask a question that you really want to answer.

Make a Hypothesis

To find out how a car's shape affects its speed, Sarah began looking at model cars. At a hobby shop she saw that model cars come in many shapes.

Sarah thought that a sleek-shaped car, such as a race car, would travel faster than a boxy car, such as her family's car. So she chose this idea as her hypothesis. A hypothesis is a possible answer to a question.

When you use what you've observed to suggest a possible answer to your question, you're making a hypothesis. Make sure that your hypothesis is an idea that you can test. If you can't test your hypothesis, try changing it.

Plan and Do a Test

At school Sarah and some friends worked together to plan an experiment that would test her hypothesis. They decided to test the speed of model cars. At the hobby shop they found three cars that had the same mass but different shapes. A blue car was low, sleek, and had a sloping roof. A gold car had a high roof and a boxy shape but with some curved parts. A red car looked like Sarah's family's car—a boxy SUV.

The students used a balance to check the mass of each model car. Then they set up a ramp to race the cars. They got a stopwatch with which to time each race. They planned to race each car three times. Then they would find the average time for each car.

One way to try out your hypothesis is to use a **test** called a **controlled experiment**. The setups in this kind of experiment are identical in all ways except one. The one difference is the **variable**. In Sarah's experiment the variable is the shape of the cars.

S7

Record and Analyze

Sarah released each car, one at a time, at the top of the ramp. Another student used a stopwatch to time how long it took for each car to reach a line drawn near the end of the ramp. A third student recorded the times in a chart like the one shown.

When you do an experiment, you make observations so that you can obtain information called data. You need to write down, or record, this data and then organize it. Graphs and tables are ways to organize data. Analyze the information that you collect by looking for patterns. To see if your results are reliable, repeat the experiment several times.

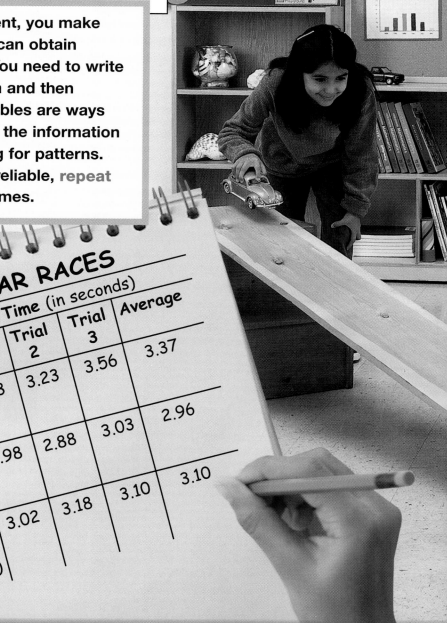

MODEL CAR RACES

Shape of Model Car	Time (in seconds)			
	Trial 1	Trial 2	Trial 3	Average
High body, boxy shape (red car)	3.33	3.23	3.56	3.37
Low, sleek with sloped roof (blue car)	2.98	2.88	3.03	2.96
Low, boxy shape, some curves (gold car)	3.02	3.18	3.10	3.10

Draw Conclusions

The students decided that their data supported Sarah's hypothesis. They looked at the average of the races. They saw that the blue car traveled down the ramp the fastest. The students concluded that a car's shape affects its speed. They also concluded that a low, sleek-shaped car is faster than a high, boxy-shaped car.

The students wondered if there were other things that might affect how fast the cars would go. They wanted to test cars that all had the same sleek shape but that had different masses. Now the group had a new question and new hypothesis to explore.

After you have analyzed your data, you should use what you learned to draw a conclusion. A conclusion is a statement that sums up what you learned. The conclusion should be about the hypothesis you made. A hypothesis supported by a lot of evidence may be called a theory.

USING SCIENCE PROCESS SKILLS

Observing involves gathering information about the environment through your five senses—seeing, hearing, smelling, touching, and tasting.

Classifying is grouping objects or events according to common properties or characteristics. Often you can classify in more than one way.

Measuring and using numbers involves the ability to make measurements (including time measurements), to make estimates, and to record data.

Communicating involves using words, both speaking and writing, and using actions, graphs, tables, diagrams, and other ways of presenting information.

Inferring means coming to a conclusion based on facts and observations you've made.

Predicting involves stating in advance what you think will happen based on observations and experiences.

Collecting, recording, and interpreting data

all involve gathering and understanding information. This skill includes organizing data in tables, graphs, and in other ways. Interpretation includes finding patterns and relationships that lead to new questions and new ideas.

Identifying and controlling variables involves determining the effect of a changing factor, called the variable, in an experiment. To do this, you keep all other factors constant, or unchanging.

Defining operationally means to describe an object, an event, or an idea based on personal observations. An operational definition of a plant might be that it is a green living thing that is attached to soil and that does not move around.

Making a hypothesis is suggesting a possible answer to a question or making an educated guess about why something happens. Your hypothesis should be based on observations and experiences.

Experimenting is testing your hypothesis to collect evidence that supports the hypothesis or shows that it is false.

Making and using models includes designing and making physical models of processes and objects, or making mental models to represent objects and ideas.

Plan and Do a Test • Record and Analyze • Draw Conclusions • Make Observations • Ask a Question • Make a Hypothesis • Plan and Do a Test • Record and Analyze • Plan an

S11

READING TO LEARN

RESOURCE

Electricity From Sunlight

Reading Focus What is a solar cell, and how is it used in a solar panel?

Did you ever use a solar calculator? **Solar energy**, or the energy of the Sun, powers the calculator. Inside solar calculators are solar cells. A **solar cell** is a device that changes light into electrical energy. Solar cells are so sensitive they even work on overcast days.

Solar Cells, Clean Energy

About 25 power plants in the United States use solar cells to produce electricity. Solar cells produce electricity in a way that helps keep the environment clean. Burning coal or oil to produce electricity can pollute the air. Using nuclear energy can create toxic wastes that pollute water and land.

Another advantage of using solar energy is that it helps to save fossil fuels. The amount of solar energy Earth receives in 12 hours is equal to the energy produced from burning fossil fuels in one year! Look at the photographs to see some uses of solar cells.

▲ One solar cell produces a [small] amount of electricity. Because of this, many cells are connected in panels.

Solar-powered airplane ▼

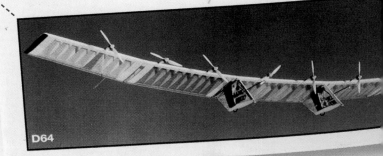

D64

Before You Read

1. **Scan** each page.
   - titles
   - subheads
   - highlighted words
   - captions
   - photos and illustrations

2. **Identify** the main topic.

3. **Ask** yourself what you know about the topic.

4. **Predict** what you will learn by turning subheads into questions.

S12

Scientists use scientific methods when they do experiments. They also use special methods when they read to learn. You can read like a scientist, too. Just follow the steps below.

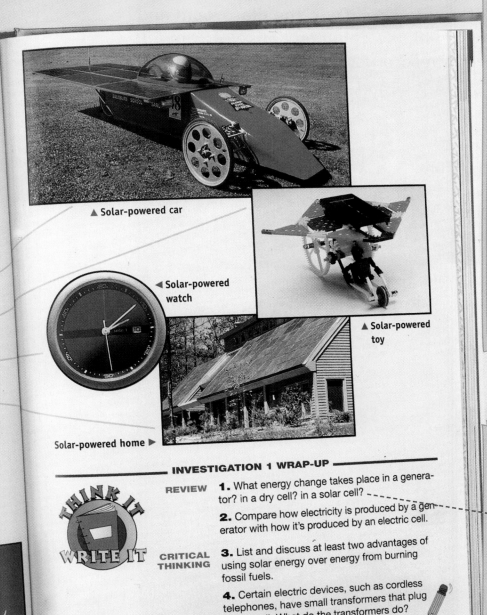

▲ Solar-powered car

◄ Solar-powered watch

▲ Solar-powered toy

Solar-powered home ▶

THINK IT WRITE IT

INVESTIGATION 1 WRAP-UP

REVIEW

1. What energy change takes place in a generator? in a dry cell? in a solar cell?

2. Compare how electricity is produced by a generator with how it's produced by an electric cell.

CRITICAL THINKING

3. List and discuss at least two advantages of using solar energy over energy from burning fossil fuels.

4. Certain electric devices, such as cordless telephones, have small transformers that plug into a wall. What do the transformers do?

D65

While You Read

1. Look for words that signal cause and effect and sequence.

2. Make inferences and draw conclusions.

3. Ask questions when you don't understand and then reread.

After You Read

1. Say or **write** what you've learned.

2. Draw, **chart** or **map** what you've learned.

3. Share what you've learned.

SAFETY

The best way to be safe in the classroom and outdoors is to use common sense. Prepare for each activity before you start it. Get help from your teacher when there is a problem. Always pay attention.

Stay Safe From Stains

- Wear protective clothing or an old shirt when you work with messy materials.
- If anything spills, wipe it up or ask your teacher to help you clean it up.

Stay Safe From Flames

- Keep your clothes away from open flames. If you have long or baggy sleeves, roll them up.
- Don't let your hair get close to a flame. If you have long hair, tie it back.

Make Wise Choices About Materials

- Use only the amount of material you need.
- Recycle materials so they can be reused.
- Take care when using valuable tools so they can be used again.

Stay Safe From Injuries

- Protect your eyes by wearing safety goggles when you are told that you need them.
- Keep your hands dry around electricity. Water is a good conductor of electricity, so you can get a shock more easily if your hands are wet.
- Be careful with sharp objects. If you have to press on them, keep the sharp side away from you.
- Cover any cuts you have that are exposed. If you spill something on a cut, be sure to wash it off immediately.
- Don't eat or drink anything unless your teacher tells you that it's okay.

Stay Safe During Cleanup

- Wash up after you finish working.
- Dispose of things in the way that your teacher tells you to.

HAIR Keep it out of the way of a flame.

EYES Wear safety goggles when you are told to.

MOUTH Don't eat or drink ANYTHING unless your teacher tells you it's okay.

CLOTHES Keep long, loose sleeves rolled up. Protect your clothes from stains. Stay away from open flames.

HANDS Keep your hands dry around electricity. Cover any cuts. Wear gloves when told to. Wash up after you finish.

DON'T MAKE A MESS If you spill something, clean it up right away. When finished with an activity, clean up your work area. Dispose of things in the way your teacher tells you to.

MOST IMPORTANTLY

If you ever hurt yourself, or one of your group members gets hurt, tell your teacher right away.

Earth's Land

Theme: Constancy and Change

THINK LIKE A SCIENTIST

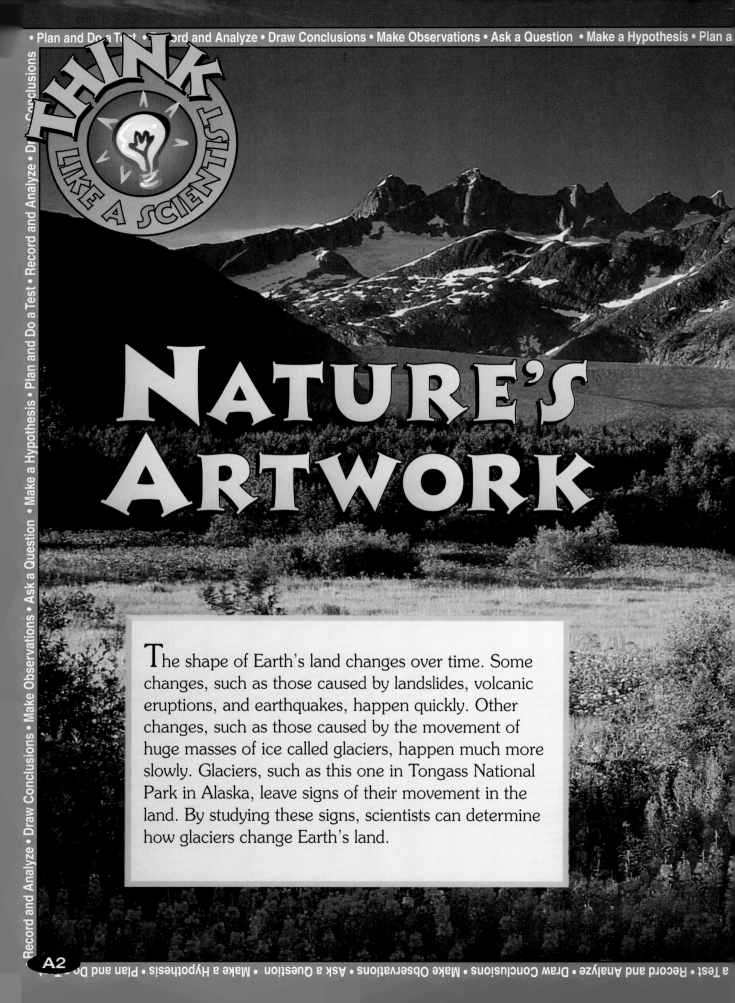

THINK LIKE A SCIENTIST

NATURE'S ARTWORK

The shape of Earth's land changes over time. Some changes, such as those caused by landslides, volcanic eruptions, and earthquakes, happen quickly. Other changes, such as those caused by the movement of huge masses of ice called glaciers, happen much more slowly. Glaciers, such as this one in Tongass National Park in Alaska, leave signs of their movement in the land. By studying these signs, scientists can determine how glaciers change Earth's land.

THINK LIKE A SCIENTIST

Questioning In this unit you'll study glaciers and other forces that shape the land. You'll investigate questions such as these.

- How Do Wind and Ice Shape the Land?
- Why Is Soil an Important Resource?

Observing, Testing, Hypothesizing In the Activity "Gigantic Frozen Sandpaper," you'll make observations about the effect of a model glacier on a rock's surface. You'll also hypothesize about the effect of a real glacier on Earth's surface.

Researching In the Resource "Glaciers—Nature's Bulldozers," you'll gather more information about how glaciers change the land.

Drawing Conclusions After you've completed your investigations, you'll draw conclusions about what you've learned—and get new ideas.

THE SHAPE OF THE LAND

Have you seen pictures or movies that show white-water rafting? Were the riders paddling wildly in a crashing, speeding river? You know that rivers can be very powerful forces. But did you know that such forces help to shape the land?

PEOPLE USING SCIENCE

Landscape Photographer Miriam Romais got her first camera from her father while on an outing in Central Park in New York City. He paid one dollar for the camera. It was, as she recalls, "old and very used." Miriam Romais was eight years old at the time. From that day to the present, she has been "taking pictures." At an early age she was, in her own words, "fascinated with the idea of taking a moment of time and saving it for later. . . ."

Today Miriam Romais is a highly regarded photographer. She travels a great deal, always taking at least one camera with her to record on film the landscapes and natural formations that capture her eye. In this chapter you will find out what forces of nature work to shape Earth's surface, creating these landscapes.

◀ Forces of nature help shape the mountains and valleys shown in these photographs taken by Miriam Romais.

HOW DOES MOVING WATER SHAPE THE LAND?

A gentle rain falls. You watch puddles form and water trickle along the ground. How can these small streams of water affect the land? In this investigation you'll find out how Earth's land is shaped by water.

Activity

Hills and Valleys

Hills and valleys don't look as if they'd ever change. But they do. Find out how moving water can change them.

Procedure

1. Spread newspaper over your work area. Pile damp sand in one end of a baking pan. Shape the sand so that it forms a hillside with a steep slope near the top. The slope should gradually level out to form an area that is nearly flat. Shape the sand down to a thin edge a short distance from the other end of the pan. With your finger, make a small hole near the top of the hill and fill it with salt to model a mineral.

2. Use a coffee can with holes in the bottom as your rain-maker. Have a group member hold the rainmaker a few centimeters above the top of the hill. Fill a container with water. **Predict** what will happen to the sand and salt if you make the "rain" fall on the top of the hill. **Record** your prediction in your *Science Notebook*.

3. Then **test** your prediction. Pour the water into the rainmaker. **Observe** the water as it flows down the hill. **Describe** where the water makes a "stream," a "river," and an "ocean."

4. **Make a drawing** of what you observe. Draw arrows to point out the stream, river, and ocean areas. Then add the labels *stream, river,* and *ocean* to your drawing.

5. With your group, **experiment** with different-shaped hills. Try using more than one rainmaker. **Make drawings** of what you observe.

Analyze and Conclude

1. How do your observations compare with your prediction? What happened to the salt? How does your model hillside differ from a real hillside?

2. **Compare** the shape of the valley that the stream made near the top of the hill with the shape of the valley that the river made near the bottom of the hill.

3. Study the drawing you made. What can you **infer** about how moving water changes the shape of the land over which it moves?

UNIT PROJECT LINK

In this project you will plan, prepare, and present an exhibit about your state's natural resources, including scenic places. With your group, make a list of scenic places in your state. Collect pictures of them if you can and make a display of the pictures.

Technology Link

For more help with your Unit Project, go to **www.eduplace.com**.

A7

Activity

At the Beach

Where does sand on a beach come from? Where does it go? Find out how moving water affects sand on a beach.

MATERIALS

- goggles
- newspaper
- large baking pan
- sand
- large container
- water
- metric ruler
- 12 to 15 pebbles (about 1 cm in diameter)
- *Science Notebook*

SAFETY

Wear goggles during this activity. Clean up spills immediately.

Procedure

1. Spread newspaper over your work area. Pile damp sand in one side of a baking pan. Shape the sand into a beach.

2. Fill a container with water. Slowly pour water into the side of the pan opposite the sand until the water is about 3 cm deep.

See **SCIENCE and MATH TOOLBOX** *page H6 if you need to review Using a Tape Measure or Ruler.*

3. Place a ruler in the water. Make waves by carefully moving the ruler back and forth.

4. **Observe** what happens to the beach. **Record** your observations in your *Science Notebook*.

5. Make a jetty by piling up pebbles in a line that extends from the middle of the shoreline into the water about 5 cm, as shown.

Step 3

Step 5

6. With your group, **predict** what will happen to the waves and the beach if you make waves that hit the jetty. Explain your prediction.

7. Use the ruler again to make waves. **Observe** what happens when waves strike the jetty. **Record** your observations.

Analyze and Conclude

1. From your observations in step 4, **infer** how ocean waves can change a shoreline.

2. **Compare** the changes you observed in step 4 with those you observed in step 7. How did your prediction compare with your observations?

3. **Hypothesize** how a jetty changes the movement of sand. **Give evidence** to support your hypothesis.

INVESTIGATE FURTHER!

EXPERIMENT

Hypothesize whether the direction from which the waves come makes a difference in what happens to a beach. Make a plan to find out, and then carry it out. Share your findings with your class.

Science in Literature

FLASH FLOOD

"Water came bubbling and singing down the arroyo. It filled the riverbed from bank to bank, then rose like a great cement wall, a flash flood that filled the canyon. It swept over the embankment, over the hut, over the old saguaro cactus."

Deserts are normally dry places. But water can and does change the shape of a desert floor. In *One Day in the Desert*, by Jean Craighead George, you'll learn how Bird Wing, a young Papago Indian, and plants and animals of the desert face the power of a wall of water.

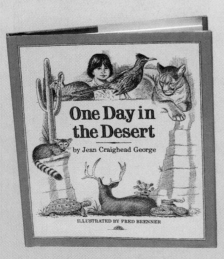

One Day in the Desert
by Jean Craighead George
Illustrated by Fred Brenner
HarperCollins, 1983

A9

Carving the Land

Reading Focus How does erosion, with weathering, shape the land?

You may have watched water flow along the ground after a rainstorm. Gravity causes the water to flow downhill until it finds a low spot. There the water forms a puddle. Often a puddle is muddy from soil that the rainwater picked up and carried with it. The process just described takes place on a much larger scale all over the world. It is called erosion (ē rō′zhən).

Partners That Shape the Land

Erosion is the process by which rock material is broken down and carried from one place to another by moving water, wind, or moving ice. Water causes more erosion on Earth than wind and moving ice combined.

Have you ever scraped your knee in a fall? Land can also be scraped—by materials that are carried by water. Over time, erosion and weathering— part of the process of erosion—work to wear away the land. **Weathering** is the process by which rock is broken into smaller pieces. The small pieces of rock in soil are formed by weathering.

OVER STEEP LAND
Fast-moving rivers can carve deep valleys. Rivers often join before reaching the ocean.

ACROSS A VALLEY FLOOR
As a river approaches the ocean, it winds in a string of S-curves across a valley floor. On the inside of each curve, the river deposits, or drops, some of the material it is carrying.

ON A FLOOD PLAIN
Melting snow often causes rivers to overflow and deposit silt on the valley floor, producing rich soil. The land formed from this silt is called a flood plain.

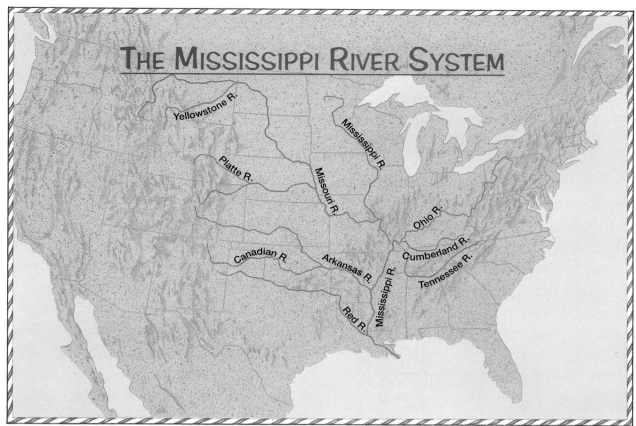

THE MISSISSIPPI RIVER SYSTEM

Using Math The longest part of the Mississippi River system is 5,970 km (3,582 mi) long. How much longer is that than the Mississippi River itself, which is 3,766 km (2,260 mi) long?

Breaking Up, Wearing Down

Rocks are changed all the time. Some rocks contain minerals that dissolve in water. When the minerals dissolve, the rocks are made weaker. Sometimes certain gases in the air mix with water, making a weak acid. This acid also can dissolve minerals in the rocks, causing the rocks to weaken.

Once a rock is weakened, cracks form in the rock. Water can seep into the cracks. Plant roots can also force their way into the cracks. Over time the freezing and thawing of the water and the growth of plant roots can cause weathering of the rock, breaking it into smaller pieces.

From Trickle to River

When rain falls on a hill or mountainside, some soaks into the ground. The rest of the rainwater trickles down the slope. Several trickles may join to form a brook. Several brooks may join to form a stream. Streams join to form a river. Small rivers join larger ones.

A river and the waterways that drain into it are referred to as a **river system**. The map above shows some rivers of the Mississippi River system. It's the largest river system in the United States.

Moving water causes more erosion than any other factor. Think of a stream or river rushing down a slope.

Either can move soil, sand, gravel, and rocks. The materials carried by moving water are called **sediments**. The activity on pages A6 and A7 shows how moving water carries away sand and minerals.

Fast-flowing rivers can even move small boulders. As boulders and rocks are carried along, they crash into each other and into rocks along riverbanks. Chips of rock break off. Over time moving water grinds rocks into grains of sand or tiny particles of rock material called clay, or silt.

How River Valleys Form

Just as a metal file wears away hard material, a fast-moving river can carve a deep, steep-sided valley. Over time the river valley deepens and widens.

As water batters the sides of the valley, the water breaks up rock and soil and carries them away. At some point the soil above the eroded sides of the valley caves in. This widens the river valley even more.

When Water Slows Down

When a river reaches the ocean, the water slows down. Then the water loses energy and can no longer carry all its sediments. The river deposits, or drops, the sediments. They build up along the banks and bottom of the river. As you can see below, when a river empties into the ocean, sediments form a flat plain called a **delta** (del′tə). The formation of a delta is just one way that weathering and erosion reshape the land. ■

The Mississippi Delta ▼

A SATELLITE VIEW OF THE DELTA
Look for a clue to why deltas are named after the triangle-shaped Greek letter *delta*.

The Changing Shoreline

Reading Focus How do the actions of wind and water change shorelines?

When you look at a map of the world, you can see the thousands of kilometers of shoreline, the boundary where the ocean meets the land. Coastal areas are among the most beautiful places in the world. However, these areas are under constant attack by water and wind.

Wearing Away the Shoreline

Moving water and wind are the major causes of weathering and erosion. Nowhere on Earth is the land more exposed to moving water and wind than along shorelines.

Waves are driven onto the shore by wind. Along rocky shorelines, sand and small rocks carried by the waves grind against large rocks. This grinding breaks down the rocks and wears them away. It produces the sand that forms coastal beaches. It also helps to form interesting shapes and formations along rocky shorelines.

The water brought in by a wave rushes back toward the ocean. Along sandy shorelines, waves remove sand from some places and deposit it in other places, often very far away.

Using Math *Much of the Pacific Ocean's shoreline erodes at a rate of about 1 m (3 ft) a year. Estimate how much shoreline erodes in one month.*

In fact, sand can be deposited hundreds of kilometers from where it was removed. Some sandy beaches change with the seasons. During the winter, strong winds produce waves that are steep and close together. These waves remove more sand from the shore than they deposit. In summer, gentler waves deposit more sand on beaches than they remove.

Building Up the Shoreline

Sometimes, sand carried by a current along the shoreline moves past a headland. A **headland** is a natural piece of land that extends out into the water. The headland may be at the mouth, or opening, of a bay. A **bay** is a body of water that is partly enclosed by land but has an opening, called a mouth, connecting the water to the ocean.

Sand is washed along an ocean shore by waves. When the sand reaches a headland, the headland directs the sand across the mouth of the bay. Over time the sand may build up and form features such as the barrier island shown. Such narrow islands stretch for hundreds of kilometers along the Atlantic and Gulf coasts of the United States.

A Tug of War at the Shore

As the ocean and land interact, movement and change are normal. This is especially true for beach areas. Beaches can change a lot—almost overnight. If no people lived in these areas, the natural changes would go almost unnoticed. However, people do live in these areas. Some of the world's largest cities are found near the shore.

Headland and bay ▼

Barrier island ▼

▲ **Sea wall and jetty**

In the United States, many people live and work on many of the barrier islands along the Atlantic and Gulf coasts. In addition, millions of tourists visit these beaches each year. These areas can be greatly damaged or even destroyed by the erosion of sand caused by the strong winds and huge waves produced by severe storms.

People have thought of different ways to protect shore areas, such as building jetties and sea walls. The activity on pages A8 and A9 shows how to build a jetty out of pebbles. A jetty, shown above, is a structure built to stop the erosion of sand. Water that strikes a jetty slows and drops the sand it is carrying.

The different methods of saving or restoring beaches are costly. Most of them will not work over a long period. And none can completely protect people or property from fierce storms, such as hurricanes. What is your answer, then, to this question: Who's winning the tug of war at the shore—people or nature? ■

Internet Field Trip

Visit **www.eduplace.com** to learn more about weathering and erosion.

INVESTIGATION 1 WRAP-UP

REVIEW

1. Describe two ways that water can help to weaken or break up rocks.

2. What causes moving water to drop sediments it is carrying?

CRITICAL THINKING

3. How is weathering related to the process of erosion?

4. Suppose you planned to build a house at the shore. Would you build it on a rocky shore or a sandy beach? Give reasons for your answer.

How Do Wind and Ice Shape the Land?

When you're hot and sweaty, wind and ice can cool you off. In winter they may keep you from playing outdoors. But wind and ice can do something more. They can shape the land. In this investigation you'll find out how.

Activity

Blowin' in the Wind

The word desert can make you think of huge dry areas and hills of sand called sand dunes. What part does wind play in shaping a desert landscape? Find out in this activity.

MATERIALS

- goggles
- newspaper
- tray or pan
- dry sand
- ruler
- cardboard box
- hair dryer
- timer
- craft sticks
- *Science Notebook*

SAFETY //////

Wear goggles during this activity. Be careful not to burn yourself when using the hair dryer. Use the coolest setting.

Procedure

1. Spread newspaper over your work surface. **Make a model** of a desert. Use a ruler to spread an even layer of sand about 2 cm deep in a tray.

2. Set one end of the tray in a cardboard box as shown. The box is to keep the sand from blowing around the room.

3. Use a hair dryer as a source of wind. Use the settings for the coolest temperature and lowest air speed. Hold the dryer far enough from the tray so that the "wind" *gently* blows across the surface of the sand, as shown. Allow the wind to blow for 15 to 20 seconds.

4. **Observe** the surface of the sand. **Record** your observations in your *Science Notebook*.

Step 3

5. Spread the sand out evenly again. Lay several sticks on top of the sand, as shown below. **Talk with your group** and together **predict** what the surface of the sand will look like if you repeat step 3.

Step 5

6. **Record** your prediction and give reasons for predicting as you did. Then **test** your prediction and **record** what you observe.

Analyze and Conclude

1. **Compare** the surface of the desert produced in step 3 with the surface produced in step 6.

2. How did your prediction compare with what you observed in step 6?

3. What role do the sticks play in helping to shape a desert surface? **Infer** what must happen in order for a sand dune to form.

INVESTIGATE FURTHER!

EXPERIMENT

Smooth out your desert sand. Put plants in the desert. Then use the hair dryer to blow wind along the surface of the sand for 15 to 20 seconds. Record your observations. Infer the effect that plants have on the erosion of sand in desert areas.

Activity

Gigantic Frozen Sandpaper

Have you ever seen what sandpaper can do to a piece of wood? In nature a huge mass of ice called a glacier (glā'shər) *can do the same thing to rock. Find out how ice shapes the land.*

Procedure

1. **Make a model** of a glacier. Scatter a handful of sand and pebbles in a small pan. Add water to the pan until it is two-thirds full. Then carefully place the pan in a freezer.

Math Hint *To fill the pan two-thirds full with water, measure the height of the pan. Fill two of three parts with water.*

2. After the water has frozen solid, remove the block of ice from the pan. The ice is your "glacier."

Step 1

Step 4

3. Use a hand lens to examine the surface of a smooth flat rock.

 See **SCIENCE** *and* **MATH TOOLBOX** *page H2 if you need to review* **Using a Hand Lens.**

4. Using a towel to protect your hands, place the glacier, sandy-side down, on the flat rock. **Talk with your group** and **predict** what will happen if you press down on the glacier and move it back and forth over the rock. **Record** your predictions in your *Science Notebook*.

5. Holding the glacier with the towel, move the glacier back and forth over the rock. Then **observe** the rock's surface with a hand lens. **Record** your observations.

Analyze and Conclude

1. Compare your observations with your prediction.

2. In what ways is your model glacier different from a real glacier?

3. Hypothesize what a real glacier would do to Earth's surface as the glacier moves over it. **Give reasons** to support your hypothesis.

Technology Link CD-ROM

INVESTIGATE FURTHER!

Use the **Best of the Net—Science CD-ROM**, Earth Sciences, *Glaciers of Blackcomb Mountain* site to find out some cool facts about glaciers and how to make model glaciers. You can also learn about the only animals known to live inside glaciers.

Sand Blasted

Wind is not as powerful as moving water. But, like water, wind can change the shape of land. Have you ever had wind blow sand into your eyes? Then you know that wind can carry sediment.

Wind Blows Away the Land

The stronger the wind, the more sediments it can carry. Wind must blow at least 18 km/h (11 mph) just to move sand along the ground. Stronger winds are needed to lift sand and carry it less than a meter above the ground.

In areas with loose sand and fine soils, wind can blow these materials away. The wind is even more likely to erode materials during dry periods, when most of the plants in an area may die off. In some areas, wind erosion can be prevented or reduced by windbreaks. Windbreaks may be fences, shrubs, grass, or trees—anything that can slow down the wind.

Wind Carves the Land

Wind erodes Earth's surface by removing sand and silt from one place and depositing them in another. The sediments that wind carries also weather Earth's surface. As windblown grains of sand move along the ground, they act as sandblasters—chipping, cutting, and polishing.

DUNES THAT MOVE Where winds blow steadily in the same direction, dunes migrate, or move, as much as 30 m (100 ft) a year. Dunes can even bury towns and forests. ▼

Sand dunes are formed on desert floors, on dry sandy flood plains, and along shorelines. Dunes vary in size. In the Sahara Desert, in North Africa, sand dunes cover an area larger than the state of Texas. Small beach dunes may be 1–2 m (3–7 ft) high. Some sand dunes in the Sangre de Cristo Mountains, in Colorado, are nearly 300 m (1,000 ft) high.

To carve buttes, polish rock, and make sand dunes move, wind has to attack, wear down, and carry away pieces of Earth's surface. Then the pieces have to be deposited somewhere else. All of these activities take a lot of sandblasting! ■

BUTTE Erosion by windblown sand can help shape the surfaces of rock formations such as this butte (byo͞ot). A butte is a narrow-topped hill with very steep clifflike sides. ▼

Wind Builds Up the Land

The sediments that wind picks up from one surface are deposited on another. The surface on which the sand is deposited is then built up.

Wind will carry its load of sediments until an object such as a boulder, a bush, or a fence slows it down. In the activity on pages A16 and A17, a hair dryer is used to model wind blowing across sticks on a desert. When an object in a desert slows down the wind, the wind deposits some of the sediments it carries. Piles of sand are often deposited in one place, forming hills called **sand dunes**.

◀ **Desert sand dunes**

Glaciers— Nature's Bulldozers

Reading Focus How do glaciers change the land over which they move?

A bulldozer pushes soil, trees, stumps, and rocks ahead of it as it moves. Nature has its own "bulldozers." They are called glaciers. A **glacier** is a huge mass of slow-moving ice that forms over land. Glaciers form in cold regions, where more snow falls in winter than melts in summer. In such places the snow piles up, becomes heavy, and turns to ice. As shown in the pictures below, there are two kinds of glaciers— continental and valley.

How Glaciers Move

As unlikely as it may seem, glaciers do move. The great weight of the ice causes a continental glacier to flow outward in all directions from its center. Gravity is the main force that makes valley glaciers flow.

Some glaciers move only a few centimeters a day. Others move a few meters a day. No matter how slowly a glacier moves, the surface beneath the glacier is changed by the weight of the ice and the material carried by the ice.

CONTINENTAL GLACIERS Also called ice sheets, these gigantic masses of ice are found only in Greenland and Antarctica. ▼

VALLEY GLACIER Also called alpine (al'pīn) glaciers, these thick "rivers" of ice form in high mountain ranges. ▼

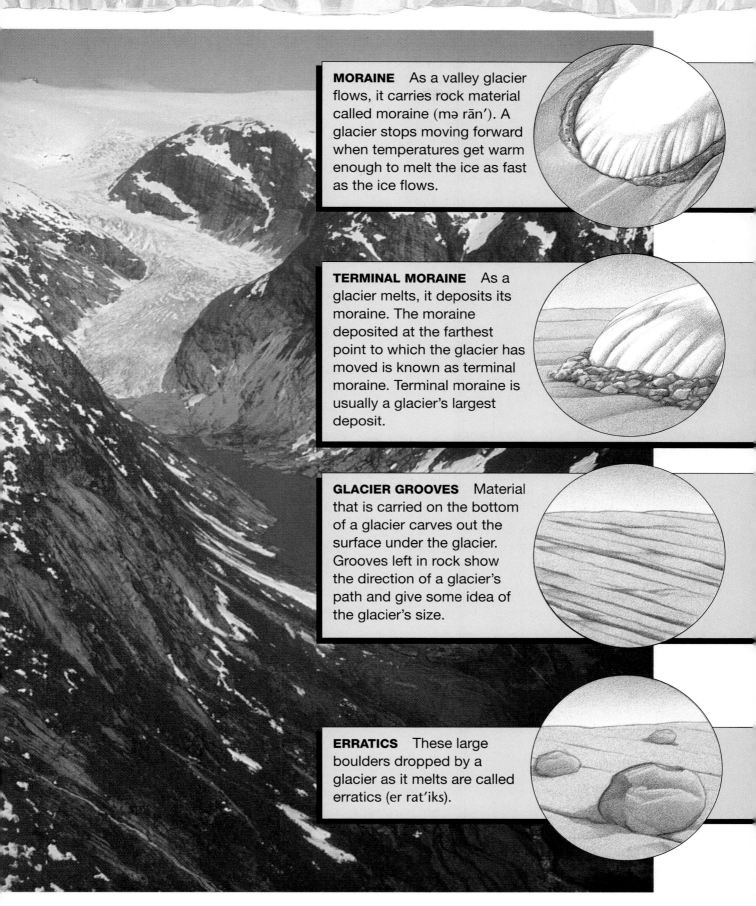

MORAINE As a valley glacier flows, it carries rock material called moraine (mə rān′). A glacier stops moving forward when temperatures get warm enough to melt the ice as fast as the ice flows.

TERMINAL MORAINE As a glacier melts, it deposits its moraine. The moraine deposited at the farthest point to which the glacier has moved is known as terminal moraine. Terminal moraine is usually a glacier's largest deposit.

GLACIER GROOVES Material that is carried on the bottom of a glacier carves out the surface under the glacier. Grooves left in rock show the direction of a glacier's path and give some idea of the glacier's size.

ERRATICS These large boulders dropped by a glacier as it melts are called erratics (er rat′iks).

A23

The Matterhorn was carved by glaciers. It has four triangular faces that are each about the same size. What space shape is this peak most like?

Often two or more valley glaciers move down a mountain at the same time. The glaciers grind away at the rocky structure between them, producing narrow ridges. The activity on pages A18 and A19 uses a piece of ice to show how a glacier grinds away rock. Around the mountain near its top, the glaciers carve out bowl-shaped holes. This action produces a pyramid-shaped peak, called a horn. Perhaps the most famous horn is the Matterhorn, located in the Alps between Switzerland and Italy.

Like wind and moving water, glaciers shape the land in two ways. As a glacier moves across the land, it carries away tons of material. Later, when the glacier stops moving and begins to melt, it deposits its load of sediments.

A glacier does more than just push materials from one place to another. Its action shapes mountains, carves valleys, and leaves huge boulders and piles of rocks along its path. Some of the most beautiful landscapes in the world have been produced by the actions of nature's bulldozers. ■

What Ice Leaves Behind

In places where a huge mass of ice once moved, signs of its presence and its power are left behind. These signs include U-shaped valleys, pointed peaks, sharp ridges, steep cliffs, lakes, and waterfalls.

INVESTIGATION 2 WRAP-UP

REVIEW

1. Name and describe two types of glaciers.

2. What are some signs that show that a giant ice sheet once covered an area?

CRITICAL THINKING

3. How do sediments that are deposited by wind compare with those deposited by glaciers?

4. Glaciers move very slowly, yet they can transport huge amounts of sediments. Explain.

REFLECT & EVALUATE

Word Power

Write the letter of the term that best matches the definition. *Not all terms will be used.*

1. Process by which rock is broken into smaller pieces
2. Body of water partly enclosed by land
3. Material carried by moving water
4. Flat plain formed where a river empties into the ocean
5. Mass of slow-moving ice
6. Movement of weathered rock materials by water, wind, or ice

a. bay
b. delta
c. erosion
d. glacier
e. headland
f. sand dune
g. sediment
h. weathering

Check What You Know

Write the term in each pair that best completes each sentence.

1. A horn is formed by the action of (wind, glaciers).
2. Materials carried by moving water are called (sediments, dunes).
3. A structure built to save sand beaches is a (headland, jetty).
4. Land that forms near the mouth of a river is a (delta, bay).

Problem Solving

1. You plan to build a rock wall in an area that receives a lot of rainfall. Would you use rocks that contain a high percentage of salt crystals? Explain your answer.

2. Think about what happens to sediments carried by water when the flow of water slows down. How does this explain why a barrier island might form near a headland?

Study the drawing, which shows grooves, or scratches, in bedrock. Infer what could cause such scratches. Record your inferences. Then tell what information you could infer about the object that produced the scratches.

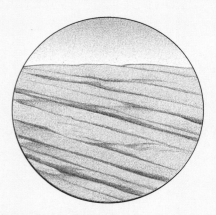

CHAPTER 2

THE IMPORTANCE OF NATURAL RESOURCES

Many natural resources come from the land. One of the most important is soil. Why is soil important? One reason is that plants, the world's food source, can grow in it. What other natural resources come from the land? Why are they important?

PEOPLE USING SCIENCE

Soil Scientist Dr. Thanh Dao is a scientist who is interested in the conservation, or wise use of, soil. If soil is conserved, it can be used a long time for the raising of livestock or for the production of crops.

Dr. Dao conducts laboratory and field experiments in his study of soil. According to him, the work he is doing in the picture deals with "protecting soil particles and plant nutrients from being washed away by rainwater." He uses a rainmaking machine to make rain. Then he collects and studies the chemical makeup of the rain that runs off the soil.

A soil scientist must know a great deal about the resource soil. In this chapter you'll find out more about this and other natural resources of the land.

Coming Up

◀ Soil scientist Dr. Thanh Dao uses a pump to collect water that runs off the soil following a rainstorm.

WHY IS SOIL AN IMPORTANT RESOURCE?

Soil is a valuable natural resource. A natural resource is any material from Earth that can be used by people. Where does soil come from? How do we use it? How can we make sure we'll always have enough? Find out in this investigation.

Activity

Little Ones From Big

You can make soil the way a mountain stream does. Find out how.

MATERIALS
- goggles
- rock chips
- water
- 2 plastic jars, 1 with screw lid
- timer
- filter paper
- funnel
- hand lens
- *Science Notebook*

SAFETY

Wear goggles during this activity. Clean up spills immediately.

Procedure

Wash some rock chips with water. Fill a plastic jar one-third full of chips. Cover them with water. Screw the lid on tightly. With a partner, take three 1-minute turns each, shaking the jar hard to model a mountain stream.

Place filter paper in a funnel. Stand the funnel in a second plastic jar. **Predict** what you would see if you poured the water through the filter. Then **test** your prediction. Use a hand lens to **observe** the material on the paper. **Record** your observations in your *Science Notebook*.

Analyze and Conclude

Compare your prediction with what you observed. **Infer** how mountain streams help to make soil.

Activity

Saving Soil

Do plants help to keep soil from being washed away? Find out in this activity.

MATERIALS

- goggles
- 2 baking pans
- topsoil
- piece of sod
- 2 wooden blocks
- 2 coffee cans, each with holes in their bottoms
- 2 large containers
- water
- *Science Notebook*

SAFETY

Wear goggles during this activity. Clean up spills immediately.

Procedure

1. Place soil in one baking pan and sod in another. Sod is soil with grass growing in it. Set one end of each pan on a wooden block so that the pans are sloped.

2. **Predict** how rain might affect the soil in each pan. **Record** your prediction in your *Science Notebook*.

3. Use coffee cans with holes in their bottoms as rainmakers. Hold the rainmakers over the pans.

4. Have two other members add equal amounts of water into each rainmaker as shown. Be careful not to add too much "rain" to the pans, causing them to overflow. **Observe** each pan. **Record** your observations.

Analyze and Conclude

1. **Compare** your observations with your predictions.

2. **Infer** how soil might be kept from washing away during a rainstorm.

Step 4

A29

Gully!
It's Soil Erosion

Reading Focus Why is soil important, and how can it be conserved?

The word *soil* means different things to different people. A construction worker sees soil as material that can be moved by digging. To a farmer, soil is the loose surface material in which plants with roots can grow.

To a person doing laundry, soil is dirt that needs to be washed from clothing.

Soil—A Limited Resource

Geologists (jē äl'ə jists) are scientists who study Earth materials. To a geologist, **soil** is loose rock material such as that produced in the activity on page A28. Soil covers much of Earth's land surface. If you've ever

watched a building crew dig a deep hole, it may seem that the soil goes on forever. Actually, the layer of soil that covers the land is very thin compared with the thick layer of rock that's under the soil.

Soil is a natural resource. A **natural resource** is any useful material from Earth. Some other natural resources are trees, coal, air, and water.

The most important thing about soil is that plants can grow in it. Without plants, life as we know it couldn't exist. That's because plants are the source of food for all living things on Earth.

Soil doesn't just happen. A well-developed soil is made up of layers that take many years to form. A side view of the different layers, called a soil profile, is shown below.

Using Soil Wisely

The greatest cause of soil loss is erosion by running water. When rain falls on bare soil, it runs across the surface, carrying soil with it. Gullies, or miniature river valleys, are formed in the soil. With each new rainfall, the gullies get bigger and deeper, and more soil is carried away.

Conservation (kän sər vā′shən) is the wise use of natural resources. There are many things people can do to conserve soil. The most important is to leave plants growing where they are whenever possible.

A SOIL PROFILE

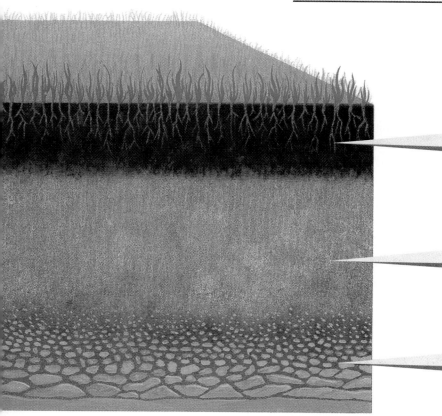

TOPSOIL Topsoil is a mixture of weathered rock and humus (hyo͞o′məs). Humus is decayed plant and animal matter. Humus provides nutrients that plants need for growth.

SUBSOIL Subsoil is a reddish or yellowish layer made up largely of clay particles that have been weathered out of the rock below.

WEATHERED ROCK Partly weathered rock lies under the looser soil above it.

CONTOUR PLOWING Contour plowing is plowing hilly land in a way that follows the shape of the land. This practice slows rainwater as it runs downhill, giving it time to sink into the soil. ▶

◀ **STRIP CROPPING** Strip cropping is planting a cover crop in strips between rows of crops. A cover crop is a crop, such as clover, that grows quickly. The closely planted cover crop absorbs rainfall. Then the rainfall will not run off the land and erode the soil.

Plants, such as trees and grass, provide protection against soil erosion. The activity on page A29 shows how rain affects sod and how it affects bare soil. When "rain" falls on both samples, less soil erodes from the sod, which has grass growing in it. Plant roots hold soil in place. Some of the ways to protect soil from erosion are described on these two pages.

Conserving soil is hard work. But it's worth the effort. Soil is important. The word *soil* has different meanings. But probably the one most important to you is that soil is a natural resource that helps to produce food. ■

DAM BUILDING Dam building helps slow or stop the formation of gullies. Dams may be built with boulders, small trees, tree branches, bushes, or boards. Water that would have run into a gully, thus carrying soil away, is stopped by a dam. ▶

▲ **TERRACING** Terracing is the building of terraces, or steplike ridges, in hilly areas to prevent or slow down water runoff.

INVESTIGATE FURTHER!

EXPERIMENT

Collect samples of soils with different textures. Plan experiments to test each sample for its ability to absorb water and to support plants. If your teacher approves your plans, conduct your experiments.

═══ INVESTIGATION 1 WRAP-UP ═══

THINK IT WRITE IT

REVIEW

1. What is the most important role of soil?

2. In what ways are terracing and contour plowing similar?

CRITICAL THINKING

3. In addition to providing food, what other important functions do plants serve?

4. How do the processes of weathering and erosion relate to soil?

WHY ARE ROCKS AND MINERALS IMPORTANT?

Below the layers of soil exists a wealth of materials that we use to build everything from computers to roads. What are these materials? Rocks and minerals! In this investigation you'll learn how we get and use these materials.

Activity

Exploring Minerals

You can explore the different properties of minerals, natural solids found in Earth. Then decide how these properties make the minerals useful.

MATERIALS
- goggles
- assorted labeled mineral samples
- hard tile
- magnet
- *Science Notebook*

SAFETY
Wear goggles during this activity.

Procedure

1. Observe the labeled minerals your teacher has displayed—magnetite (mag'nə tīt), hematite (hem'ə tīt), chalcopyrite (kal kō pī'rīt), gypsum (jip'səm), sphalerite (sfal'ər īt), and quartz (kwôrts). In your *Science Notebook*, **make a chart** like the one shown. In the first column, write the names of the minerals.

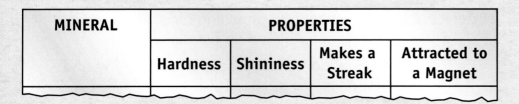

MINERAL	PROPERTIES			
	Hardness	Shininess	Makes a Streak	Attracted to a Magnet

2. A softer mineral can be scratched by a harder one. With your group, handle the minerals and **predict** their hardness, from softest to hardest. Then rub the minerals together to test them. Under *Hardness* in your chart, write a letter from *A* to *F* to tell each mineral's hardness, with *A* representing the softest and *F* the hardest.

3. Minerals that are shiny, like a coin, are said to have metallic luster. **Observe** each of the minerals. Under *Shininess*, write *yes* if the mineral has a metallic luster. Write *no* if it doesn't.

4. Some minerals leave a colored streak when they are rubbed on a hard tile. Rub each mineral on a hard tile. Under *Makes a Streak*, write *yes* if the mineral makes a streak. Write *no* if it doesn't.

5. **Test** each mineral with a magnet. Under *Attracted to a Magnet*, write *yes* if the mineral is attracted to the magnet. Write *no* if it isn't.

6. Go on a scavenger hunt. Use reference books to find out what materials come from the minerals. **Record** your findings.

Analyze and Conclude

1. Which of the minerals is hardest? Which is softest? **Compare** your results with your predictions.

2. **Infer** which property might be common to all minerals.

3. Use what you learned in this activity to **infer** how the different properties of mineral resources make them useful for different things.

UNIT PROJECT LINK

As you study this chapter, write and design a class newsletter that informs others about the need to conserve natural resources, such as soil. Choose natural resources that are important in your own community. Distribute the newsletter locally.

For more help with your Unit Project, go to **www.eduplace.com**.

Activity

Being Polite About Resources

Suppose at dinner your favorite food is passed. To be polite, you must take only your fair share. In this activity you'll find out why being polite about mineral resources is important, too.

Procedure

1. You will play a game in which a bowl of paper clips at your work station represents the total supply of a metal resource that is present in Earth's crust today. Place the role cards face down on the table. Each group member selects one card. Hold up your card so that the other group members can read it. The card tells you the name of your generation group—parent, children, or grandchildren—and how many people are in that group.

Step 1

2. When your turn comes, take five paper clips for each person in your generation group. The student with the "Parent" card goes first.

Step 2

3. The student with the "Children" card goes next, followed by the student with the "Grandchildren" card.

4. In your *Science Notebook*, **record** the results of this activity.

Analyze and Conclude

1. Based on the results, what can you **infer** about the number of paper clips that represents a fair share of the world's present supply of this metal?

2. **Hypothesize** about what would happen to the supply of the metal in several more generations.

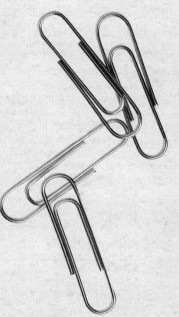

INVESTIGATE FURTHER!

TAKE ACTION

Make a list of items that you use that are made of metals—for example, paper clips. Brainstorm with members of your group to think of some ways that you can help to make sure that people in future generations will have their fair share of metal resources. Record your ideas in your *Science Notebook* and share them with your classmates.

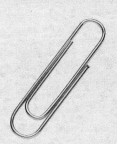

Minerals Through the Ages

Reading Focus How did the understanding of minerals and their uses develop over time?

People have always found ways to use materials that are taken from the ground. Some of these materials are called minerals. Metals come from a group of minerals that contain metal ore, or rock that can be mined to obtain metals.

Suppose no one had ever found out how to use metals. You wouldn't be sitting at a desk. There would be no desks because there would be no metal tools for making desks. Look at the time line to discover some things that people have learned about minerals over time.

THE STONE AGE
2 million years ago to 4000 B.C.

58,000 B.C.
People in what are now Europe, the Middle East, and North Africa shape flint, a mineral, into spear points for hunting. They shape other rocks into tools for scraping hides.

7000 B.C.
In what is now China, people make stone spades for digging up plants and roots. In what is now North America, people use stone tools for woodworking.

THE BRONZE AGE
4000 B.C. to 1000 B.C.

4000 B.C.
The Egyptians and Sumerians find that gold and silver are easy to hammer and shape. They also use copper alloys (al′σiz). An alloy is a mixture of metals. Bronze, for example, is an alloy of copper and tin.

1000 B.C.
The use of bronze for weapons, armor, and tools is widespread. Better ways to make bronze are developed.

THE INDUSTRIAL AGE
1700 to the 1900s

1770s
The Industrial Revolution begins in the textile, or cloth, industry in Great Britain and later spreads to the rest of Europe and to America. Machines replace hand methods. Factories are built. In 1789, Samuel Slater, a British textile worker, opens the first factory in the United States.

1800
The first copper-and-zinc battery is invented.

1874
A steel bridge that spans the Mississippi River is built at St. Louis, Missouri. This bridge is the first major steel structure in the United States.

1912
Stainless steel is invented. Its ability to resist rusting makes it an ideal material for surgical instruments and kitchen utensils.

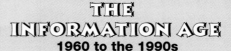

BEYOND 2000

THE IRON AGE
1000 B.C. to A.D. 1700

350 B.C.
In China, ironworks produce better tools for farming and stronger weapons. At ironworks, iron is separated from the rock it's in.

1452
Metal plates are used for printing. These plates are usually made of copper.

1668
The first cast-iron pipeline is used in Versailles, France, to supply water to the city.

THE INFORMATION AGE
1960 to the 1990s

1960s
Computers help guide spacecraft to the Moon and back.

1981
The silicon chip is invented and used in computers.

1990s
Scientists are finding newer and better ways to use metals and other minerals. For example, gold is used in making very small computers called microcomputers.

From Rocks to Riches

Reading Focus Why are minerals important, and why should they be conserved?

The next time you look at jewelry, pick up a coin, or pedal away on your bicycle, think a minute. Where did the materials that were used to make those objects come from? The materials came from rocks. The next time you pick up a rock, look at it carefully. It may contain a little iron, copper, lead, or even gold!

Where Rocks Are Found

Earth is made up of layers as you can see in the drawing below. The thinnest, outermost layer is called Earth's crust. It is made mostly of rock. The thickest parts of the crust are the continents (kän'tə nənts). The thinnest parts are the ocean floors.

The surface of Earth's crust may be covered with rocks or soil or water or plants. But if you were to dig down far enough at any place on the surface, you'd find solid rock.

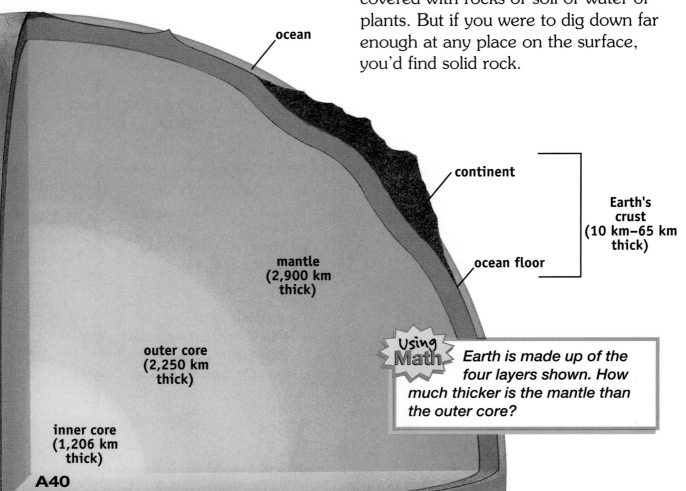

ocean

continent

Earth's crust (10 km–65 km thick)

ocean floor

mantle (2,900 km thick)

outer core (2,250 km thick)

Using Math *Earth is made up of the four layers shown. How much thicker is the mantle than the outer core?*

inner core (1,206 km thick)

▲ **Many items you use came from or are minerals.**

An Inside Look at Rocks

Rock is a solid material made up of one or more minerals. A **mineral** is a natural solid that has a definite chemical makeup, found in Earth's crust. Just as different foods can make up a cookie, different minerals can make up a rock. Most rocks are made up of at least two kinds of minerals.

Uses of Rocks & Minerals

The way rocks are used depends on their properties. For example, granite (gran'it) is a very hard rock. Because granite doesn't weather easily, it's commonly used as a building material. Marble is a rock used for its beauty. Many of the most famous statues are carved from marble.

Rocks may be valuable because of the minerals they contain. If you tried to list all the uses of minerals, your list couldn't fit on all the pages in this book. In fact, you might need a whole sheet of paper just to list the things in your classroom that are made from minerals. In the activity on pages A34 and A35, different minerals are examined to determine how they could be useful.

The pictures at the top of the page show some familiar minerals. The lead in your pencil is made from the mineral graphite (graf'īt). Chalk is a mineral called calcite (kal'sīt). The salt you sprinkle on food is a mineral called halite (hal'īt).

Minerals in Ore

All the metals in your classroom come from minerals found in ores. An **ore** is a rock that can be mined for the minerals it contains.

If you look closely at a rock, you may see specks of different minerals. ▶

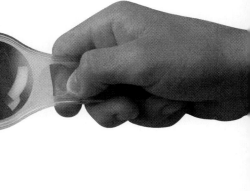

Most minerals come from ores. Some rocks are made up of a single mineral. Rock salt, for example, is rock made up of the mineral halite. Rock salt is an ore that is mined for its one mineral—salt.

Metals are perhaps the most valuable substances that come from ores. Iron, copper, aluminum, gold, and tin are some metals found in ores. Obtaining pure metals from ores is a long and costly process. The first step in this process is to find an ore deposit, or place where there is a large amount of ore. The pictures on page A43 show what is done after a metallic ore deposit is found.

Resources Worth Saving

Some natural resources can be replaced fairly easily. For example, an area that once had trees can be replanted with trees that grow quickly. A resource that can be replaced is called a **renewable resource**.

Many natural resources, such as metallic ores, can't be replaced. A natural resource that can't be replaced is called a **nonrenewable resource**. Nonrenewable resources should be conserved, or people someday will have to do without them. What happens to the paper clip "resource" in the activity on pages A36 and A37 could happen to actual mineral resources.

Science in Literature

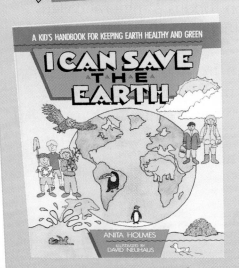

I Can Save the Earth
by Anita Holmes
Illustrated by David Neuhaus
Julian Messner, 1993

YOU-ME-ALL-OF-US

"Help! There's a monster on the rampage! This monster eats up the earth's resources. Then it spits them out all over the land. Do you know the name of this monster? It is You-Me-All-of-Us."

This passage is part of the introduction to Chapter 4 of *I Can Save the Earth* by Anita Holmes. This book is filled with ideas about small things you, your family, and your neighbors can do to save Earth's natural resources.

1 First a metallic ore is mined, or dug out of the ground.

2 The ore is taken from the mine to a crusher.

3 The ore is crushed and the valuable metal is collected.

4 The pure metal is taken away to be used.

INVESTIGATION 2 WRAP-UP

THINK IT WRITE IT

REVIEW

1. What does the chalk in your classroom have in common with the salt you put on your food?

2. Why is it important to conserve Earth's mineral resources?

CRITICAL THINKING

3. Pretend you have discovered a new mineral. Name the mineral and describe one property that makes the mineral especially useful.

4. Write a short paragraph explaining why rocks are important natural resources.

WHY ARE ENERGY RESOURCES SO IMPORTANT?

INVESTIGATION 3

People need energy for many things—to move things, to make things, and to keep themselves warm or cool. In this investigation you'll explore how people get energy to meet their current needs, and you'll think about what fuels might be used in the future.

Activity

Sun-Toasted Marshmallows

You can feel the energy from the Sun on a hot, sunny day. Can you make this energy work for you? Find out as you try to make a Sun-powered marshmallow toaster.

MATERIALS

- goggles
- 3 pieces of aluminum foil
- glue
- scissors
- 3 sheets of cardboard
- several books
- 3 thermometers
- 4 wooden dowels
- tape
- marshmallows
- *Science Notebook*

SAFETY

Wear goggles during this activity.

Procedure

1. Glue a sheet of aluminum foil, shiny side out, to a cardboard square to make a sun reflector. Repeat this procedure to make two more reflectors.

2. Carefully bend one reflector into a V shape and another into a U shape. Use stacks of books as shown to help these reflectors hold their shapes. Keep the third reflector flat. Tape a thermometer to one end of each of three wooden dowels.

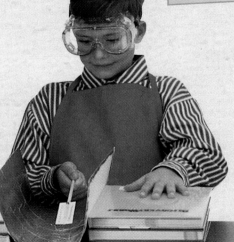

A44

3. Talk with your group and predict which thermometer will show the highest temperature if held in the center of each reflector placed in direct sunlight. Also predict whether the time of day will affect the temperature readings. In your *Science Notebook*, record your predictions and explain why you made them.

4. Test your predictions and record your observations.

See **SCIENCE** and **MATH TOOLBOX** page H8 if you need to review *Using a Thermometer.*

5. Use your results from step 4 to design a solar cooker that will toast a marshmallow.

6. After getting your teacher's approval, test your design. Carefully put a marshmallow on the end of a wooden dowel. Use the dowel to hold the marshmallow in or over your solar cooker. Observe the marshmallow and record your observations.

Analyze and Conclude

1. Which reflector produced the highest temperature? How did the time of day affect the temperature? Compare your results with your prediction.

2. What kind of energy was used to heat the marshmallow? How did you apply what you learned in step 4 to design and use your cooker?

Technology
Link
CD-ROM

INVESTIGATE FURTHER!

Use the **Best of the Net—Science CD-ROM**, Physical Sciences, *Energy Quest: California... Discover Its Energy!* to learn more fascinating facts about fossil fuels.

Step 4

A45

Fuels Around the World

Reading Focus How does the use of fossil fuels in the United States compare with that of other nations?

What is happening when a car engine starts up and when hamburgers sizzle on a grill? Fuel is being burned to produce energy. People around the world burn different kinds of fuels to produce energy.

Fuel From Living Things

Wood has been used as a fuel for thousands of years. It's still a very important fuel in some parts of the world. Wood, of course, comes from trees. A tree stores energy from the Sun. This energy is released when wood is burned.

In some areas solid animal waste, called dung, is burned as fuel. The energy in dung comes from energy stored in plants that are eaten by animals. Dung is used, in a limited way, in the United States. An electric power plant in California uses cow manure as fuel!

WORLD SOURCES OF FOSSIL FUELS

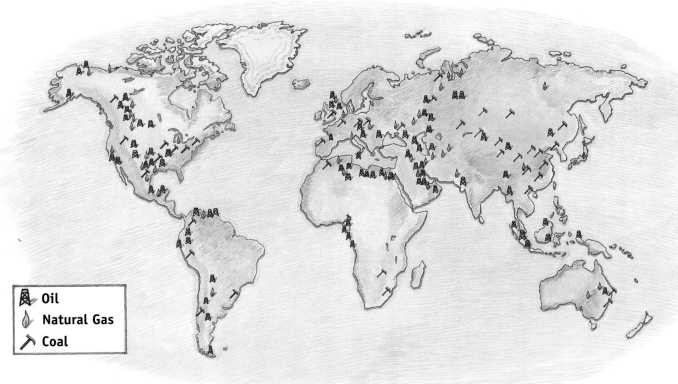

Oil
Natural Gas
Coal

Fossil Fuels

Much of the energy that people use comes from burning fossil fuels. **Fossil fuels**—natural gas, coal, and petroleum, also called crude oil—are fuels made from the remains of once-living things. Peat, another fuel, comes from the remains of ancient swamp plants. In time and with enough pressure, peat can change into coal.

Supply and Demand

As you can see from the map and graphs, the world's fossil fuels are not shared equally. What country today uses the most petroleum? the most natural gas? the most coal?

Fossil fuel use per person is even less equal. The average person in the United States uses about 47 times as much petroleum as the average person in India. And the United States uses more than three times as much coal per person as does China.

Fossil fuels are nonrenewable resources. Suppose all people used as much fossil fuel as do people in the United States. Imagine how quickly fossil fuels would disappear. In the future more people might use solar energy, the kind used in the activity on pages A44 and A45. ■

Using Math *China's population is about four times that of the United States. Explain how the graph shows that the United States uses three times as much coal per person as does China.*

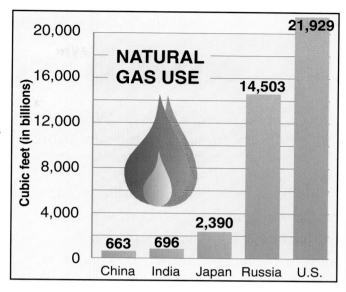

NATURAL GAS USE

Cubic feet (in billions)

China 663
India 696
Japan 2,390
Russia 14,503
U.S. 21,929

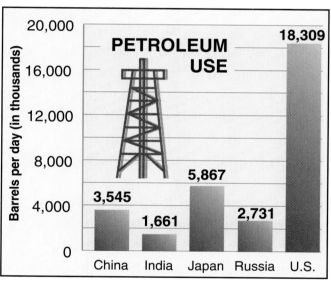

PETROLEUM USE

Barrels per day (in thousands)

China 3,545
India 1,661
Japan 5,867
Russia 2,731
U.S. 18,309

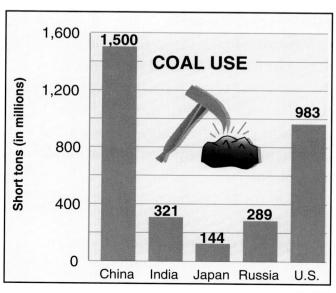

COAL USE

Short tons (in millions)

China 1,500
India 321
Japan 144
Russia 289
U.S. 983

Coal, Gas, and Black Gold

Reading Focus What are the major drawbacks of using fossil fuels as the main source of energy?

It's hard to imagine what life would be like without fossil fuels—fuels made from once-living things. And fossil fuels are valuable. In fact, petroleum is sometimes called black gold.

Energy From Ancient Sunlight

All fossil fuels contain energy that was once stored in the cells of living things. In turn, those living things—plants and animals—got their energy from the Sun. As today, plants used the Sun to make food. Animals ate the plants to get the energy they needed to carry out their life activities. So the energy stored in fossil fuels can be traced back to the Sun, the major source of energy for Earth.

Fuel From Fossils

Millions of years ago tiny living things in the ocean died and sank to the sea floor. Over time they were covered with layers of mud and sand. Heat and pressure slowly changed the once-living things into petroleum and natural gas.

While these changes were taking place on the ocean floor, other changes were taking place on land. In swampy areas giant ferns and trees were dying. The plants were then covered by sand and mud. Over time they changed into a type of fuel called peat. If peat is buried long enough, it changes into coal.

Bad News About Fossil Fuels

Fossil fuels that we use today cannot be replaced in our lifetime. Natural gas and petroleum take millions of years to form. Today people are using these fuels at an alarming rate. Just think about all the car motors running and homes being heated. Once a gallon of oil or cubic meter of gas is burned, it is gone forever!

Coal is more plentiful than oil or natural gas, and it isn't being used up as quickly. However, even Earth's supply of coal won't last forever.

Even if supplies of fossil fuels were plentiful, there would still be problems. For example, mining coal destroys huge areas of land. And even though mine operators try to repair the damage, the process is very costly and takes many years.

Burning fossil fuels adds carbon dioxide and other harmful gases to air.

Land that is strip-mined (*left*) is ripped up by power shovels. The same land can be restored (*right*).

Carbon dioxide traps and holds heat close to Earth's surface, much like the glass in a greenhouse. Some scientists fear that too much carbon dioxide in the air will cause climates on Earth to change.

Good News About Fossil Fuels

We know how fast we are using our supplies of fossil fuels. So it's possible to estimate when the supplies might run out long before that ever happens. That's part of the good news—fossil fuel supplies are dependable.

Because fossil fuels are formed and stored in the ground, they can be removed as they are needed. Fossil fuels can also be transported from where they are formed to where they are needed.

Coal is made from the remains of plants that lived long ago. ▼

To find coal buried deep underground, miners dig hundreds of meters into Earth's crust.

▲ **A windmill farm uses the wind as a source of energy.**

A small amount of a fossil fuel has a great deal of energy. This energy can be used to warm rooms or heat water or power machines.

New Energy Sources

In the activity on pages A44 and A45, it may take a very long time to cook the marshmallow in the solar cooker. The cooker uses **solar energy**, or energy from the Sun.

Sunlight is a cheap, clean energy. Solar energy is being used more today than ever before. Over half the homes in Israel, and nearly all the homes in Cyprus, use solar energy to heat water.

As Earth's supply of fossil fuels runs low, people will continue to search for cleaner and better sources of energy. New energy sources include the wind, energy from inside Earth, and sea water. Chances are that sea water might become an important source of energy in the future. ■

Internet Field Trip
Visit **www.eduplace.com** to learn more about energy sources.

INVESTIGATION 3 WRAP-UP

REVIEW

1. Why are petroleum, natural gas, and coal known as fossil fuels?

2. Why are fossil fuels nonrenewable resources?

CRITICAL THINKING

3. Cars are being designed to use less fuel and burn fuel more cleanly. Why is this important?

4. Choose one of these kinds of energy—solar energy, wind energy, or energy from inside Earth. Explain why using that kind of energy might be better than using energy from fossil fuels.

REFLECT & EVALUATE

Word Power

Write the letter of the term that best completes each sentence. *Not all terms will be used.*

1. Any useful material from Earth is called a (an) ——.
2. Rock that can be mined for its minerals is called a (an) ——.
3. Loose material that covers much of Earth's surface is ——.
4. Wise use of natural resources is called ——.
5. Energy from the Sun is ——.

a. conservation
b. fossil fuel
c. natural resource
d. ore
e. rock
f. soil
g. solar energy

Check What You Know

Write the word in each pair that correctly completes each sentence.

1. Decayed plant and animal matter in soil is (subsoil, humus).
2. Ores are valuable because they contain (marble, minerals).
3. Peat is an early stage in the formation of (coal, natural gas).

Problem Solving

1. As in the past, living things today are dying and being covered by mud and soil. Why can't people count on these changes to meet fossil fuel needs in the future?

2. Suppose you're on a mission to discover new elements in space. What special properties would you look for? Explain your choices.

Using the picture shown here, make a sketch of a soil profile. Label each of the layers in your sketch. Briefly describe each layer. Then in a short paragraph, discuss the importance of soil and some ways to conserve it.

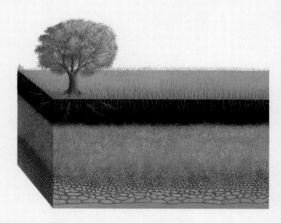

CHAPTER 3

THE PROBLEM WITH TRASH

Trash—it's what becomes of many of our land resources. In fact, Americans throw out enough trash every day to fill 63,000 garbage trucks. Where does all the trash go? And how does trash affect our natural resources?

PEOPLE USING SCIENCE

Garbologist William Rathje is an unusual kind of archaeologist (är kē äl'ə jist). An archaeologist is a scientist who digs up buried objects and studies them to learn about the people who left them. Rathje is sometimes called a garbologist. He is part of a team that digs up, sorts, and catalogs garbage from old landfills and dumps. In garbage that had been buried for 40 years, the team made these two discoveries. Newspapers were still readable, and hot dogs were still recognizable.

These and other discoveries have led people to think about new ways to dispose of, or get rid of, wastes. As you explore this chapter, think about how you dispose of wastes. Can you make some changes?

◄ Dr. Rathje is a scientist who studies garbage.

INVESTIGATION ①

WHAT DO PEOPLE THROW AWAY, AND WHERE DOES IT GO?

Think of a 13-story building the size of a football field. Americans produce enough trash to fill 10,000 of these buildings every year. Where do we put it all? In Investigation 1 you'll find out!

Activity

Looking at Trash

Think about the trash your family throws away. What materials make up the trash most people throw away? Find out!

Procedure

1. Your teacher will give your group a bag of trash that a family might dispose of. Before the bag is opened, **talk with your group** and **predict** what material most items will be made of. **Record** your prediction in your *Science Notebook*.

2. **Make a chart** like the one shown.

Group (Material Item Is Made Of)	Item of Trash

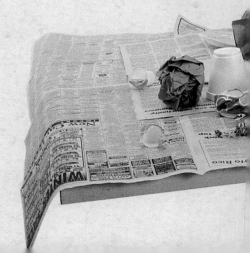

3. Carefully empty the bag onto newspaper and examine the trash. Classify the trash into groups based on the material each item is made of. Count and record the number of trash items in each group.

4. Analyze the data in your chart. Then make a bar graph to show your data.

 See SCIENCE and MATH TOOLBOX page H3 if you need to review Making a Bar Graph.

Analyze and Conclude

1. Which material was most of the trash made of?

2. How did your prediction compare with what you found out?

3. Resources were used to make the materials in the trash. What resources were being thrown away?

Step 3

INVESTIGATE FURTHER!

EXPERIMENT

Make a list of all the trash that is produced by your class during the school day. Classify the trash and then make a large bar graph of the results. What material would you infer is thrown away in schools in the greatest amount?

Activity

Making a Landfill

Many towns dispose of trash in a landfill. What happens to trash buried in a landfill? Build a model and find out!

MATERIALS

- goggles
- plastic gloves
- small items of trash
- newspaper
- shoebox
- plastic wrap
- soil
- tray
- metric measuring cup
- water
- watering can
- *Science Notebook*

SAFETY

Wear goggles during this activity. Wear plastic gloves when handling trash and soil.

Procedure

1. Look at different items of trash. **Predict** what will happen to each kind of waste after it has been buried for two weeks.

2. Spread newspaper on your work surface. Work with your group to **build a model** landfill as shown in the cutaway drawing. Press down the layers. End with a layer of soil on top. Set the landfill on a tray where it won't be disturbed.

Step 2

3. Each day, sprinkle the landfill with 60 mL of "rain" as shown.

 See **SCIENCE** and **MATH TOOLBOX** page H7 if you need to review **Measuring Volume.**

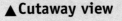

plastic wrap

soil

trash

shoebox

▲ **Cutaway view**

4. At the end of two weeks, dump the wastes onto newspaper. **Record** in your *Science Notebook* any changes you observe.

Analyze and Conclude

1. **Compare** your results with your predictions.

2. **Infer** what happens to the different items of trash buried in a landfill.

3. What material served as a liner in your model landfill? **Hypothesize** what would happen if wastes were buried in the ground without a liner.

INVESTIGATE FURTHER!

EXPERIMENT

Bury trash in a model landfill for three months. Predict what will happen. Check your predictions. Infer what happens to trash in a landfill over long periods of time.

Trashing Trash

Reading Focus What are some good points and bad points of using landfills and burning to dispose of trash?

"It's time to take out the trash!" Do you ever hear that reminder? People produce a lot of trash. The average American produces 1.8 kg (4 lb) of trash each day.

Look at the circle graph below. It shows the kinds of trash a town produces and how much space each kind takes up. What kind of trash is missing from the graph?

Trash can be a problem. It's ugly, smelly, and can be harmful to living things. Let's take a look at where trash goes, what problems it can cause, and how people try to prevent those problems.

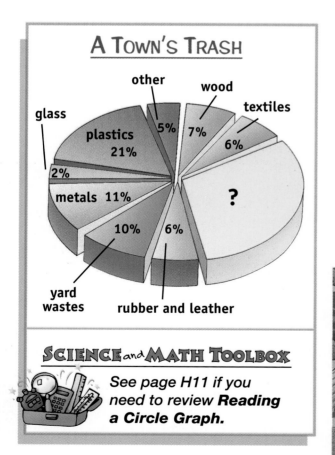

A TOWN'S TRASH

other 5%
wood 7%
textiles 6%
glass 2%
plastics 21%
metals 11%
yard wastes 10%
rubber and leather 6%
?

SCIENCE and MATH TOOLBOX

*See page H11 if you need to review **Reading a Circle Graph.***

TRASH Trash is brought to the landfill by trucks. The trash is spread in a layer and squeezed together to take up less room.

Trashing Trash in the Past

Until recently, most trash was put in dumps far away from people. These dumps were usually holes in the ground that were covered over when they were filled. Such dumps have many drawbacks. The wastes in uncovered dumps attract birds, rats, mice, flies, and other disease-carrying animals. Dumps also smell bad, and rainwater moving through a dump picks up harmful chemicals. If this water reaches underground drinking water supplies, the water becomes unsafe to drink.

Today most places have laws against simply dumping trash. Instead the Environmental Protection Agency (EPA) suggests four ways of dealing with trash—bury it, burn it, make new things out of it, or make less of it.

The activity on pages A56 and A57, shows how landfills are made. A **landfill**, like a dump, is a large hole that is filled with trash over time. But landfills are built to keep trash from harming the environment. Examine the layers in the landfill pictured below. How is the trash kept from getting outside the landfill? How is this landfill like the model?

When a landfill is full, the area can be covered over, planted with grass, and made into a park or used for other purposes. Some cities build recreational areas on old landfills.

BURYING TRASH IN A LANDFILL

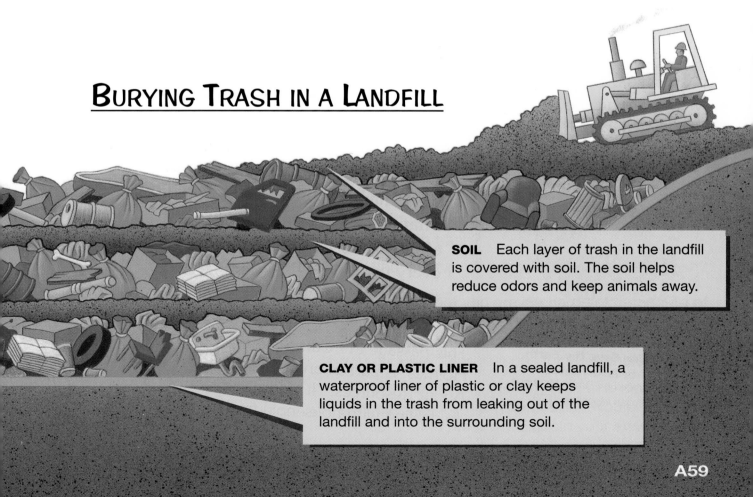

SOIL   Each layer of trash in the landfill is covered with soil. The soil helps reduce odors and keep animals away.

CLAY OR PLASTIC LINER   In a sealed landfill, a waterproof liner of plastic or clay keeps liquids in the trash from leaking out of the landfill and into the surrounding soil.

INVESTIGATION 2

HOW CAN TRASH AFFECT RESOURCES?

Some trash isn't "lucky" enough to end up in a landfill or incinerator. It's thrown out of car windows, dropped on city streets, or piled up in illegal dumps. Find out in Investigation 2 what effects this trash has on our environment.

Activity

A Litter Walk

MATERIALS
• Science Notebook

SAFETY
Do not pick up trash.

Trash thrown on the ground is litter. How does litter affect your school's environment?

Procedure

Take a walk outdoors to look for litter. In your *Science Notebook*, make a list of the kinds of litter you see. When you return to the classroom, work with your group to decide how you would like to classify the litter. Using the categories your group decides on, classify the litter on your list. Make a chart or bar graph to help you analyze your data. Share your results with the class.

Analyze and Conclude

1. What material was most litter made of? What else did you learn about litter?

2. How was the litter affecting the environment? Infer how litter can waste resources.

A62

Activity

Clean It Up!

Find out why oil spills present special problems for the environment.

- -

Procedure

1. Half-fill a plastic cup with sand. Pour 20 mL of vegetable oil on the sand. The vegetable oil represents motor oil.

2. After an hour, **observe** the oily sand. **Discuss with your group** ways to remove the oil from the sand. **Predict** which method will best clean up the oil.

3. Make a plan to test one of your ideas. Show the plan to your teacher and then carry it out. Note how long you work to remove the oil. **Record** all your results in your *Science Notebook*.

Step 1

Analyze and Conclude

1. How well did your plan work? **Hypothesize** whether your plan would work on a real oil spill on land. Explain.

2. Motor oil is made from crude oil, a vital natural resource. How does improper disposal of used motor oil affect the environment and Earth's limited supply of crude oil?

INVESTIGATE FURTHER!

RESEARCH

Find out about the methods used to clean up oil spills. Research one of the following: the 1993 *Braer* tanker spill off the Shetland Islands into the North Sea; the 1996 *Sea Empress* oil spill near the southwest of Wales; or another spill.

Don't Teach Your Trash to Swim!

Reading Focus What are some harmful effects of dumping trash into the ocean?

SCIENCE TECHNOLOGY & SOCIETY

You might think that litter is only a problem on land. But littering is a big problem in the ocean, too. For centuries, sailors have thrown their garbage over the sides of their boats. And for a long time, trash produced in coastal cities was taken out to sea and dumped.

Ocean dumping does more than make the water dirty. Trash that's dumped at sea washes up on beaches, making them unsafe areas for swimming. Animals that live in or near the ocean can become ill from the trash or can become trapped in broken fishing nets that have been discarded in the ocean.

Some fishers are trying very hard to change their habits. In Newport, Oregon, fishers bring their garbage back to land. There it is sorted and disposed of properly. Some fishers are even picking up trash they see floating in the ocean. They are hoping that their motto—Don't teach your trash to swim!—catches on. ■

◄ **These plastic objects were found in the nest of this albatross. Birds are attracted to colorful plastics, which are harmful if eaten.**

Trashing Resources

Reading Focus How does the improper disposal of trash affect the environment and waste resources?

Earth is full of treasures. Soil, rocks, minerals, water, and petroleum are all natural resources that people get from the land. Sometimes people add un-wanted materials to the environment, causing **pollution** (pə lo͞o′shən). These unwanted materials are called **pollutants**.

People cause pollution when they improperly dispose of trash. Look at the picture below. It shows how pollu-tants can seep into the ground from oil cans that have been disposed of improperly. Trace the oil as it moves through the ground and into the water. What will happen to the soil in this area? How will the environment of the stream change?

The activity on page A63 shows how difficult it can be to clean up the oil from the soil.

Hazardous Wastes

There are many materials that can harm soil or water supplies. They include motor oil, paint, pesticides, many cleaning supplies, and chemicals from the inside of batteries. These pollutants are called hazardous wastes. **Hazardous wastes** are wastes that can pollute the environment even when they are in very small amounts.

The improper disposal of trash can pollute the environment. ▼

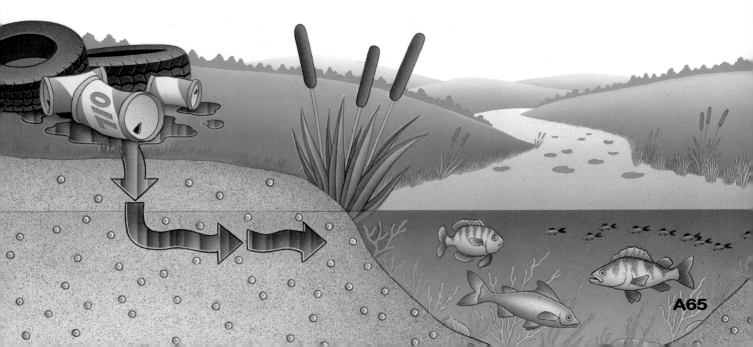

▲ **Littering reduces natural resources and harms the environment.**

PETROLEUM Plastics are made from petroleum, or crude oil. Since this is a non-renewable resource, every time you throw away a plastic bottle the amount of available petroleum is reduced. How does throwing away plastic harm the environment? ▶

Hazardous wastes in soil or drinking water can cause diseases.

Litter—An Ugly Trash Problem

Litter is solid waste, or trash, that is discarded on the ground or in water. Littering can hide the beauty of the land and be harmful to living things.

Some animals are attracted to and collect litter to feed to their young. This can cause serious health problems in the young animals.

Internet Field Trip

Visit **www.eduplace.com** to learn more about protecting your environment.

◀ **PAPER** Paper is made from trees. Even though we can plant more trees, it takes time for them to grow. And processing trees into paper produces many pollutants.

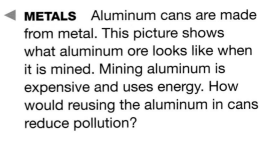

◀ **METALS** Aluminum cans are made from metal. This picture shows what aluminum ore looks like when it is mined. Mining aluminum is expensive and uses energy. How would reusing the aluminum in cans reduce pollution?

Littering also wastes available resources. In the activity on page A62, students take a walk outdoors to look for litter. What resources do you think are being thrown away? Look at the pictures on these pages to see some other ways that littering wastes resources. ■

───── **INVESTIGATION 2 WRAP-UP** ─────

THINK IT WRITE IT

REVIEW

1. What are hazardous wastes? Name some.

2. What natural resource is used to produce plastics?

CRITICAL THINKING

3. Look for evidence of land pollution in your community. Record your observations. Then suggest the cause of the pollution and how it might be prevented.

4. Describe two ways that trash can affect available natural resources.

HOW CAN YOU HELP SOLVE THE TRASH PROBLEM?

"Please take out the trash!" How many times a week do you hear that? How can your family reduce the amount of trash it produces? Find out in Investigation 3.

Activity

A New Life for Trash

MATERIALS
• street map of your community
• telephone directory
• colored markers
• *Science Notebook*

Make a map that shows places to take items for recycling and reuse.

Procedure

With your group, use a telephone directory to identify recycling centers and stores that sell used items. Using a street map, mark the location of each place you identify. In your *Science Notebook,* make a chart like the one below. Record information about places you marked on your map.

WHERE TO RECYCLE AND REUSE			
Name and Address	**Telephone Number**	**Kinds of Items Accepted**	**Payment Given for Items**

Analyze and Conclude

What kinds of items can be accepted for recycling or reuse? How does recycling or reusing help conserve resources?

Activity

The Rethink Link

You've heard of the three R's—reading, 'riting, and 'rithmetic. Now you'll learn about the four R's—reduce, reuse, recycle, and rethink. They can help you find ways to save resources.

Procedure

1. The pictures on this page show some ways to save resources. Think of a way to save resources that you would like to try. **Make a plan** for what you'll do and show it to your teacher.

2. **Predict** how your plan will work. **Record** your prediction in your *Science Notebook*. Carry out the plan. Then share your results.

Analyze and Conclude

1. **Compare** your results with your prediction.

2. How will your plan help save resources?

▲ Collect leaves and grass clippings for compost.

▲ Have a yard sale to sell items that you no longer use.

▲ Use a sponge or cloth instead of paper towels.

▲ Start a recycling center in your home.

Conserving Resources

Reading Focus What are some different reasons people have recycled materials over the ages?

Have you ever given away clothing that you've outgrown or toys that you no longer play with? If you have, you were conserving resources. Using materials that otherwise would be thrown away is one important method of conserving valuable natural resources.

Today many communities recycle paper, aluminum cans, glass, and plastic items. They try to save resources and reduce the amount of trash going into landfills.

Study the time line shown here. As you can see, conserving resources by recycling and reusing materials is not a new idea at all.

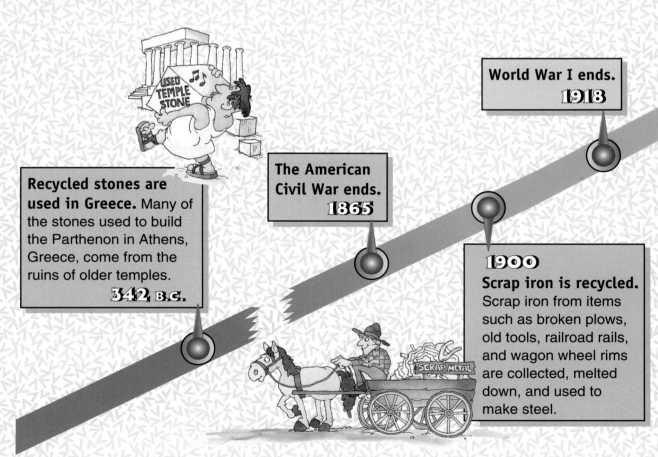

Recycled stones are used in Greece. Many of the stones used to build the Parthenon in Athens, Greece, come from the ruins of older temples.
342 B.C.

The American Civil War ends.
1865

World War I ends.
1918

1900
Scrap iron is recycled. Scrap iron from items such as broken plows, old tools, railroad rails, and wagon wheel rims are collected, melted down, and used to make steel.

The first aluminum can recycling program is begun in the United States. In the late 1960s, people begin to worry that the world might run out of both renewable and nonrenewable resources. The idea of reusing and recycling items becomes popular again.

1968

BEYOND 2000

1998
The United States recycles 27% of its waste. The goal is 35% by 2005.

1970
The first Earth Day is held.

1942
Rubber, metal, and paper are recycled during World War II. Resources are needed to build ships, tanks, and planes. Even children collect scrap metal, old rubber tires, tin foil, and tin cans for recycling.

UNIT PROJECT LINK

Choose one resource in your state. Use the information in Investigation 1 to figure out how much of this resource is thrown away. Make a plan for reducing this amount. Then carry out your plan.

**Technology**Link
For more help with your Unit Project, go to **www.eduplace.com**.

A71

Recycling

Reading Focus What steps are common to the recycling processes of plastics, glass, and aluminum?

Each day, Americans make enough trash to fill two football stadiums. This trash could be reduced by half if people would **recycle**, or process items and use them again.

Recycling Paper

As you learned earlier, paper makes up about one third of a typical town's trash. So the recycling of paper, especially newspapers, is a very important part of any recycling program.

Paper to be recycled is first ground up and mixed with water to form a mushy pulp. The pulp is treated with chemicals to remove ink and other impurities. Then bleach is added to make it white. Finally the pulp is processed in different ways to make a variety of paper products, from egg cartons to greeting cards.

Recycling Plastic

The diagram below shows the stages in recycling plastics. Although many plastic bottles look alike, they may contain different materials. That's why the plastics industry created a number code that shows what kind of plastic an item is made of. As you can see in the picture on the next page, the code is stamped on the bottom of plastic containers.

1 Recyclable plastic items are carried along a belt.

2 Items are chopped into small pieces and dropped into a flotation tank.

3 The pieces of plastic are washed in the tank. Dirt and nonplastic items, which sink, are separated from the floating plastic pieces.

4 The plastic pieces are dried in a dryer.

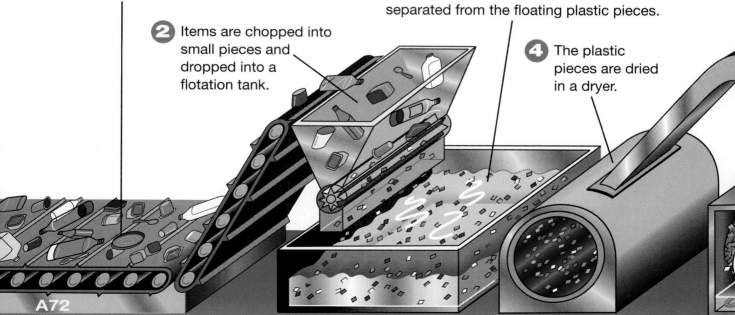

Recycling Plastics

Code	Original Plastics	New Products
1	soft-drink bottles, peanut-butter jars, frozen-food trays	surfboards, film, skis, carpets, soft-drink bottles
2	detergent bottles, milk and water jugs, toys	flowerpots, trash cans, stadium seats, toys
3	shampoo bottles, clear food wrap	floor mats, pipes, hoses, mud flaps on trucks
4	bread bags, frozen-food bags, grocery bags	grocery and other types of bags
5	ketchup bottles, yogurt cups, other food containers	food trays, car battery parts
6	videocassette cases, plastic spoons, food trays, foam cups	trash cans, egg cartons, hangers
7	packages with many layers of materials	plastic lumber

The plastic coded 1 is called PET or PETE. PET is used to make plastic soda bottles. It is the easiest plastic to recycle. The plastic coded 2, called HDPE, is also easy to recycle. Look at the table above to find out what products are made from the plastics you recycle.

▲ **Number code on plastic container**

5 The plastic pieces are melted, filtered, and shaped into strands.

6 The plastic strands are chopped into small bead-shaped pieces that are bought by manufacturers, who make new plastic products from them.

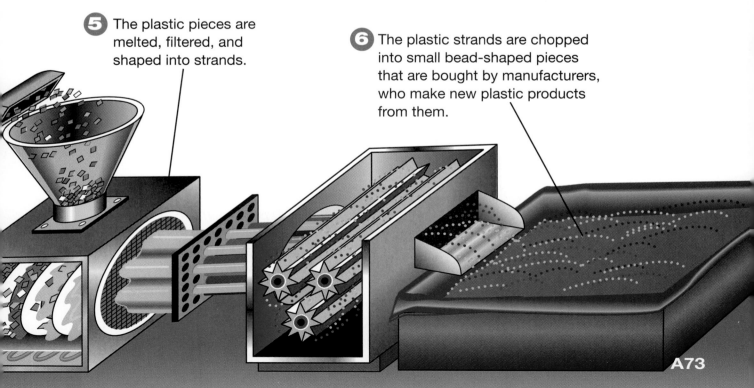

A73

Recycling Glass

1. Used glass bottles are sorted by color and checked for metal caps.

2. The bottles are crushed into small pieces.

3. The glass pieces are cleaned and mixed with sand, soda ash, and limestone.

4. The mixture is melted, and the melted glass is shaped and cooled.

Recycling Aluminum

1. Aluminum cans are crushed.

2. The crushed cans are melted.

3. The liquid aluminum is poured into molds and cooled.

Recycling Glass

Some types of glass—such as that used in light bulbs, windows, and auto headlights—can't be recycled. These types of glass can cause damage to a glass furnace when they're mixed with glass bottles. Study the process used to recycle glass bottles.

Recycling Aluminum

Aluminum cans may be melted down to make new cans. The steps above show the process of recycling aluminum cans. How does it compare with recycling glass and plastics?

Recycling materials helps save resources. However, recycling is not free. It takes energy resources to collect the materials and run the machines used in recycling. But the energy used to recycle materials is usually less than what is needed to make the same materials from scratch. ■

Using Math

Each person in the United States produces about 87 pounds of glass waste per year. A glass bottle weighs about 8 ounces. About how many glass bottles is that per person per year?

A74

The Wrap Trap

Reading Focus What are some of the unwanted effects of overpackaging products?

In the activity on page A69, a plan is made to reduce, reuse, or recycle. All the methods shown in the activity help solve the problem of too much trash. And they help conserve natural resources. But one of the most important things that can be done to help reduce the amount of trash is to rethink. Rethinking is making choices before you buy or use a product.

Wrap Rap

Packaging is the wrappings and containers of items for sale. Think about the trash and litter discussed earlier in this chapter. How many of those items are wrappings or containers? In the United States about one third of the trash in landfills comes from packaging. Think about the many products for sale and their wrappings. Could less wrapping have been used? Why not just stop making packaging? The answer is that packaging serves many purposes.

Look at the diagram. It shows some of the purposes for packaging and an example of each. What other examples can you think of?

▲ Layers of packaging keep products fresh, safe, and unbroken. They also add to the trash problem.

Technology Link
CD-ROM

INVESTIGATE FURTHER!

Use the **Best of the Net— Science CD-ROM**, Physical Sciences, *Energy Quest: Saving Energy* site, to find out more about conserving energy and recycling. You can also learn how to start an "Energy Patrol" in your school.

You Decide

Many of the items people buy are wrapped several times. Some bags of snack food come packed within larger bags. Fruit is often put on paper or plastic-foam trays and then covered with plastic wrap.

How can you help with the "wrap trap" of overpackaging? You have a choice of products when you go shopping. What type of packaging will you look for? If you choose products wisely, you can help reduce the amount of trash in landfills.

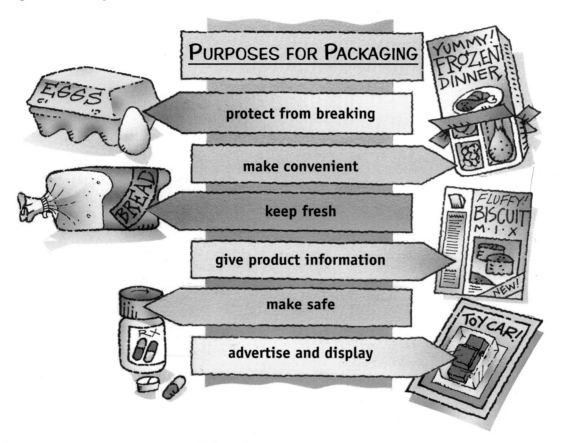

PURPOSES FOR PACKAGING

protect from breaking

make convenient

keep fresh

give product information

make safe

advertise and display

INVESTIGATION 3 WRAP-UP

THINK IT WRITE IT

REVIEW

1. Why is the recycling of paper an important part of any recycling program?

2. What are the first two "steps" in the recycling of certain materials?

CRITICAL THINKING

3. Name and describe four ways that you can help reduce trash.

4. Most people agree that reducing the amount of packaging would help conserve natural resources. Why is it difficult to reduce packaging?

REFLECT & EVALUATE

Word Power

Write the letter of the term that best matches the definition. *Not all terms will be used.*

1. Burning of trash
2. Process items and reuse them
3. Wrappings and containers of items for sale
4. Trash discarded on the ground or in water
5. Wastes that can pollute even in small amounts
6. Large hole filled with trash over time

a. hazardous wastes
b. incineration
c. landfill
d. litter
e. packaging
f. pollutant
g. recycle

Check What You Know

Write the term in each pair that best completes each sentence.

1. The addition of unwanted materials to the environment is called (packaging, pollution).
2. Trash discarded along a roadside is (litter, landfill).
3. Keeping an item fresh is one purpose of (incineration, packaging).
4. Each layer of trash in a landfill is covered with (plastic, soil).

Problem Solving

1. Suppose your town found it was more expensive to recycle certain materials than it was to dump them in a landfill. As a voter, what would you choose to do? Explain your choice.

2. A town has a problem with unsafe drinking water. Draw a map showing how the location of the town dump might be related to the problem with the drinking water.

Copy the drawing shown here. Then use the drawing to write a paragraph that describes how newspapers are recycled.

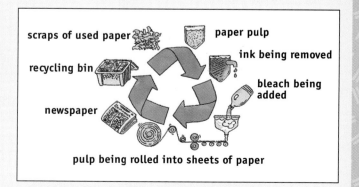

scraps of used paper

paper pulp

recycling bin

ink being removed

newspaper

bleach being added

pulp being rolled into sheets of paper

Main Idea and Details

When you read science, it's important to recognize which facts and details support or explain the main idea. First identify the main idea by looking for clues such as a title, or a topic sentence that states the main idea. Then look for statements that support that idea.

Look for clues to find the main idea.

Look for statements, facts, and details that support the main idea.

Read the paragraphs below. Then complete the exercises.

Partners That Shape the Land

Erosion is the process by which rock material is broken down and carried from one place to another by moving water, wind, or moving ice. Water causes more erosion on Earth than wind and moving ice combined.

Have you ever scraped your knee in a fall? Land can also be scraped—by materials that are carried by water. Over time, erosion and weathering—part of the process of erosion—work to wear away the land. **Weathering** is the process by which rock is broken into smaller pieces. The small pieces of rock in soil are formed by weathering.

1. Write the letter of the sentence that states the main idea of the paragraphs.

    a. Weathering breaks rocks into small pieces.

    b. Most of the land's erosion is caused by water.

    c. Erosion, with weathering, works to change the land.

    d. Erosion moves rock from one place to another.

2. What clue helped you find the main idea?

3. List the most important facts and details that support the main idea.

Circle Graph

People in the United States use energy in many ways. The circle graph shows the main purposes for which crude oil products, such as gasoline and heating oil, are used.

Use the data in the circle graph to complete the exercises that follow.

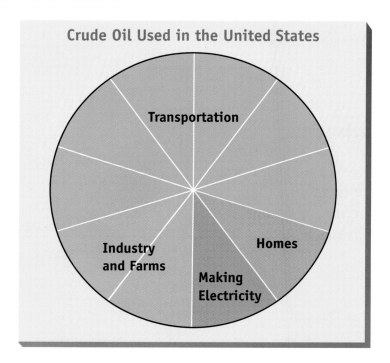

Crude Oil Used in the United States

Transportation

Homes

Industry and Farms

Making Electricity

1. For what purpose is the greatest amount of crude oil used? the least amount?

2. What uses twice as much crude oil as homes do?

3. Which two groups, added together, use $\frac{8}{10}$ of the crude oil used in the United States?

4. How much more crude oil is used for industries and farms than is used for making electricity?

5. Is more crude oil used for transportation or for all of the other purposes combined? Tell how you know.

WRAP-UP!

On your own, use scientific methods to investigate a question about Earth and its resources.

THINK LIKE A SCIENTIST

Ask a Question

Pose a question about Earth and its resources that you would like to investigate. For example, ask, "What effect does contour plowing have on soil?"

Make a Hypothesis

Suggest a hypothesis that is a possible answer to the question. One hypothesis is that contour plowing helps to hold soil in place.

Plan and Do a Test

Plan a controlled experiment to find the effect that contour plowing has on soil. You could start with two pans, soil, a craft stick, a coffee can with holes in the bottom, and a pitcher of water. Develop a procedure that uses these materials to test the hypothesis. With permission, carry out your experiment. Follow the safety guidelines on pages S14–S15.

Record and Analyze

Observe carefully and record your data accurately. Make repeated observations.

Draw Conclusions

Look for evidence to support the hypothesis or to show that it is false. Draw conclusions about the hypothesis. Repeat the experiment to verify the results.

WRITING IN SCIENCE
Persuasive Letter

Write a letter that persuades farmers to plant cover crops to help stop erosion. Follow these guidelines for writing a persuasive letter.

• State your opinion about what you want to persuade the farmer to do.
• Include facts and reasons that support your opinion.
• End with a strong conclusion.

UNIT B

Populations and Ecosystems

Theme: Systems

THINK
LIKE A SCIENTIST

BLOOMING DESERT

The Anza-Borrego Desert State Park, shown here, is a flowering desert stretching out below stark mountains in southern California. Scientists study things that affect the organisms living in this desert, such as the temperature, the amount of rainfall, and the kind of soil. They also study how desert organisms behave and survive in an environment where temperatures can be high and water is scarce.

THINK LIKE A SCIENTIST

Questioning In this unit you'll study how living and nonliving things in the environment interact. You'll find out how nonliving materials, such as water, carbon dioxide, and oxygen, cycle within the environment. You'll investigate questions such as these.

- How Do Earth's Major Ecosystems Differ?
- What Is Biodiversity, and How Is It Changing?

Observing, Testing, Hypothesizing In the Activity "Make a Mini-Biome!" you'll put together a biome of your choice. You'll observe how nonliving things affect the growth of living things in your biome.

Researching In the Resource "Earth's Biomes," you'll learn about diverse land environments and organisms that populate the land.

Drawing Conclusions After you've completed your investigations, you'll draw conclusions about what you've learned—and get new ideas.

LIVING THINGS AND ENVIRONMENTS

Nature—it's amazing! Everything works together so smoothly. In every environment each plant and animal finds what it needs to survive. Together with other organisms in the environment, plants and animals form a busy, healthy community.

PEOPLE USING SCIENCE

Environmental Engineer Juho So (jōō hō tsä) works to clean up environmental pollution. For example, he has cleaned up water that was polluted by a company that made fertilizers. Since leaving his native Korea, Dr. So has monitored and corrected many kinds of water and soil pollution in the United States and England.

Dr. So first thought about cleaning up the environment when he was about ten years old. A pond where he played was filled with frogs and toads. One day he found the pond covered by a slick of oil from a nearby broken oil tank. A week later he was heartbroken to find that all the frogs and toads were gone. Today Dr. So cleans up environmental pollution after it happens. But he wants to prevent pollution from ever taking place.

Coming Up

◀ Juho So at work in his laboratory

B5

WHAT IS AN ECOSYSTEM?

Do you need living things to survive? Do you need nonliving things? If you answered "yes" to both questions, then you are part of an ecosystem. In this investigation you'll find out what an ecosystem is.

Activity

A Local Ecosystem

All ecosystems include living and nonliving things. How do these parts interact?

- -

Procedure

1. Use a meterstick to **measure** a plot of ground that is 1 m square. Push a wooden stake into the ground at each corner. Mark off the square by tying string around the four stakes.

Math Hint *To make sure your plot of ground is reasonably square, measure the diagonals of the plot. The length of each diagonal should be about 1.4 m.*

2. Predict the kinds of living and nonliving things you'll find in your plot and how they'll interact. **Record** your predictions in your *Science Notebook*.

3. Make a chart like the one shown on page B7. **Describe** the location of your plot.

MATERIALS

- gloves
- meterstick
- 4 wooden stakes
- string (5 m long)
- garden trowel
- aluminum or plastic tray
- paper towel, moistened with water
- hand lens
- toothpick or probe
- *Science Notebook*

SAFETY //////

Wear gloves during this activity. Do not touch any plants until they have been identified as safe by your teacher. Some plants—poison ivy, for example—can cause skin rashes.

	Living Things	Nonliving Things	Unsure If Living or Nonliving	Interactions
Plot				
Soil Sample 1				
Soil Sample 2				

Step 6

4. In your chart, **list** the number and kinds of living and nonliving things that you see in your plot. Then **list** any interactions you see between living things or between living and nonliving things.

5. Place a moist paper towel in the bottom of a tray. Use a garden trowel to take a small sample of soil from the plot. Spread the soil on the towel.

6. With a hand lens and a toothpick or probe, gently probe the soil for living and nonliving things. Do not injure any living things you find. **List** living and nonliving things in your soil sample and **describe** any interactions between them that you see. **Record** your observations.

7. Empty the tray in the same spot from which you took the soil sample. Take another sample of soil from a different part of your plot of ground and repeat steps 5 and 6. Be sure to **record** your observations in the chart.

Analyze and Conclude

1. Write a paragraph that describes which living and nonliving things make up the plot you observed and any interactions you noted.

2. What do you think was the purpose of repeating part of the activity, using a second sample of soil?

3. How do living things in the plot depend on and interact with nonliving things?

4. *Eco-* means "environment." A *system* is made up of parts that interact. Was your plot an example of an ecosystem? **Provide evidence** to support your answer.

Technology Link CD-ROM

INVESTIGATE FURTHER!

Use the **Best of the Net—Science CD-ROM**, Life Sciences, *African Primates at Home* site to meet primates such as mountain gorillas and monkeys in their natural habitats. You'll learn about their physical characteristics and discover environmental threats to their existence. You can hear their screams, roars, and chirps.

The Nature of an Ecosystem

Reading Focus In what ways are forest and water ecosystems alike and different?

Imagine that you have spent the night camping in the woods. As the Sun rises, you see green leaves overhead and you hear squirrels chatter. You are seeing and listening to the sights and sounds of your environment.

All the living and nonliving things around an organism make up its environment. As seen in the activity on pages B6 and B7, organisms interact with their environment. Animals such as birds and insects pollinate plants and help to scatter their seeds. Plants are a source of food and shelter for many animals.

Organisms interacting with one another and with their physical environment make up an **ecosystem** (ek′ō sis təm). In the forest ecosystem, birds eat insects that may feed on decomposing animals. Dead plants rot, adding nutrients (n oo ′trē ənts), substances living things need for growth, to the soil. Bees produce honey from nectar they gather from flowers, squirrels bury acorns that grow into oak trees, and skunks nest in hollow trees.

The living (and once-living) things in an ecosystem are called the biotic (bī ät′ik) factors. Biotic factors include plants, animals, and fallen logs. The nonliving things in an ecosystem are called abiotic factors. Abiotic factors include soil, rocks, water, air, land and water temperatures, and sunlight.

Ecosystem Dwellers

Organisms that live together in an ecosystem make up a **community**. A community contains many different populations of organisms. Each **population** contains all the organisms of the same kind in a community. A forest may have populations of squirrels, maples, and woodpeckers.

Together with other populations, they form a community. All the members of a population are members of the same species (spē′shēz).

Organisms of the same species have the same general physical characteristics and other adaptations (adəp tā′shənz). An **adaptation** is a structure or behavior that enables a species to survive and reproduce in its environment.

The role that each species plays in a community is its **niche** (nich). Where an organism lives and how it obtains food are parts of its niche. No two species in a community have exactly the same niche.

The niche of each species in an ecosystem is a result of its adaptations. For example, a redheaded woodpecker has a beak that is an adaptation for digging insects out of dead wood. In the same community a

blue jay is adapted to eat mainly flying insects. So each species of bird occupies a different niche.

A Watery Ecosystem

In a forest ecosystem, living things live on the land. But in a water ecosystem, plants and animals live in and on water. For example, in a pond, fish live under the water, while turtles sun themselves on a fallen log. Lily pads float on the water's surface.

Like land ecosystems, water ecosystems contain both biotic and abiotic factors. Water and land ecosystems differ in the specific organisms and the abiotic factors that make up each type of ecosystem.

Living things live in the ecosystems to which they are adapted and that meet their needs. For example, water lilies grow well in a water ecosystem, but would not survive in a forest

ecosystem. For any particular ecosystem, some kinds of living things survive well, some survive less well, and some cannot survive at all.

Ecosystem Size

An ecosystem may be small, containing only a few interacting species. A puddle that forms on the sidewalk after a rain is a small ecosystem. It may contain four species of microbes. An ecosystem may be large, such as a rain forest, which stretches for thousands of kilometers. It may contain millions of different species, from monkeys to beetles, from moss plants to oak trees. Large ecosystems are made up of many smaller ecosystems.

Changing Ecosystems

Logging, farming, road construction, industries, and building homes all change ecosystems. When ecosystems change, some organisms will survive. Others will die unless they move and find a new home. What did humans

▲ **The ecosystem of Mount St. Helens changed drastically—but naturally.**

do to change the ecosystem shown below from a forest to a warehouse?

Humans aren't responsible for all changes to ecosystems. Ecosystems change naturally, too. Lightning strikes, starting a forest fire. An earthquake cracks open the ground. These natural events change physical environments and as a result change ecosystems. At first such events may appear to be disastrous. In fact, they are often called natural disasters. With time, however, the number of populations in these communities will slowly increase again.

▲ **A forest ecosystem may be changed by development.**

▲ **The new ecosystem may not support all the living things of the forest.**

▲ **What used to be living trees looked like giant toothpicks after the eruption.**

▲ **Regrowth soon began.**

The Mount St. Helens volcanic eruption proved how suddenly an ecosystem can change without human interference. On May 18, 1980, the slopes of Mount St. Helens in Washington fell strangely still. Suddenly the mountain burst apart. Hot rock, ash, and steam billowed into the air, then rained down on the forest.

Boiling mudflows surged down the mountain. Within minutes, trees were flattened and wildlife disappeared. From the air, the once-lush mountainside looked gray and lifeless.

Although the land looked dead, it was really just "napping." Before long, plants protected by a layer of snow began to grow. Twenty years after the eruption, Mount St. Helens is again populated with a rich variety of species.

Ecosystems are constantly changing. Some changes might be hard to see. Other changes, whether caused by nature or by humans, are dramatic. ■

Internet Field Trip

Visit **www.eduplace.com** to see examples of animals in their niches.

INVESTIGATION 1 WRAP-UP

THINK IT WRITE IT

REVIEW

1. Define biotic and abiotic factors. Give an example of each kind of factor.

2. Distinguish between a community and a population.

CRITICAL THINKING

3. Analyze the adaptive characteristics of red-headed woodpeckers and blue jays. Describe how those characteristics result in each organism having a unique niche.

4. Predict some adaptations that enable an animal such as a bird to survive and reproduce in a desert ecosystem.

HOW ARE LIVING THINGS IN AN ECOSYSTEM RELATED?

How did you get energy this morning? Did you eat a bowl of cereal? In this investigation you'll see how the members of an ecosystem are related by the ways they get energy.

Activity

A Meal Fit for an Owl

By examining the remains of an owl's meal, you can find out how owls are related to other organisms in their ecosystem.

Procedure

Unwrap an owl pellet and place it on a paper towel. **Observe** the outside of the pellet with a hand lens. **Predict** what you will find inside the pellet. **Record** your predictions. Use tweezers and a toothpick to separate the pellet's contents. **Examine** the parts carefully with the hand lens. **Record** your observations.

Analyze and Conclude

1. **Compare** your findings with your predictions.

2. Based on your observations, **infer** what an owl eats. In what kind of an ecosystem would this owl live?

Activity
Lunch Time!

Find out how the members of an ecosystem get their energy.

MATERIALS
- marker
- paper
- collecting net
- hand lens
- *Science Notebook*

Procedure

1. With your group, go to the area that your teacher has selected. Look for every organism in the ecosystem. You may wish to use a collecting net to find insects.

2. Have one member of your group make a chart like the one below. That person can **record** the data for the group.

See **SCIENCE** and **MATH TOOLBOX** page H10 if you need to review *Making a Chart to Organize Data.*

Organism	How It Gets Energy

3. Have another member use the hand lens for "close-up" studies of the organisms you see. **Record** all observations.

4. **Discuss** with your group how each organism obtains energy and **record** your conclusions.

5. Back in the classroom, copy your observations into your *Science Notebook*. Work with your group and other groups to **construct a map** of the area surveyed.

Step 3

Analyze and Conclude

1. **Infer** how most of the organisms studied got energy for life processes.

2. **Identify** any organisms that produced energy for other organisms.

B13

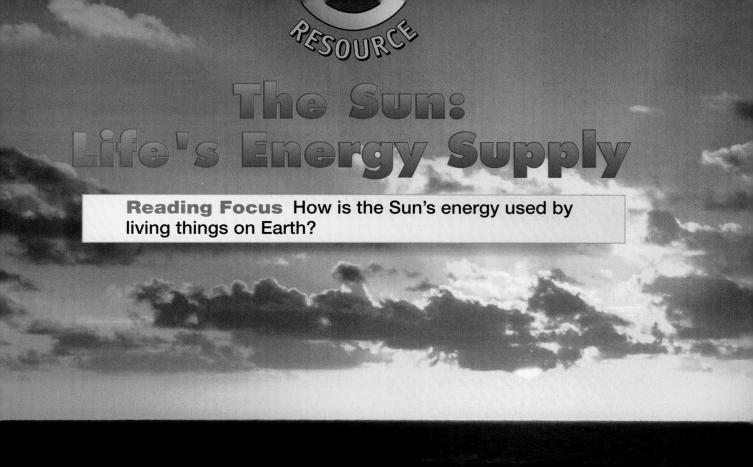

The Sun: Life's Energy Supply

Reading Focus How is the Sun's energy used by living things on Earth?

▲ **The Sun provides energy for Earth's organisms.**

SCIENCE TECHNOLOGY & SOCIETY

Have you heard people say, "It's so hot outside, you could fry an egg on the sidewalk"? Fry an egg? Don't you need a stove for that?

No, you don't need a stove. You just need plenty of heat energy. And sometimes, when it's sunny and extremely hot, it can feel as though there is enough heat energy from the Sun to fry an egg.

Energy from the Sun reaches Earth as light and other forms of wave energy, such as infrared rays. Much of this energy is changed to heat energy in Earth's air, land, and oceans. Day after day, year in, year out, the Sun lights and warms Earth.

Green Organisms Need the Sun

What do you think would happen to Earth's ecosystems if the Sun's energy were blocked? If you said that most life on Earth would soon disappear, you would be correct. Almost all life on Earth depends on the Sun for energy, either directly or indirectly. All green plants depend directly on the energy of the Sun. Certain groups of plantlike organisms also depend on the Sun. Included in this group are organisms called algae (al'jē). Plants and plantlike organisms use light energy from the Sun to make food through a process called photosynthesis (fō tō sin'thə sis). These living things take in water and carbon dioxide, a gas that is in the air and water, and change them to sugar and oxygen. The sugar is the plant's food and contains stored energy. So a plant actually "stores" the Sun's energy. When animals eat plants, they also use the solar energy stored in the sugar.

Organisms that carry out photosynthesis contain a chemical called chlorophyll (klôr′ə fil). Chlorophyll is the substance in plants that gives leaves and stems their green color. It also stores light energy from the Sun. Organisms that do not contain chlorophyll can't store light energy and therefore can't make their own food.

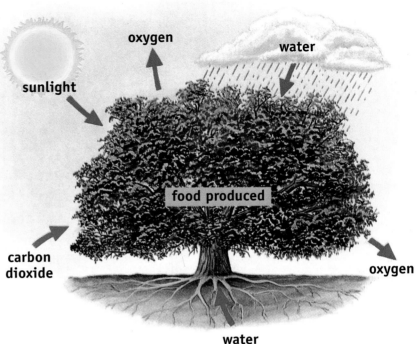

▲ **During photosynthesis, plants turn the energy of sunlight into food energy.**

Nongreen Organisms Need the Sun

What would happen to nongreen organisms—such as you, a dog, or a mushroom—if the Sun's energy were blocked? You may think that you and these other organisms could get along just fine—after all, none of you needs the Sun to make your own food. But think again!

Although animals and many other organisms can't use the Sun's energy directly, they still depend on the Sun.

To obtain energy, animals must eat plants, or they must eat other animals that eat plants. Fungi (fun′jī), such as mushrooms, get energy by breaking

down the remains of dead animals and plants. You can see that nongreen organisms also depend on the Sun for energy. ■

INVESTIGATE FURTHER!

RESEARCH

The Sun is important to you in many ways. Find out whether solar power is used in your area. Hypothesize why it is a common or uncommon source of energy. Research solar power. Decide whether a house in your area could be powered by solar energy alone.

What's to Eat?

Reading Focus In what ways do organisms in a forest obtain energy?

◀ **Great horned owls prey on small animals for food energy.**

It is mid-autumn, and the Sun is setting in the forest. A gray squirrel ventures into a nearby clearing to nibble on fallen berries. High above, a great horned owl perches on the branch of a red oak tree. The owl has begun its nightly search for prey. It hears the squirrel moving in the clearing. The owl focuses its eyes and prepares to attack. In one swift, silent swoop it seizes the squirrel in its talons.

Everyone Needs Food

Great horned owls thrive in forest ecosystems. There they find plenty of small mammals to feed on. In every ecosystem each organism has its own way of getting food energy. You know that some organisms can use the Sun to make food because they can carry on photosynthesis. These organisms are called **producers**. In forest ecosystems, producers include green plants, such as trees, vines, shrubs, ferns, and mosses.

Organisms that obtain energy by eating other organisms are called **consumers**. To get energy, consumers must eat producers or other consumers. Both owls and squirrels are consumers in a forest ecosystem. Squirrels eat acorns, berries, tree sap, and more than 100 kinds of plants. Owls eat squirrels, many other small mammals, and sometimes insects.

Another kind of consumer, called a **decomposer**, feeds on the wastes of living organisms and on dead, decaying plants and animals. Fungi, bacteria, insects, and worms are forest decomposers.

Three Kinds of Consumers

Consumers can be classified by the kinds of food they eat. Plant-eating consumers are called **herbivores** (hʉr′bə vôrz). Meat-eating consumers are called **carnivores** (kär′nə vôrz). Consumers that eat both plants and animals are known as **omnivores** (äm′ni vôrz).

Squirrels, deer, rabbits, mice, and most insects are examples of forest herbivores. Carnivores feed on herbivores and on other carnivores. The owl pellets in the activity on page B12 contain fur, bones, and other animal remains that owls cannot digest. You might be surprised to know that some owls can capture mammals as large as cats, rabbits, and skunks!

Omnivores eat both plants and animals. They often eat whatever is available. The forest-dwelling box turtle, for example, is an omnivore. It eats strawberries, blackberries, and mushrooms. It also eats insects and spiders.

Many forest birds are omnivores. For example, the wood thrush eats beetles, ants, and caterpillars as well as wild fruits and seeds. The Eastern bluebird feeds on grasshoppers and weevils. It also eats the fruits of holly, dogwood, and other plants.

Other ecosystems may contain organisms that are different from those of a forest. But all ecosystems contain producers, consumers, and decomposers. ■

UNIT PROJECT LINK

For this Unit Project you will make a science museum exhibit showing how ecosystems change over time. List the living things you might find in your area. Then map the area and do a survey, marking the location of all the living things you find. Draw or photograph some of these organisms in their environment.

Technology Link
For more help with your Unit Project, go to **www.eduplace.com**.

▼ **Deer are herbivores.**

Wolves are meat eaters, or carnivores. ▶

Eat or Be Eaten

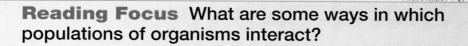

Reading Focus What are some ways in which populations of organisms interact?

The cycle of organisms eating and being eaten is a major part of life in an ecosystem. Every consumer has to eat. An organism that hunts and eats other organisms is called a predator (pred′ə tər). An organism that is hunted and eaten is called the prey.

The interaction between a predator and its prey is called a predator-prey relationship. Predator-prey relationships occur between different populations of animals.

The Size of a Population

As a predator population increases, it consumes more prey. Eventually, the prey become scarce. As a result the predators have less to eat. Then their population decreases. With fewer predators, the prey population increases again. This pattern is shown in the graph below. The lynx feeds on the hare. The lynx population increases when there are many hares. It decreases when hares are scarce.

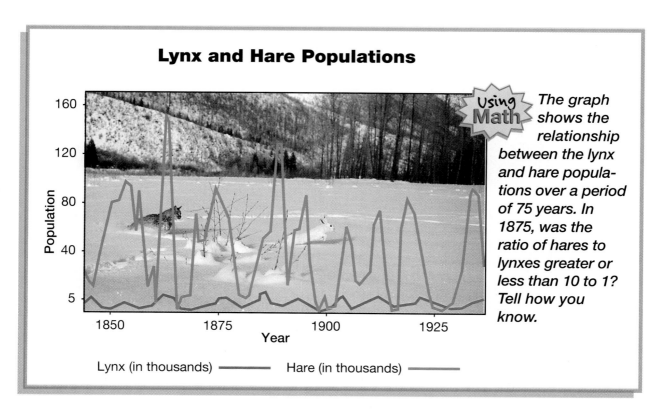

Lynx and Hare Populations

Using Math

The graph shows the relationship between the lynx and hare populations over a period of 75 years. In 1875, was the ratio of hares to lynxes greater or less than 10 to 1? Tell how you know.

Lynx (in thousands) ——— Hare (in thousands) ———

It is not only predator-prey relationships that affect population size. Population size depends also on resources such as water and soil nutrients. For example, if a drought partly dries up a pond, the number of frogs in the pond will decrease. The size of the population of plants in a grassland depends on the supply of nutrients in the soil as well as the amount of rainfall.

For Better or for Worse

Some species form long-term close relationships with other species. This kind of relationship is called symbiosis (sim bī ō'sis). Symbiosis can occur between plants and microscopic organisms, animals and plants, and animals and other animals. Read on to learn about the three kinds of symbiosis.

Ouch! That Hurts!

In **parasitism** (par'ə sīt iz əm), one organism lives in or on, feeds upon, and harms another organism. An organism that feeds on other organisms is called a parasite; the organisms that are fed upon are called hosts. A familiar example of parasitism is the relationship between a dog (host) and fleas and ticks (parasites). Fleas and ticks live and feed upon dogs and other animals. The fleas and ticks benefit, and the dogs are harmed—and irritated!

Science in Literature

City Bees Drink Soda

The City Kid's Field Guide
by Ethan Herberman
Simon & Schuster, 1989

"It turns out that in addition to seeking out flowers, bees have made an important adaptation to city life by learning to drink soda and other sugary junk they find downtown and in city lots. The soda substitutes for nectar . . . although it's hard to imagine how the insects can stand it. Soda must taste awfully sour. Some nectar, after all, is at least four times as sweet."

Read *The City Kid's Field Guide* by Ethan Herberman to learn what goes on in vacant lots, parks, and garbage cans.

No Harm Done

In **commensalism** (kə-men'səl iz əm), one species benefits, while the other species is unaffected. Many kinds of animals have such relationships with plants. In some cases the animal resembles a certain part of a plant. When it is on that plant part, the animal cannot be seen by predators or prey. For example, a kind of crab spider resembles flower petals. The spider sits in a flower. When insects land on the flower, they are quickly eaten by the spider. While the spider profits, the flower neither benefits nor is harmed.

In **mutualism** (myoo'choo əl iz-əm), all species that take part benefit from the relationship. For example, bees drink nectar from flowers. In the process they carry away pollen, which pollinates other flowers. Both the bees and flowers benefit. Lichens are fungi

▲ **A crab spider hiding in a flower (*left*) and lichens on a tree (*right*)**

and algae that live together. The algae produce sugars that the fungi use. The fungi supply the algae with water and nutrients.

Although some microorganisms cause disease, most do not. In fact, many are beneficial to humans. For example, large numbers of bacteria have mutualistic relationships with humans. In the human large intestine, bacteria live off parts of foods that humans can't use. These bacteria also make some nutrients that our bodies can use. ■

INVESTIGATION 2 WRAP-UP

REVIEW

1. By what basic process are the organisms in an ecosystem related?

2. Distinguish among herbivores, carnivores, and omnivores in an ecosystem.

CRITICAL THINKING

3. How might carnivores be affected by a decline in the number of producers in an ecosystem? Explain.

4. Classify an organism in your neighborhood as a consumer, decomposer, or producer. Explain how the organism gets its energy. Describe its diet and the place where it lives.

REFLECT & EVALUATE

Word Power

Write the letter of the term that best matches the definition. *Not all terms will be used.*

1. Relationship that benefits one species and harms another
2. Organism that makes its own food
3. Animal that eats both plants and animals
4. Role of a species in a community
5. All the organisms living together in an ecosystem
6. Organism that eats only producers

a. community
b. herbivore
c. mutualism
d. niche
e. omnivore
f. parasitism
g. producer

Check What You Know

Write the term in each pair that best completes each sentence.

1. Soil and water in an ecosystem are (biotic, abiotic) factors.
2. Worms and bacteria in the soil are (producers, decomposers).
3. A meat-eating animal is a (carnivore, herbivore).
4. A community is made up of the living things in a/an (niche, ecosystem).

Problem Solving

1. Like other organisms, you interact with your environment and are part of an ecosystem. Give three examples of ways that you interact with the living and nonliving parts of your environment.

2. Compare a fish and a turtle. What adaptations help each animal survive in a pond ecosystem?

BUILD YOUR PORTFOLIO

Study the photograph. Write the name of the type of relationship shown. Then write a paragraph explaining how the organisms benefit or are harmed by the relationship.

flea

cat's ear

CHAPTER 2

ENERGY AND MATTER IN ECOSYSTEMS

An ecosystem is like a bustling city. Producers are busy storing energy. Consumers are always "shopping" for energy. And decomposers keep the city clean. The citizens of this "city" are plants, animals, and other living things.

PEOPLE USING SCIENCE

Ecologist Cynthia Wentworth is an ecologist, a scientist who studies how living things interact with each other and their environment. She works for the U.S. Forest Service.

Before becoming an ecologist, Wentworth spent 14 years as a medical technician. But her childhood love of the outdoors drew her away from the indoors and out into nature. Hoping to work at her first love, Wentworth returned to school to learn forestry. As an ecologist, Wentworth must be able to identify different species of plants and animals. Also, she must recognize animal habitats. Her work helps ensure that the environments she studies are preserved for their inhabitants.

The Cycle of Food

Reading Focus What is the basic path that energy follows as it moves through an ecosystem?

Why do you eat lunch? If you didn't eat, you'd get very hungry, right? You'd probably also have trouble concentrating during the afternoon.

All living things need energy to survive. This energy comes from food. The food you eat gives you the energy you need to grow, move, breathe, and even think. But how does energy get into your food? The source of most life-giving energy is the Sun.

Capturing the Sun's Energy

Plants and other producers can change energy from the Sun into food energy. Recall that producers change the Sun's energy into food energy through a process called photosynthesis (fot ō sin'thə sis). Some of this energy is stored in cells for later use. Cells are the basic units that make up all organisms.

When a consumer eats a producer, some of the matter that makes up the producer, as well as some of its stored energy, is passed on to the consumer. If this consumer is eaten by another consumer, energy stored in the first consumer's cells is passed on to the second consumer. This transfer of energy creates a food chain. A **food chain** is the path of energy transfer from one organism to another. Plants are the primary source of matter and energy entering most food chains. They form the base of the food chain.

Using Math *People are consumers in food chains. Food energy is measured in units called Calories. One slice of bread contains about 75 Calories. Estimate the number of Calories you get from bread in one week.*

B27

Moving up the Chain

You know that plants convert the Sun's energy into a usable form that can be passed on to other organisms. Plants are called producers. Organisms that eat producers are called first-order consumers. Second-order consumers eat first-order consumers, and so on.

Trace the energy path in the ecosystem shown on page B29. When the crickets eat grass, they get only part of the energy that the grass received from the Sun. When the mice eat the crickets, the mice get only part of the energy that the crickets received from the grass. This pattern continues up to the owls and the hawks. Because less energy is available at each higher level in the food chain, there are fewer organisms at each higher level. So this ecosystem can support more mice than owls or hawks.

Starting Over Again

All food chains include decomposers. Decomposers include worms, mushrooms, and many microorganisms and insects. They get energy by

Mushrooms are decomposers. ▼

breaking down wastes and dead plant and animal matter. Decomposers break down wastes and the remains of organisms into simpler substances. This process is called decay. The simpler substances are then recycled back to the soil and water. These recycled substances become nutrients for plants and other organisms. So decomposers, including microorganisms, are beneficial to other living things.

Overlapping Food Chains

Most consumers and decomposers can get energy from more than one kind of food. An organism can be part of many food chains, causing food chains to overlap. In the activity on page B26, overlapping food chains form a **food web**. In a food web, an organism can be a first-order consumer in one food chain and a second- or third-order consumer in another food chain.

Animals in a food web often compete for the same resources. Look at the food web on page B29. Which organisms may compete for the same food? What organisms in the salt marsh ecosystem are both second- and third-order consumers?

What About Us?

What is *your* place in food chains and food webs? Humans differ from many other consumers because of

Internet Field Trip

Visit **www.eduplace.com** to find out more about organisms that are part of different food chains.

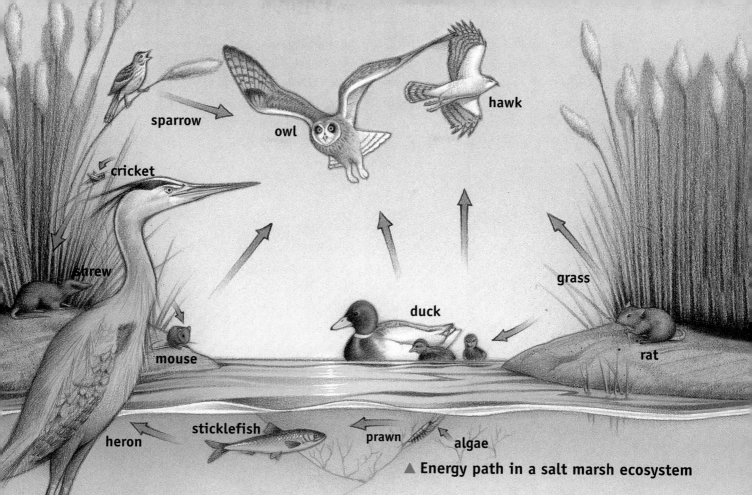

sparrow

hawk

owl

cricket

shrew

grass

mouse

duck

rat

heron

sticklefish

prawn

algae

▲ **Energy path in a salt marsh ecosystem**

what they eat. Recall that herbivores eat only plants, and carnivores eat only animals. Most humans, however, are omnivores. Omnivores eat both plants and animals.

As an omnivore, you can eat "high" or "low" on the food chain. If you eat animal foods, such as meat, eggs, and fish, you are eating high on the food chain. You are consuming other consumers. If you eat mostly plant foods, such as grains, fruits, and vegetables, you are eating low on the food chain. You are eating producers. ■

INVESTIGATION 1 WRAP-UP

REVIEW

1. What is a food chain, and how is a food chain related to a food web?

2. Which type of organism, herbivore or carnivore, eats higher on the food chain?

CRITICAL THINKING

3. Describe a food web of which you are a part. What other organisms are in your food web?

4. Make a drawing that shows what happens to the amount of available energy in an ecosystem as the energy flows from producers through several levels of consumers.

Investigation 2

How Is Matter Cycled In An Ecosystem?

Matter matters in ecosystems! Matter cycles between living and nonliving portions of the ecosystem. How is this cycling done? Find out in Investigation 2.

Activity

Where's the Water?

Water is matter. Plants help water cycle through an ecosystem. Find out how.

MATERIALS
- bean plant (in cup) with 4 or 5 leaves
- water
- small plastic bag
- rubber band
- *Science Notebook*

Procedure

Your teacher will give you a bean plant in a cup. Add water to the cup so that the soil is moist. Loosely cover two or three leaves of the plant with a plastic bag. Hold the bag in place with a rubber band.

Leave the cup in a sunny spot for two days. Each day, observe the plant and record any changes in your *Science Notebook*. Observe the leaves and the inside of the bag.

Analyze and Conclude

1. What happened to the water in the soil over the two days? How do you know?

2. Plants take in water and return some of it to the air through their leaves. What evidence do you have of this?

Activity

Take a Breath

Your body uses the oxygen you inhale to release energy from the food you eat. A waste product of that process is carbon dioxide. What happens to that carbon dioxide?

MATERIALS

- goggles
- beaker (250 mL)
- 2 wide-mouthed plastic cups
- water
- dropper
- bromothymol blue (BTB) solution
- plastic straw
- *Elodea* plant
- 2 test tubes
- timer
- *Science Notebook*

SAFETY //////

Wear goggles. Do not suck on the straw. If you accidentally do, do not swallow. Spit out the liquid. Rinse your mouth several times with tap water.

Procedure

1. Fill a beaker about two-thirds full with water. Use a dropper to add enough BTB solution to turn the water blue. Using a plastic straw, blow into the BTB solution. **Record** in your *Science Notebook* what happens.

2. Put an *Elodea* plant in a test tube. Completely fill each of two test tubes with the BTB solution from the beaker.

3. Place your thumb over the mouth of the first test tube to seal it. Turn the test tube upside down and put it in a plastic cup, as shown. Do not let air get into the test tube. Do the same thing with the second test tube. Wash your hands.

4. Put the test tube setups in a sunny place for one hour. **Predict** what changes, if any, will take place. **Record** your predictions. After one hour, **observe** both test tubes and **record** your observations.

See **SCIENCE** *and* **MATH TOOLBOX** page H12 if you need to review *Measuring Elapsed Time.*

Analyze and Conclude

1. In step 1, the carbon dioxide that you breathed out caused a change in the BTB. Describe that change.

2. In step 4, how did the BTB change after one hour? **Compare** the BTB in each test tube. What can you **infer** about the carbon dioxide you breathed into the BTB?

3. In what way are you and plants cycling matter?

Step 4

The Carbon Dioxide–Oxygen Cycle

Reading Focus How do photosynthesis and cell respiration work together in the cycling of matter?

1 During cell respiration, living things use oxygen, given off by plants, to break down food and obtain energy. When organisms carry out this process, carbon dioxide is given off into the air and the water.

▲ **How carbon dioxide and oxygen are cycled in ecosystems**

Take a deep breath. As you inhale, you take in oxygen, as well as nitrogen, carbon dioxide, and water vapor in the air. When you exhale, you breathe out less oxygen than you took in. You also breathe out more carbon dioxide than you took in. Each time you breathe, you take part in the worldwide **carbon dioxide–oxygen cycle**.

Into the Soil

The drawing above shows that soil is a major part of the carbon dioxide–oxygen cycle. Plant roots deep in the soil take in water. In the plant the water is combined with carbon dioxide to form sugar, a carbon compound rich in energy. Carbon is released as carbon dioxide when decomposers break down plant and animal matter. The use of oxygen to break down carbon compounds and release energy is called **cell respiration** (res pə-rā′shən). Carbon dioxide is a waste product of cell respiration. The activity on page B31 tests exhaled breath for carbon dioxide. Its presence is evidence of cell respiration.

The Nitrogen Cycle

Reading Focus How does nitrogen help people live?

Nitrogen is an important substance found in the cells of all organisms. Living things need it to make proteins. **Proteins** are compounds that form the building blocks of living things.

How do living things get the nitrogen they need to make protein? More than three fourths of Earth's atmosphere is nitrogen gas. But your body can't take in nitrogen gas directly from the air and use it to make proteins. Neither can most other organisms.

Certain kinds of bacteria can take nitrogen from the air, change it, and make it useful to other living things. Some plants, such as clover, alfalfa, beans, and peas, have these kinds of bacteria on their roots. So although some bacteria cause illness, most do not. In fact, bacteria that make nitrogen available to other living things are essential to life on Earth.

How, then, do people get the proteins they need? They eat plants or they eat animals that eat plants.

Decomposers, including bacteria and fungi, also change nitrogen compounds into forms that plants can use. Look at the nitrogen cycle on the next page to find out how this happens. Then use the diagram to find out how lightning changes nitrogen in air.

Look at the amount of nitrogen in inhaled and exhaled air. Is nitrogen in air used directly to form protein? How do you know? ▼

nitrogen

78 percent

78 percent

oxygen

21 percent

17 percent

argon

0.03 percent — carbon dioxide — 4 percent

other gases

Air breathed in

Air breathed out

1 In the **nitrogen cycle**, nitrogen gas is converted to a usable form and eventually returned to the atmosphere as nitrogen gas.

2 Lightning changes some nitrogen gas into nitrogen compounds. These compounds are washed to Earth in rain. Some of the nitrogen compounds enter the soil with rainwater.

5 Proteins in wastes and in the remains of dead organisms are broken down by decomposers to ammonia, nitrites, and nitrates. These compounds are used by plants or break down into nitrogen gas, which passes into the air.

3 Nitrogen is made usable by bacteria that grow on the roots of plants such as beans and peas. These bacteria turn nitrogen into ammonia. Other bacteria change ammonia into nitrates that can also be used by plants.

4 Plants use ammonia and nitrates to make proteins. Animals get nitrogen by eating plants or other animals.

▲ **How nitrogen is cycled in ecosystems**

INVESTIGATION 2 WRAP-UP

REVIEW

1. Sketch how water is recycled in ecosystems.

2. What are the roles of oxygen and carbon dioxide in cell respiration and photosynthesis?

CRITICAL THINKING

3. Modern farming practices speed up the decomposition of matter in soil. How might this affect the nitrogen cycle?

4. Compost, which is made from grass clippings, leaves, and food wastes that are broken down, can be used to enrich soil. What organisms must be part of a compost pile?

REFLECT & EVALUATE

Word Power

Write the letter of the term that best matches the definition. *Not all terms will be used.*

1. The use of oxygen to release energy from food
2. Overlapping food chains in an ecosystem
3. A group of compounds that are building blocks of living things
4. Consumer that eats only animals
5. Path of energy transfer from one organism to another
6. Process of changing water vapor to liquid water

a. carnivore
b. cell respiration
c. condensation
d. evaporation
e. food chain
f. food web
g. proteins

Check What You Know

Write the term in each pair that best completes each sentence.

1. A carnivore's position on the food chain is (high, low).
2. During cell respiration, oxygen is (used up, released).
3. Photosynthesis is an important process in the (carbon dioxide–oxygen, nitrogen) cycle.
4. Nitrogen is a substance found in (protein, sugar).

Problem Solving

1. Imagine that Earth stopped receiving light from the Sun. What effect would this have on food chains and food webs? on the carbon dioxide–oxygen cycle? on the water cycle? on the nitrogen cycle?

2. Suppose you work on a farm. Identify a way that you could improve the nitrogen content of the soil.

BUILD YOUR PORTFOLIO

Study the drawing. Then write a paragraph explaining each organism's role in food chains and food webs.

CHAPTER 3

DIFFERENT KINDS OF ECOSYSTEMS

If you live in the American Southwest, you may see cactuses outside your window. In the Northeast you may see maple trees or in the Southeast, palms. Wherever you live, you are part of a large ecosystem.

PEOPLE USING SCIENCE

Biologist If you had visited Kenya in 1977, you would have seen a land stripped of trees. Ninety percent of Kenya's forests had been cut down. As the forests disappeared, so did Kenya's streams and wildlife. Wood for fuel had nearly vanished. Without fuel it was difficult to cook healthful foods. As a result, children were not eating well. The natural ecosystem was being destroyed. Every organism in the ecosystem suffered.

That same year a Kenyan biologist named Wangari Maathai began to save the ecosystem. She started a tree-planting project, called the Green Belt Movement, in which young trees are given to women farmers to plant. Maathai's idea has been a great success. In just the first ten years of the project, the Green Belt planted 5 million trees!

Coming Up

INVESTIGATION 1

How Do Earth's Major Ecosystems Differ?
.... B44

INVESTIGATION 2

What Is Biodiversity, and How Is It Changing?
.... B54

▲ Wangari Maathai's Green Belt Movement helped restore Kenya's ecosystem.

HOW DO EARTH'S MAJOR ECOSYSTEMS DIFFER?

Some ecosystems, like a backyard garden, are very small. In this investigation you'll find out about characteristics of each of Earth's major ecosystems.

Activity

Make a Mini-Biome!

Biomes are ecosystems that cover large areas of Earth's land surface. In this activity you can make a model of a biome and see how abiotic factors affect it.

Procedure

1. From the table on the next page, choose the kind of plant you wish to grow. Your teacher will give you several specimens of that kind of plant.

2. Work on newspaper. Cover the bottom of a large jar with a layer of activated charcoal 0.5 cm thick. Use the table on page B45 to find the kind of soil your plants need. Place a layer of this kind of soil, 3 cm deep, on top of the charcoal.

Math Hint Remember that 0.5 cm equals $\frac{1}{2}$ cm.

MATERIALS
- goggles
- newspaper
- gardening gloves
- plants (several of the same kind)
- large plastic jar
- activated charcoal
- metric ruler
- potting soil
- sand
- grass seed
- water in a spray bottle
- *Science Notebook*

SAFETY
Use gardening gloves to handle plants that have needles or spines. Wear goggles when handling soil.

Kind of Plant	Soil Type	How Often to Water
Broad-leaved	potting	every 2–3 days
Cactus	sand	lightly, every 2 weeks
Grass	potting	every other day
Needle-leaved	potting-sand mixture	weekly

3. Carefully lift the plants out of their pots, making sure that some soil clings to the roots. Place the plant roots in the soil in the jar. Be sure the roots are completely covered so that the plants are well anchored. If you choose to grow grass, scatter the seeds on the soil and cover them with a thin layer of soil.

4. Place your mini-biome in a sunny spot. Use a spray bottle to moisten the soil. Use the table as a guide to watering the plants. **Observe** your mini-biome daily. **Record** your observations in your *Science Notebook*.

5. **Observe** and **compare** the mini-biomes of the other students.

INVESTIGATE FURTHER!

EXPERIMENT

Plan your own experiment to find out how well the plants in your mini-biomes can live under different conditions (see Question 2 under Analyze and Conclude). Write a question you can test about what might happen to plants if you changed their conditions. Then write a procedure for your experiment that other students can follow.

Analyze and Conclude

1. The biomes varied as to the kind of plants, type of soil, and amount of watering. What abiotic factors were the same for all the biomes represented?

2. Which two biomes had the most similar growing conditions? Which two had the least similar conditions? **Infer** what would happen if you switched the plants growing under the least similar conditions.

3. What is the relationship between abiotic factors in a biome and the kind of plant life found there?

Step 3

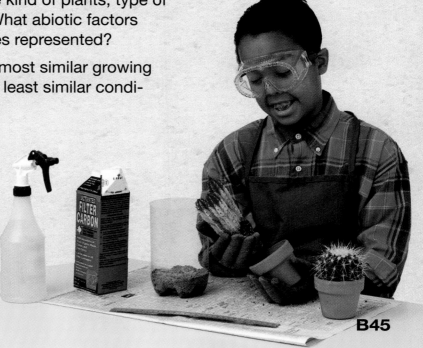

Earth's Biomes

Reading Focus What are some abiotic and biotic factors of each kind of biome?

The abiotic factors of an area include climate and soil type. Along with the biotic factors, such as plants and animals, abiotic factors determine an area's ecosystem. Ecosystems that cover large areas of land are called **biomes**.

The major biomes on Earth are the deciduous (dē sij′o͞o əs) forest, the desert, the grassland, the taiga (tī′gə), the tropical rain forest, and the tundra. This world map shows you where these biomes are found. Humans live in all biomes, but some biomes support human populations better than others do.

UNIT PROJECT LINK

Create a model of the biome where you live. Find out which biome you live in and how biomes can change over time. Work with others to create a model of your biome as it may have looked before people inhabited it. Include extinct plants and animals that once lived there.

Technology Link
For more help with your Unit Project, go to **www.eduplace.com**.

The largest number of people live in biomes that have a lot of plant and animal resources. These biomes, which include temperate and tropical regions, have milder climates. Temperate and tropical regions are close to the equator. These biomes receive enough solar energy to support a great many living communities.

On the next two pages, you'll find out about the abiotic and biotic factors of each biome. And you'll learn how these factors make each biome like no other.

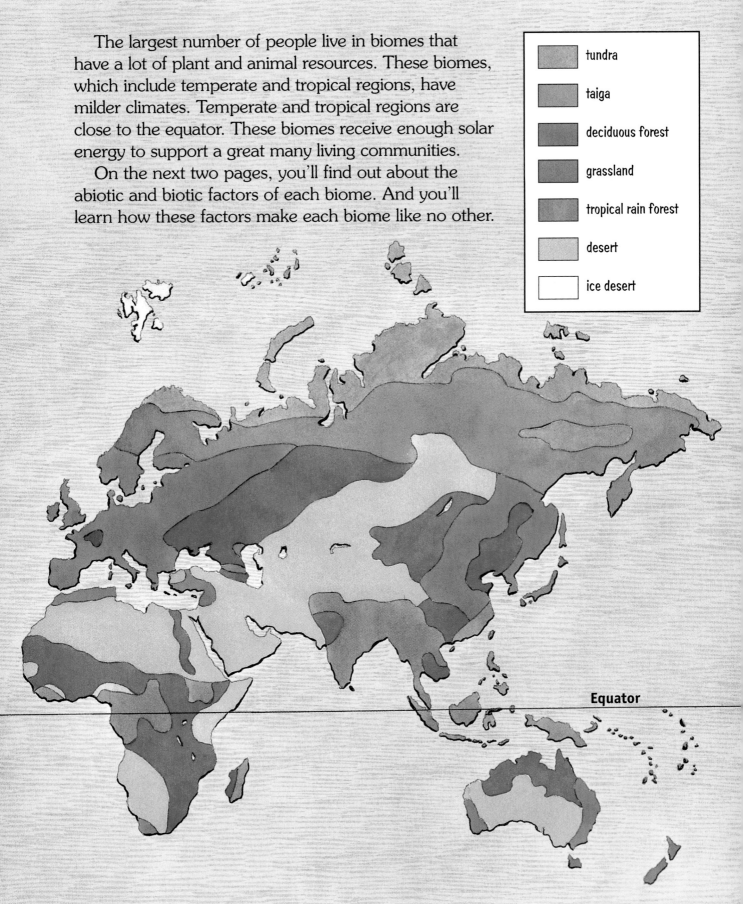

tundra

taiga

deciduous forest

grassland

tropical rain forest

desert

ice desert

Equator

toucan

◀ **TROPICAL RAIN FOREST**
Tropical rain forests are lush and green year-round. Heavy rainfall and a warm climate create an environment in which an amazing variety of plants and animals thrive. These organisms live in "layers" of the forest, from the ground to the tops of trees. Tree branches form one layer known as the canopy.

GRASSLAND **Grasslands** are ▶ wide-open fields of grass that once covered vast areas of nearly every continent. The kinds of grasses that grow in a grassland depend on the amount of rainfall. Wetter areas have taller grasses; drier areas have shorter grasses. Grasslands attract grazing animals and rodents, as well as their predators.

field mouse

◀ **DESERT** **Deserts** can be either hot or cold, but they are always very dry. So desert plants and animals have to survive without much water. As a result, few types of plants grow in desert ecosystems. Animal populations also are not diverse.

horned lizard

B48

▲ **DECIDUOUS FOREST** **Deciduous forests** grow where winters are cold and summers are warm and wet. The large leaves of deciduous trees—maple, oak, and birch, for example—carry out photosynthesis. Their leaves are lost in autumn. There is plenty of food for insects, birds, rodents, and other animals in these forests.

beetle

TAIGA The **taiga** contains ▶ coniferous forests where evergreens grow. In the taiga the winters are long and cold. On the forest floor are low-growing mosses and lichens. Many birds and mammals prey on needle-eating insects and seed-eating rodents.

lodgepole pine cone

◀ **TUNDRA** The **tundra** is the Arctic grassland north of the taiga where the subsoil is frozen year-round. The tundra has long, cold winters and cool summers. There is little precipitation. A thin layer of snow and ice covers the ground most of the year. The plants that live in the tundra survive a growing season that is only a few months long.

saxifrage

B49

Water Ecosystems

Reading Focus What are some abiotic and biotic factors of freshwater and saltwater ecosystems?

Look back at the map on pages B46 and B47. As you read earlier, about three fourths of Earth's surface is covered by water! There are two main kinds of water ecosystems: freshwater ecosystems and saltwater ecosystems. A great variety of organisms live in each of these ecosystems.

Freshwater Ecosystems

Only about three one-hundredths of the water on Earth is fresh. And more than two thirds of the fresh water is locked in ice at the North Pole or the South Pole or at the tops of mountains. The remaining fresh water is in the ground or is surface water.

Fresh water fills the lakes, ponds, rivers, streams, and swamps of the world. The variety of living things in a freshwater community depends on whether the water is still or flowing, slow-moving or fast-moving. It also depends on other abiotic factors, such as the water temperature and how much oxygen the water contains. All these factors are connected. Cold water, for example, holds more oxygen than warm water; fast-moving water holds more oxygen than slow-moving water. Look at the picture to get the idea about the variety of life forms some freshwater ecosystems support.

great blue heron

RIVER A river is running water that empties into a lake, an ocean, or another river. The underwater ecosystems of rivers vary a great deal. Rivers support freshwater fish, shrimp, plants, birds, and other life forms.

pickerelweed

Freshwater Ecosystems

deciduous trees

WETLAND A wetland is an area where land and water meet. The soil of a wetland is watery. There is less oxygen in the water of wetlands than in that of rivers or lakes. Many types of wetlands exist. A marsh has mostly grasses and cattails. A swamp is similar to a marsh but has mostly trees and shrubs. A bog consists primarily of mosses.

LAKE A lake is a large standing body of fresh water. Lakes range in size from huge expanses, such as Lake Superior, to small bodies of water. The place in which an organism lives is its habitat. A lake contains a variety of habitats, but each lake is different. Lake fish include perch and bass. Lakes also support frogs, insects, and other water life.

blue-winged teal

waterlily

cattail

leopard frog

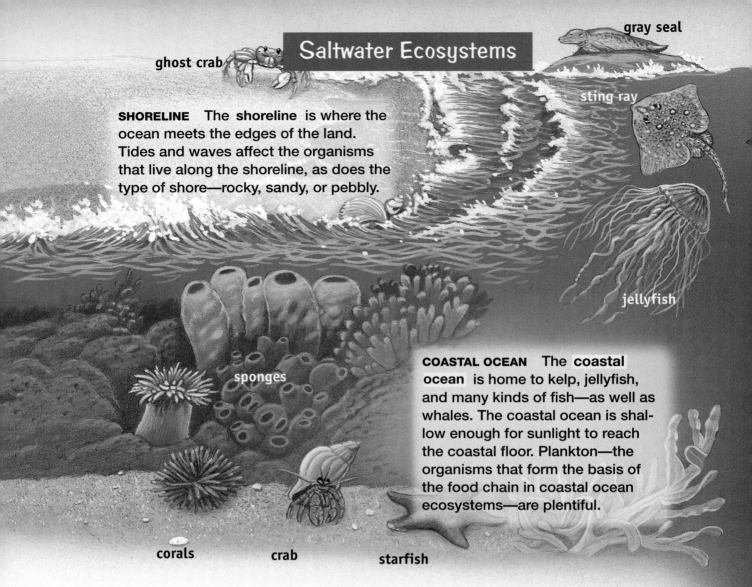

Saltwater Ecosystems

SHORELINE The shoreline is where the ocean meets the edges of the land. Tides and waves affect the organisms that live along the shoreline, as does the type of shore—rocky, sandy, or pebbly.

COASTAL OCEAN The coastal ocean is home to kelp, jellyfish, and many kinds of fish—as well as whales. The coastal ocean is shallow enough for sunlight to reach the coastal floor. Plankton—the organisms that form the basis of the food chain in coastal ocean ecosystems—are plentiful.

ghost crab

gray seal

sting ray

jellyfish

sponges

corals

crab

starfish

Saltwater Ecosystems

Ninety-seven percent of Earth's water is salty ocean water. The oceans are one continuous body of water. The forms of life this ecosystem supports vary from tiny one-celled organisms to enormous mammals.

Ocean water generally contains about 3.5 percent salt, but this amount can vary. The amount of salt in water can either support organisms or kill them. Water pressure, temperature, and light also affect the types of organisms that live in salt water. So, there are really several different saltwater ecosystems.

The next time someone talks about the ocean as if it were one big ecosystem, you may want to set them straight. Explain that saltwater ecosystems are not as simple as they seem. To understand them, you must observe and study them. ■

Internet Field Trip

Visit **www.eduplace.com** to learn more about plants and animals in ocean ecosystems.

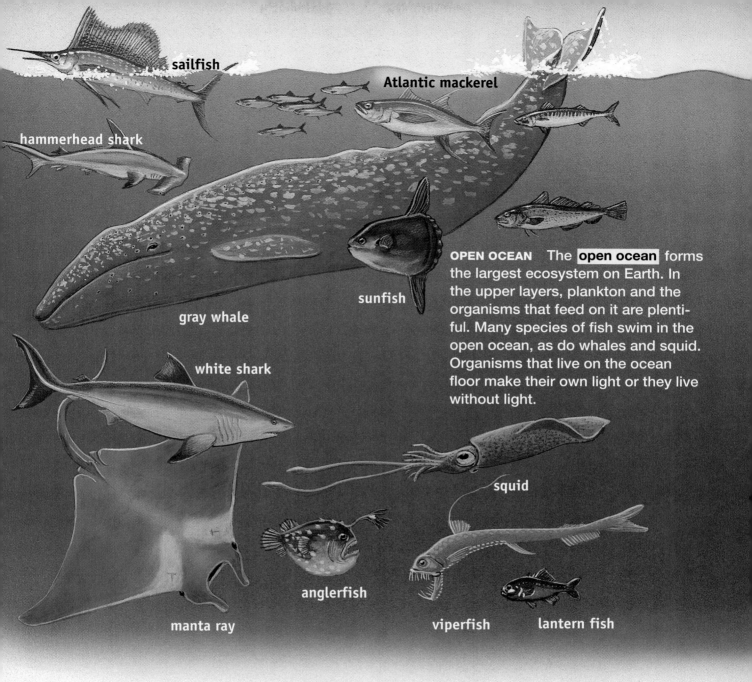

sailfish

Atlantic mackerel

hammerhead shark

gray whale

sunfish

white shark

OPEN OCEAN The open ocean forms the largest ecosystem on Earth. In the upper layers, plankton and the organisms that feed on it are plentiful. Many species of fish swim in the open ocean, as do whales and squid. Organisms that live on the ocean floor make their own light or they live without light.

squid

manta ray

anglerfish

viperfish

lantern fish

INVESTIGATION 1 WRAP-UP

THINK IT WRITE IT

REVIEW

1. Describe some abiotic and biotic factors that vary among different land biomes.

2. Give an example of each of the two main kinds of water ecosystems.

CRITICAL THINKING

3. Deciduous forests and grasslands have supported large human populations. Why do you think this is so?

4. Explain how desert plants and animals are adapted to live in their ecosystem.

WHAT IS BIODIVERSITY, AND HOW IS IT CHANGING?

Earth's ecosystems are home to millions of species of living things. Each species in an ecosystem plays a role. In this investigation you'll find out how changes in diversity affect an ecosystem.

Activity

Vanishing Species

MATERIALS

- globe
- graph paper
- metric ruler
- *Science Notebook*

When ecosystems change, some species may die out. Try to find one factor that has led to the decline of rain forests in Ecuador.

- -

Procedure

1. Look at the maps. They show how the area covered by tropical rain forests in Ecuador has changed since 1938. Forests are shown in green. In your *Science Notebook*, describe what has happened between 1938 and 1988.

2. Refer to the table on the next page. Make a bar graph that shows the change in Ecuador's forested area based on the data from 1961, 1971, 1991, and 1995.

 See **SCIENCE** and **MATH** **TOOLBOX** page H3 if you need to review *Making a Bar Graph.*

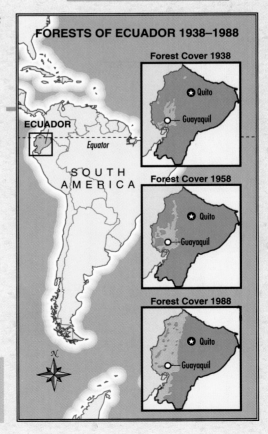

FORESTS OF ECUADOR 1938–1988

Forest Cover 1938

ECUADOR

Equator

SOUTH AMERICA

● Quito
○ Guayaquil

Forest Cover 1958

● Quito
○ Guayaquil

Forest Cover 1988

● Quito
○ Guayaquil

N

Ecuador	1961	1971	1991	1995
Forest & Woodland	173,000 km^7	153,000 km^2	112,000 km^2	110,920 km^2
Human Population	5,162,000	7,035,000	10,782,000	11,920,000

3. Look again at the table. Notice how the human population in Ecuador grew over the 34-year period. **Make a bar graph** that shows the change in Ecuador's human population based on the data from the table.

Analyze and Conclude

1. **Compare** the graphs you drew. What appears to be the relationship between the change in the population and the change in the amount of forested land in Ecuador?

2. Based on your knowledge of food webs, **infer** what happens to a rain forest community when the trees are cut down.

 # Science in Literature

PROTECTING PANDAS

"Heavy mists and rains shroud bamboo and coniferous forests in the mountains of China's Sichuan province, home to giant panda bears. Of the estimated 750 pandas in the wild, more than half live in 12 reserves set aside for their protection. Farming, logging, and building have eliminated much of their habitat. . . ."

Bears by Joni Phelps Hunt describes sloth bears, sun bears, spectacled bears, and other kinds of bears found in almost every part of the world.

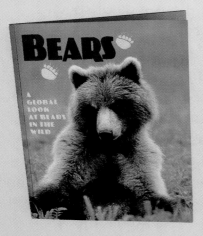

Bears
by Joni Phelps Hunt
Blake Books, 1993

Variety in Ecosystems

Reading Focus What is biodiversity?

Try to imagine 1,000 beetles, each a different species. Difficult, isn't it? But in the forests of Central and South America, you can find more than 1,000 different beetles on a *single tree*. In fact, there probably are at least *300,000* different species of beetles. Scientists think they have actually identified only a tiny fraction of all the species of beetles in the world.

Scientists believe our planet may be home to more than 100 million different species of organisms. So far only about 1.75 million species have been identified!

The great variety of organisms that live on Earth is called **biodiversity** (bī ō də vʉr′sə tē). *Biodiversity* is a combination of the words *biological* and *diversity*. The term refers to the millions of species that can live in Earth's many ecosystems. Look at the circle graph on the next page. It shows known species of each major group of organisms. What fraction of the species is insects? Is it closer to one third or one fourth?

Biodiversity refers not only to the variety of species on Earth but also to diversity within a single species. Think about how you are different from your mother, brother, neighbor, and classmates. Yet humans are members of the same species—*Homo sapiens*. Earthworms, regardless of differences in length or color, are all members of the same species—*Lumbricus terrestris*.

Diversity—A Lot or a Little?

The amount of biodiversity varies among ecosystems. One ecosystem may contain thousands of species; another, fewer than 50. What makes the difference? The biodiversity of an ecosystem depends on three major factors: its size, its land features, and its distance from the equator.

Large ecosystems support more species than do smaller ecosystems. Over a larger area, abiotic factors tend to vary. For example a small island covered by forests may be home to 50 species of butterflies. A larger island may contain 100 species of butterflies. Why? Perhaps a mountain rises on the larger island.

Mountains can cause the amount of rainfall and the temperature to vary across the island. The result? The larger island has more ecosystems than does the smaller one. And different eco- systems have different populations of organisms. Thus, the larger island, with more varied abiotic factors and more ecosystems, supports more species of butterflies.

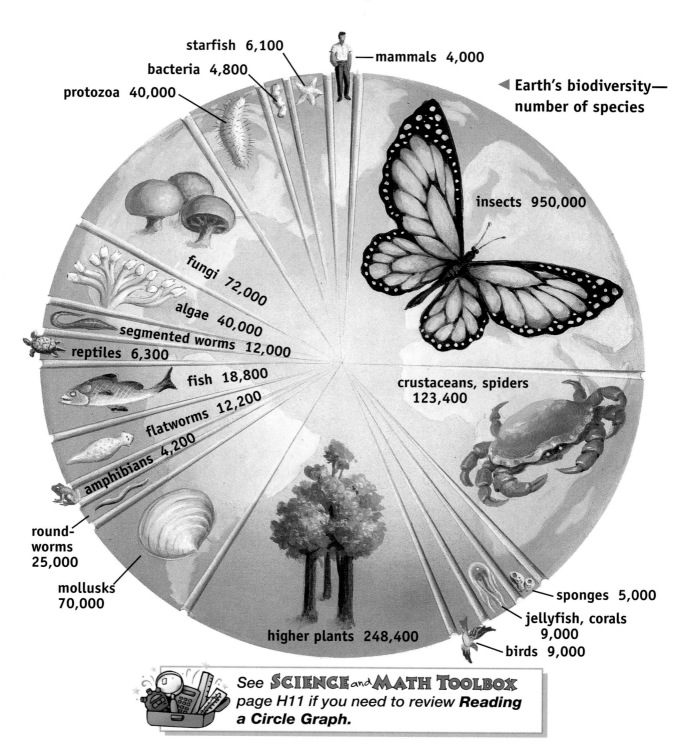

starfish 6,100

bacteria 4,800

protozoa 40,000

mammals 4,000

◀ Earth's biodiversity— number of species

insects 950,000

fungi 72,000

algae 40,000

segmented worms 12,000

reptiles 6,300

fish 18,800

flatworms 12,200

amphibians 4,200

crustaceans, spiders 123,400

round- worms 25,000

mollusks 70,000

higher plants 248,400

sponges 5,000

jellyfish, corals 9,000

birds 9,000

See SCIENCE and MATH TOOLBOX page H11 if you need to review **Reading a Circle Graph.**

Latitude also affects abiotic factors. In places further away from the equator, temperatures are lower. Sunlight is strong only part of the year. Rainfall is less steady. These conditions become more extreme as the distance from the equator increases.

Close to the equator, temperatures are high, sunlight is intense, and rain is plentiful. Plants can grow all year. As a result, producers in tropical ecosystems are numerous and varied. These producers can support consumers of a greater number and variety than can the producers in colder or drier climates.

Most rain forests are in tropical locations. Thus, rain forests have the highest biodiversity of any ecosystem. Maps of the forests of Ecuador are shown in the activity on pages B54 and B55. In the forests of Ecuador, Colombia, and Peru—just one fiftieth

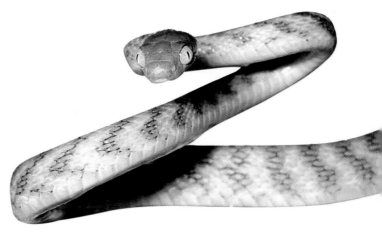

▲ **A brown tree snake**

of the world's land surface—there are more than 40,000 species of plants!

The stable climate of the tropics supports increased biodiversity. As you know, a single tree rooted in the ground is part of a forest. But the tree also supports another whole ecosystem in its canopy layer. The canopy has much plant life—mosses, ferns, and orchids. This miniforest is home to a great many consumers, from one-celled organisms to snakes, frogs, and mammals.

Tinkering With Biodiversity

If you think the dandelions in your schoolyard, the tumbleweed that rolls across the prairie, and the Norway maple in front of the library are "all-American," you'd be wrong! These plants are three of the more than 3,000 species that were brought to the United States by accident or on purpose.

Animal species have been brought from other places, too. Sometimes native species are driven from their habitats by these new species. ■

▲ **The rain forest canopy**

The Challenge of Biodiversity

Reading Focus Why should habitats of endangered or threatened species be preserved?

Have you ever heard anyone say "dead as a dodo"? The dodo was a bird that lived several hundred years ago. It was hunted until all members of its species were dead.

No one has *ever* seen a live dinosaur, and no one *ever* will. Dinosaurs and dodos are all **extinct**. None remain alive. They are gone forever.

Some species, such as the giant panda, are not *yet* extinct. However, many species are **endangered** or threatened. Endangered species are those in danger of becoming extinct.

Threatened species are those that may soon become endangered. Eleven percent of the world's bird species are endangered.

The greatest threat to biodiversity is habitat destruction. Over time, habitats have been destroyed in many ways. Many centuries ago, farmers cut down Europe's forests, destroying these native ecosystems. Settlers plowed under the prairies of the midwestern United States and planted crops. Today some developers fill in wetlands or cut down wooded areas to build housing developments.

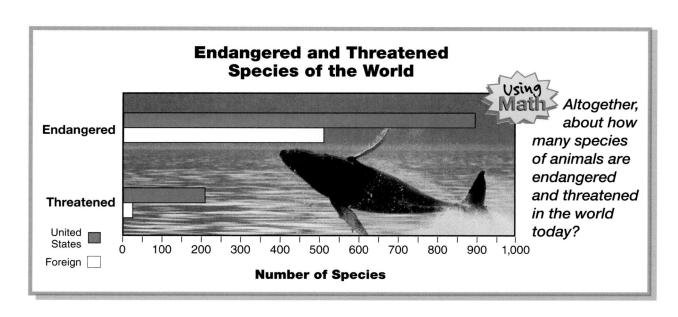

Endangered and Threatened Species of the World

Endangered

Threatened

United States ■
Foreign □

0   100   200   300   400   500   600   700   800   900   1,000

Number of Species

Using Math Altogether, about how many species of animals are endangered and threatened in the world today?

Habitats can also be harmed without being destroyed. Pollution can poison a habitat. The introduction of a species can drive out native organisms.

But why should anyone care about biodiversity? Why should anyone care what happens to plants and animals, as long as people are all right?

Humans cannot live alone on Earth. Plants and animals provide people with food, raw materials for clothing, and building materials. More than 40 percent of all medicines come from living organisms. The complex web of plant life on Earth provides oxygen for life processes. Decomposers keep soils fertile for growing crops. Although some bacteria cause disease, bacteria and other microscopic organisms break down waste and purify water. These are just some reasons why people should care about biodiversity.

▲ **Many species in the rain forests seem to be headed toward extinction, such as the red-leafed *Rafflesia arnoldii* shown.**

Aside from these reasons, many people believe that human beings have a responsibility to preserve Earth. People have the power to destroy ecosystems and drive species to extinction. They also have the power—and the knowledge—to save ecosystems and encourage species' survival. You've learned about the consequences of doing both. What will you do? ■

═══════════════ **INVESTIGATION 2 WRAP-UP** ═══════════════

REVIEW

1. What does biodiversity mean on Earth and within a species?

2. What are the three major factors that affect biodiversity in an ecosystem?

CRITICAL THINKING

3. Why does biodiversity vary among ecosystems?

4. Identify a favorite species you have read about that you fear is in danger of becoming extinct. Why is it endangered? Can anything be done to save it?

REFLECT & EVALUATE

Word Power

Write the letter of the term that best completes each sentence. *Not all terms will be used.*

a. biodiversity
b. desert
c. endangered
d. extinct
e. grassland
f. taiga
g. tundra
h. wetland

1. A species that is ⎯ has no living members.
2. In a ⎯ it may be hot or cold, but it is usually dry.
3. It is cold, and there is low rainfall in a ⎯.
4. The great variety of life forms is called ⎯.
5. Rainfall is moderate, and there are many conifers in a ⎯.
6. An area where land and water meet is a ⎯.

Check What You Know

Write the term in each pair that best completes each sentence.

1. Most of Earth's water is (fresh, salty).
2. Whales live in the (coastal, deep) part of the ocean.
3. The number of species on Earth is closer to (2 million, 100 million).
4. The most species are supported by (rain forests, wetlands).

Problem Solving

1. Compare the variety of ecosystems in the ocean and on land. Suggest reasons why there is greater variety on land than in the ocean.

2. Explain how Earth's biodiversity has been affected by the development of civilization.

BUILD YOUR PORTFOLIO

Draw or trace the animals shown. Cut out each drawing. Arrange the drawings on a sheet of paper. Identify each animal and the water ecosystem in which it lives. Then write a brief description of the main conditions of that ecosystem.

Summarizing

Summarizing helps you remember what you have read. A summary is a short paragraph that states the main points of a selection. Follow these guidelines to write a good summary.

> **Use these guidelines to write a summary.**
> - List topic sentences.
> - Restate main ideas.
> - Group similar ideas.
> - Omit unimportant ideas.

Read the paragraphs. Then complete the exercises that follow.

Ecosystem Dwellers

Organisms that live together in an ecosystem make up a **community**. A community contains many different populations of organisms. Each **population** contains all the organisms of the same kind in a community. A forest may have populations of squirrels, maples, and woodpeckers. Together with other populations, they form a community. All the members of a population are members of the same species.

Organisms of the same species have the same general physical characteristics and other adaptations. An **adaptation** is a structure or behavior that enables a species to survive in its environment.

1. **Write the letters of two statements that you would put in your summary.**

   a. A forest may have populations of squirrels, maples, and woodpeckers.

   b. A population is made up of members of the same species in a community.

   c. An ecosystem is made up of many different populations.

   d. An adaptation is a structure or behavior that enables a species to survive in its environment.

2. **Write a summary of the paragraphs, using the guidelines.**

B62

Using Math — Analyze Data

The average lengths in meters of various dolphins and whales are shown in this table.

Average Lengths of Dolphins and Whales

Type of Dolphin or Whale	Length (m)
Bottlenosed dolphin	3.9
Dusky dolphin	1.6
Humpback dolphin	2.4
Killer whale	8.0
Long-finned pilot whale	7.0
Melon-headed whale	2.6

Use the information in the table to complete the exercises that follow.

1. Which animal has the greatest length? the shortest length?

2. Which two types of animals, lined up nose to tail, would have a length of exactly 5 m?

3. Which animal is as long as five dusky dolphins lined up nose to tail?

4. About how many times longer is a killer whale than a bottlenosed dolphin?

5. The range of a set of data is found by subtracting the smallest number from the largest number in the set of data. What is the range of data in the table?

6. Estimate how many of your arm spans would equal the length of the killer whale.

WRAP-UP!

On your own, use scientific methods to investigate a question about a living thing in its environment.

THINK LIKE A SCIENTIST

Ask a Question

Pose a question about a living thing in its environment that you would like to investigate. For example, ask, "Could a land plant survive in the ocean?"

Make a Hypothesis

Suggest a hypothesis that is a possible answer to the question. One hypothesis is that a land plant would not survive if it was watered with only salt water (ocean water).

Plan and Do a Test

Plan a controlled experiment to find out the effect of ocean water on a land plant. You could start with 8–10 radish seedlings, fresh water, and ocean water. To simulate ocean water, dissolve 24 g of salt in 1 L of fresh water. Develop a procedure that uses these materials to test the hypothesis. With permission, carry out your experiment. Follow the safety guidelines on pages S14–S15.

Record and Analyze

Observe carefully and record your data accurately. Make repeated observations.

Draw Conclusions

Look for evidence to support the hypothesis or to show that it is false. Draw conclusions about the hypothesis. Repeat the experiment to verify the results.

WRITING IN SCIENCE
Note Taking

Prepare a list of different food chains that occur in a pond ecosystem. Use Internet searches and library resources to gather information. Follow these guidelines for taking notes.

- Write notes in your own words.
- Keep track of the name of each source and page references.
- Organize your notes into main topics.
- Draw conclusions based on the information you found.

UNIT C

The Solid Earth

Theme: Constancy and Change

THINK LIKE A SCIENTIST

COOL CAVERN

Reed Flute Cavern, shown here, is found in the People's Republic of China. It is an underground cavern that was produced slowly over tens of thousands of years by the dripping of ground water. The dripping water contains a chemical compound called calcium carbonate. The slow dripping causes giant columns to hang down from the roof of the cavern and tall columns to build up from the floor. Geologists, scientists who study Earth's formations, observe and take samples from caverns to learn how the caverns form.

THINK LIKE A SCIENTIST

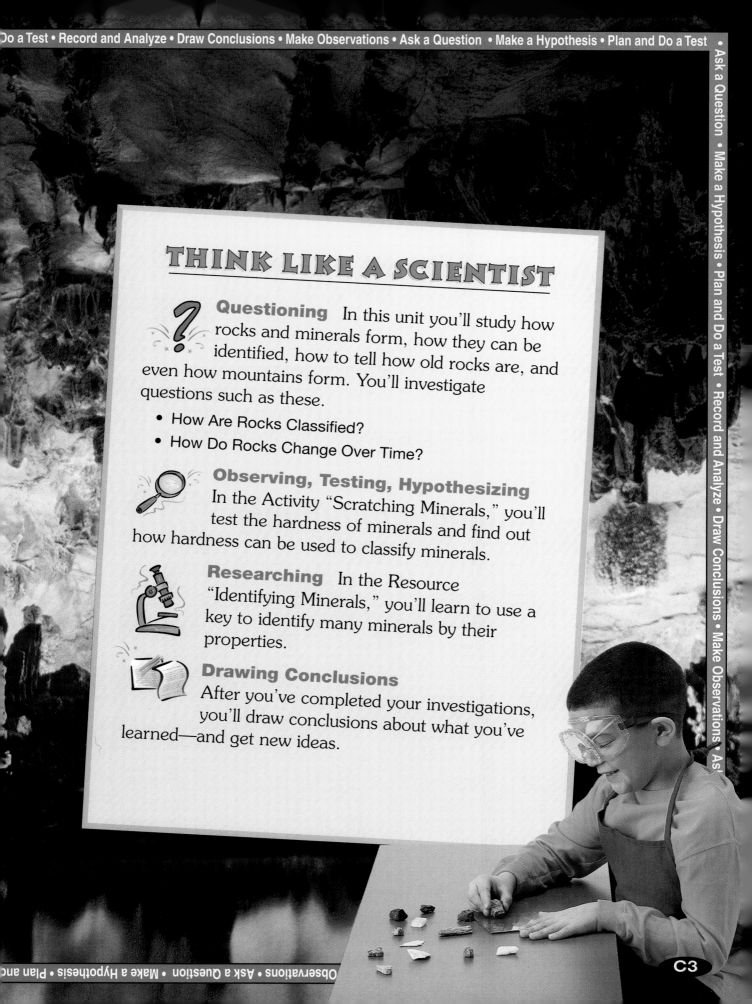

Questioning In this unit you'll study how rocks and minerals form, how they can be identified, how to tell how old rocks are, and even how mountains form. You'll investigate questions such as these.

- How Are Rocks Classified?
- How Do Rocks Change Over Time?

Observing, Testing, Hypothesizing In the Activity "Scratching Minerals," you'll test the hardness of minerals and find out how hardness can be used to classify minerals.

Researching In the Resource "Identifying Minerals," you'll learn to use a key to identify many minerals by their properties.

Drawing Conclusions After you've completed your investigations, you'll draw conclusions about what you've learned—and get new ideas.

MINERALS

Have you ever admired jewelry containing gemstones such as rubies or diamonds? Have you ever seen bracelets or necklaces made of shiny metals such as silver or gold? Both gemstones and metals have something in common. They are *minerals*.

Connecting to Science
ARTS

Wearable Art The beautiful jewelry pieces seen here are the work of Debbie Noiseux. She is a self-taught artist who has designed jewelry for many years. She uses colored gemstones, such as amethysts, opals, and garnets, in her work. Noiseux refers to her jewelry as wearable art.

The artist's fascination with colored gemstones shows in her designs. She carefully handpicks each gemstone according to its special properties. She gets ideas for how to use a particular stone from its color, texture, shape, and size. Her jewelry creatively displays the beauty of each stone.

In this chapter you'll study minerals such as those used in Debbie Noiseux's jewelry. You'll discover much about their physical and chemical properties.

Coming Up

◀ Gemstone jewelry designed by Debbie Noiseux

How Can You Identify Minerals?

A mineral is a solid element or compound from Earth's crust. See if you can name this mineral. In nature it is usually black or brown. It's used in tools for drilling and cutting. In its colorless or blue-white form, it is highly prized. If you said "diamond," you are right!

Activity

The Way Minerals Look

Think about it—you identify most things just by looking at them. Minerals aren't any different. When you get to know them, you'll be able to look at them and name them.

- -

Procedure

1. Open an egg carton and use a marker to number the pockets from 1 through 12.

2. Observe each mineral in your set. Does each look like it is made up of all the same kind of material? Is there any evidence of crystal structure in the minerals? Record your observations in your *Science Notebook*.

3. Make a chart like the one shown, with 8 columns and 12 rows. Any columns you don't fill in during this activity will be used during later activities.

MINERAL PROPERTIES							
Mineral Number	Luster	Color	Streak	Hardness	Cleavage	Special	Name

4. The way a mineral reflects light is called **luster** (lus′tər). Some minerals look like pieces of metal. They have a *metallic* luster. Others don't look like metal. They have a *nonmetallic* luster. Separate your minerals into two sets, one set with minerals that look like metal (such as gold or iron) and one with minerals that don't look like metal.

Step 5

5. Put each mineral in your egg carton. In your chart, record the number of the pocket you put each piece in. Then for each mineral, record *metallic* or *nonmetallic* under the column head *Luster*.

6. Inspect each mineral and record its color in the next column of your chart. If needed, use more than one word, such as *yellow-brown*.

7. The color of the powder left behind by a mineral is called its **streak**. Predict each mineral's streak. With each mineral, try to make a mark (like a pencil mark) on the tile. The color of the mark is the color of the streak. Record the color of each mineral's streak in your chart.

Analyze and Conclude

1. Compare the color and streak of each mineral in your collection. What conclusions can you draw about the color and streak of a mineral?

2. How are the properties of streak and luster useful in getting to know minerals?

Technology Link CD-ROM

INVESTIGATE FURTHER!

Use the **Science Processor CD-ROM**, *The Solid Earth* (Investigation 1, Who Am I?) to identify two unknown mineral samples.

Activity

Scratching Minerals

Hardness is an important property in identifying minerals. Geologists test a mineral's hardness by seeing what objects will scratch or be scratched by the mineral. Try this scratch test yourself.

MATERIALS

- goggles
- mineral set in egg carton from previous activity
- Mineral Properties chart
- square glass plate
- steel nail
- copper wire, 10 cm in length
- *Science Notebook*

SAFETY ///////

Wear goggles during this activity. When using the glass, keep it flat on the desk. Press the mineral onto the glass and pull it across the glass. DO NOT HOLD THE GLASS IN YOUR HAND.

Procedure

1. Try scratching one mineral with another; make just a little scratch. Don't scrub the minerals together or you'll damage them. Can you find the hardest and softest minerals in your set? **Record** your findings in your *Science Notebook*.

2. Geologists often use a set of tools to judge the hardness of a mineral. The tools include a piece of glass, a fingernail, a steel nail, and a piece of copper. **Predict** which of these items will be the hardest. Then scratch each tool with the others to rank the tools from softest to hardest.

3. Try to scratch each mineral with the edge of your fingernail. Always rub your finger over a mark to make certain it's a scratch and not a streak. A streak will rub off, but a scratch won't. If your fingernail scratches the mineral, **record** H < F for that mineral in your chart.

 Math Hint H < F *means "the hardness is less than that of a fingernail."*

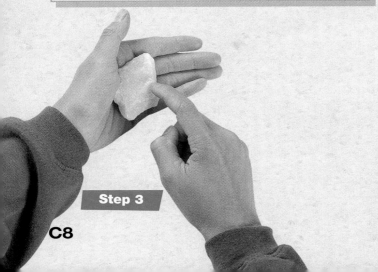

Step 3

Step 4

4. Find out if a copper wire will scratch the minerals that your fingernail did not scratch. For the minerals that the copper scratches, record $F < H < C$ (hardness is greater than that of a fingernail but less than that of copper) in your chart.

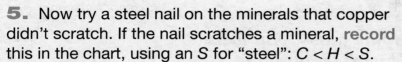

Step 5

5. Now try a steel nail on the minerals that copper didn't scratch. If the nail scratches a mineral, record this in the chart, using an *S* for "steel": $C < H < S$.

6. Finally, try scratching the glass plate with any mineral that was not scratched by the steel. Record those that scratch the glass as $H > G$.

Math Hint $H > G$ *means "the hardness is greater than that of glass."*

Analyze and Conclude

1. What was the order of hardness for your hardness tools?

2. Did your predictions match your results? Which mineral did you find to be the hardest? Which was the softest? Compare your results with those of your classmates. Did your classmates get the same results? If not, hypothesize why results varied. Then repeat the test and compare.

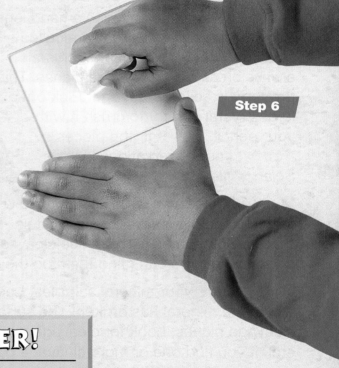

Step 6

INVESTIGATE FURTHER!

RESEARCH

One important property of gemstones is that they are hard. After all, you wouldn't want to wear a gem if it scratched easily. Look up the hardness of diamonds, rubies, sapphires, emeralds, topazes, and garnets. How do they compare? What scale is used to compare hardness?

Mineral Properties

Reading Focus What are minerals, and what properties do they have?

Did you know that the "brain" of a computer, called a computer chip, is made from a mineral found in sand? A **mineral** is a solid element or compound from Earth's crust that has a definite chemical makeup and crystal shape. Minerals can look very different from one another—colorless like quartz, silver or red like hematite, or shiny like gold and silver—but we find ways to use them all.

Look around and you'll see minerals being used. People may be wearing jewelry made of a gemstone such as a ruby, an emerald, or an opal. The walls in your home are probably made of wallboard, which is gypsum sandwiched between layers of paper. The glass windows in your classroom are made from quartz. The body powder you use may be made from the mineral talc. The point of your pencil is made of the mineral graphite. Your lunch may be wrapped in aluminum foil, made from the mineral bauxite. Perhaps you can think of other minerals you use every day. How many are there?

Why are minerals used in so many ways? They have different properties that make them right for many different uses. These same properties help scientists tell minerals apart. In the activities on pages C6 through C11, several properties of minerals are examined and tested.

▲ The mineral gypsum is used to make wallboard, or drywall.

▲ Talc is a mineral that you may sprinkle on your skin after a shower.

▲ A mineral's luster is a clue to its identity. Silver (*left*) has a metallic luster. Fluorite (*right*) has a nonmetallic luster.

Luster

Luster refers to the way light reflects from the surface of a mineral. Look at a piece of aluminum foil or some silver or gold jewelry. The shiny appearance of these minerals is called metallic luster. Any mineral that reflects light like a metal has metallic luster. All other minerals have non-metallic luster. Minerals that have non-metallic luster may appear dull like cinnabar, pearly like mica, or glassy like quartz.

Hardness

Hardness is a measure of how easily a mineral can be scratched. Talc is the softest mineral. It can be scratched by all other minerals. Diamond is the hardest mineral. It can scratch every other mineral, but no mineral can scratch a diamond.

Mohs' Scale of Mineral Hardness		
Mineral	**Hardness**	**Simple Test**
Talc	1	easily scratched by fingernail
Gypsum	2	scratched by fingernail
Calcite	3	barely scratched by copper
Fluorite	4	easily scratched by steel knife
Apatite	5	scratched by steel knife
Orthoclase feldspar	6	scratches glass with difficulty
Quartz	7	scratches glass and steel
Topaz	8	scratches quartz
Corundum	9	no simple test
Diamond	10	no simple test

Which mineral in the table has a hardness greater than that of quartz but less than that of corundum?

Mohs' scale, shown on page C13, lists the hardness of ten common minerals. To test a mineral for hardness, find out which mineral on the scale is the hardest one your mineral scratches. For example, a mineral that can scratch calcite but can't scratch fluorite has a hardness between 3 and 4.

In the activity on pages C8 and C9, some common materials—a fingernail, copper, steel, and glass—are used to test the hardness of some minerals. Using the same materials and the tests listed in Mohs' scale, you can estimate the hardness of any mineral. For example, the hardness of a mineral that can be scratched by copper but not by a fingernail is about 3.

Hardness is determined by the way in which the particles of matter in a mineral are arranged. For example, diamond and graphite are both made up of only carbon. The arrangement of carbon particles in diamond makes it the hardest mineral. The arrangement of the particles in graphite makes it one of the softest minerals.

Color

The color of a mineral is determined by the elements that make up the mineral. For example, chromium gives the mineral ruby its red color. While color is an easy property to observe, it is not very reliable for identifying minerals. The presence of

Science in Literature

FASCINATING STONES

"The popularity of birthstones and the belief that they bring good luck reveal the fascination that rare and beautiful stones have exerted on people ever since the Stone Age. The most prized gemstones are diamonds (birthstones for April)."

In *Rocks, Minerals and Fossils* by Keith Lye, you will find out just how fascinating minerals can be. Read this book if you are interested in starting a mineral collection or learning how beautiful gemstones form.

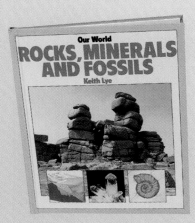

Rocks, Minerals and Fossils
by Keith Lye
Silver Burdett Press, 1991

tiny amounts of impurities can affect the color of a mineral. For example, pure quartz is colorless. Traces of other substances can result in quartz that is white, pink, or purple.

Streak

Streak is the color of a mineral in powdered form. You test for streak by scratching a mineral against a ceramic tile call a streak plate. Most minerals leave a powdery line, or streak, on the surface of the tile.

The streak of most minerals is either colorless or the same color as the mineral. However, the streak of some minerals is a different color than that of the mineral itself. For example, a silvery-gray form of hematite has a red streak.

Cleavage

Cleavage is the tendency of a mineral to split easily along flat surfaces called cleavage planes. The mineral

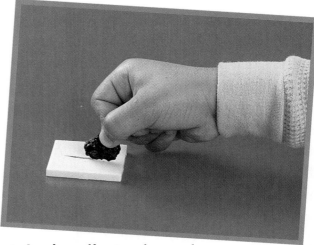

▲ **A mineral's streak may be different from its color.**

mica has cleavage planes that are all in the same direction. This type of cleavage allows mica to split into thin sheets. Can you see the cleavage planes in the photo of mica below?

Salt is a common name for the mineral halite. In the activity on page C10, halite is seen to have cleavage planes in three directions, producing cube-shaped pieces. Which mineral below has similar cleavage?

▲ **Calcite cleaves along three planes.**

▲ **Rubies, like many gemstones, have no cleavage.**

▲ **Mica cleaves along one plane and peels in thin sections.**

Most gemstones don't split naturally along several cleavage surfaces. Gem cutters grind the gems to create the flat, shiny surfaces called facets. These facets give gemstones their different shapes and cause them to "sparkle" as they reflect light. The ruby shown in the picture on page C15 has been cut so that it sparkles.

Using Mineral Properties

How are mineral properties useful? If you were a gold miner, using the properties you just learned about might make you a fortune! You would need to use mineral properties to tell gold from other minerals you might find.

▲ **Pyrite, shown here, has some properties similar to those of gold.**

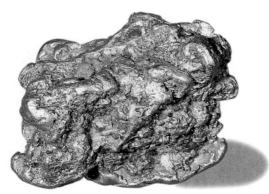

▲ **Gold, shown here, is softer than pyrite and has a different streak.**

Look at the samples of gold and pyrite shown below. At first glance they seem alike. Notice that they both have a brassy yellow color. Both minerals also have a metallic luster, and neither has cleavage.

Pyrite is known as fool's gold. Based on color, luster, and cleavage alone, you might easily mistake pyrite for gold. A smart gold miner would also compare the minerals' hardness and streak. Pyrite has a hardness of about 6, and gold has a hardness of about 3. Pyrite leaves a black streak; gold's streak is golden yellow. Gold has a greater value than pyrite, so it pays to be able to tell them apart. ■

UNIT PROJECT LINK

For this Unit Project you will start a collection of minerals. There are many ways to get mineral samples. You could join a mineral club. There may be some collectors in your community who could help you. You could write to students in schools in other parts of the country and trade minerals through the mail. Or you could collect local mineral samples from road cuts and stream beds. To determine the names of any unknown minerals in your collection, see the activity on page C11.

TechnologyLink For more help with your Unit Project, go to **www.eduplace.com**.

Identifying Minerals

Reading Focus How can you identify an unknown mineral?

The table on page C19, "Properties of Minerals," is designed to help you identify minerals. To identify an unknown mineral, match the properties you observe in your sample with those listed in the table.

Say you are given the unknown mineral shown below. What is it?

Using the Table: Nonmetallic Minerals

Step 1 Luster

How does it reflect light?

What kind of luster does your mineral have? It doesn't look like metal, so its luster is nonmetallic. Find the column labeled *Luster* and locate all the nonmetallic minerals.

Step 2 Hardness

What scratches it?

You would use the tools listed in the activity on page C8 to test for hardness. Your mineral can be scratched with a fingernail. In the column labeled *Hardness,* only six minerals are both nonmetallic and softer than a fingernail. Your mineral must be one of those six.

Step 3 Cleavage

Does it split? If so, in how many directions?

You can see that your sample has cleavage in one direction, or along one cleavage plane. You can rule out all minerals that don't show this type of cleavage.

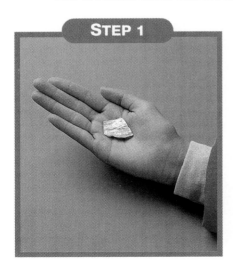

STEP 1

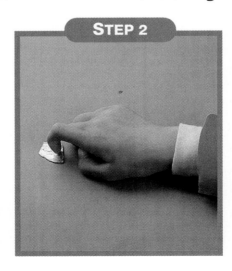

STEP 2

STEP 3

Step 4 Color
What color is it?

Observe that your sample is colorless. Look under the column labeled *Color*. Two minerals fit that description: mica and gypsum. Which is it?

Step 5 Special Properties
Are there any special properties?

Find the column labeled *Special*. Since your sample peels easily in thin sheets, it must be mica. Now try the procedure for a metallic mineral.

Using the Table: Metallic Minerals

Step 1 Luster
How does it reflect light?

The sample shines like metal. It has metallic luster. You can rule out all nonmetallic minerals.

Step 2 Hardness
What scratches it?

If you could test it, you'd find that your sample can scratch glass. Notice in the table that there are only two metallic minerals harder than glass: magnetite and pyrite.

Step 3 Color
What color is it?

Observe that your sample is black. Look in the column labeled *Color* and notice that pyrite is brassy yellow. Your mineral must be magnetite. To make sure, check its other properties.

Step 4 Streak
What color is its streak?

If you could scratch your sample along a streak plate, you would see that its streak is black. This agrees with the data for magnetite in the column labeled *Streak* in the table.

Step 5 Special Properties
Are there any special properties?

If you had a magnet, you would see that your sample is attracted to it. You can use this property and others in the table to confirm that your unknown sample is indeed magnetite.

STEP 1

STEP 4

STEP 5

PROPERTIES OF MINERALS					
Luster	**Hardness**	**Color**	**Streak**	**Special**	**Name**
Metallic	H > G	black	black	magnetic	MAGNETITE
Metallic	H > G	brassy yellow	black	fool's gold	PYRITE
Metallic	S < H < G	steel gray	red or reddish brown	may have reddish patches	HEMATITE
Metallic	C < H < S	brassy to golden yellow	black	often has blue, red, and purple tarnish	CHALCO-PYRITE
Metallic	F < H < C	silver gray	gray to black	heavy, shows cleavage (3)	GALENA
Luster	**Hardness**	**Cleavage**	**Color**	**Special**	**Name**
Non-metallic	H > G	yes (2)	white, pink, gray	hardness is very close to glass	FELDSPAR
Non-metallic	H > G	yes (2)	black, green, white	cleavage planes make a diamond shape	HORNBLENDE
Non-metallic	H > G	yes (2)	black, green	cleavage planes make a square shape	PYROXENE
Non-metallic	H > G	no	colorless, white, pink, smoky, purple	looks glassy, chips or breaks like glass	QUARTZ
Non-metallic	C < H < S	yes (6)	yellow to brown or black	yellowish-white streak	SPHALERITE
Non-metallic	C < H < S	yes (4)	purple, green, yellow	crystals are cubes, transparent	FLUORITE
Non-metallic	C < H < S	yes (3)	white, pink	crystal faces are usually curved	DOLOMITE
Non-metallic	F < H < C	yes (3)	colorless, white, yellow	cleavage planes make parallelograms	CALCITE
Non-metallic	H < F	yes (3)	colorless, white	tastes salty, breaks in cubes	HALITE
Non-metallic	H < F	yes (1)	colorless, white	sometimes transparent	GYPSUM
Non-metallic	H < F	yes (1)	colorless, silvery, black	peels in thin sheets, can be green	MICA
Non-metallic	H < F	yes (1)	light green to white	usually flaky	TALC
Non-metallic	H < F	no	yellow to brown	looks like rust	LIMONITE
Non-metallic	H < F	no	red	earthy	HEMATITE

*Numbers in parentheses give number of cleavage planes.

Key: *H*—hardness; *G*—glass; *S*—steel; *C*—copper; *F*—fingernail; <—less than; >—greater than

INVESTIGATION 2

WHAT ARE MINERALS USED FOR?

Look around at your classmates. How many are wearing jewelry? You know that minerals are used to make much of that jewelry. Try to name as many minerals used in jewelry as you can. (Think in terms of gems and metals.) Can you think of other uses for minerals?

Activity

Growing Crystals

Mineral crystals are used in jewelry and in electronics. Some crystals are grown in laboratories. Find out how to grow your own crystals!

- -

Procedure

1. Use a measuring cup to pour 500 mL of hot water into a large jar. Dissolve as much alum as possible in the water (about 100 g). Put a lid on the jar and let it stand overnight.

 See SCIENCE and MATH TOOLBOX page H7 if you need to review **Measuring Volume.**

2. The next day, pour a small amount of the solution from the jar into the bottom of a bowl and let it stand overnight. The following morning, you should find some small crystals in the bowl. Use a spoon to remove one or two good-sized crystals and pour the solution back into the jar.

MATERIALS
- goggles
- plastic gloves
- measuring cup
- large jar with lid
- hot tap water
- alum
- shallow bowl
- plastic spoon
- polyester thread
- large baby-food jar
- sheet of paper
- scissors
- metric ruler
- *Science Notebook*

SAFETY //////
Wear goggles and gloves at all times. Be sure to wash your hands after handling the alum.

3. Tie one of the crystals to the end of a piece of thread. Suspend the crystal in a baby-food jar.

Step 3

4. Nearly fill the baby-food jar with solution from the large jar. Be careful not to pour any crystals into the baby-food jar. Fold a square piece of paper to form a tent. Place it over the jar to keep the dust out. **Predict** how much the crystal will grow each day.

5. **Observe** your crystal growing. Each day, **estimate** the size of the crystal. If the level of solution in the jar goes down, add more. After a few days, remove the crystal from the solution. **Make a drawing** of it in your *Science Notebook*.

 Math Hint *Estimate the length and width of the crystal in millimeters or centimeters.*

Analyze and Conclude

1. About how large was the crystal when you started? How large was the crystal when you stopped?

2. How many days did the crystal grow? Did your crystal grow by the same amount each day? **Describe** your evidence.

3. Think of ways people use crystals. **Infer** why scientists might want to grow crystals in a laboratory.

INVESTIGATE FURTHER!

EXPERIMENT

You can grow crystals from other substances. Instead of alum, try sugar, Epsom salts, or rock salt. Compare the shapes of the crystals and how easy or difficult they were to grow.

Quartz: A Versatile Mineral

Reading Focus What is quartz, and how is it used?

If you've ever been to a beach or seen pictures of one, you know that beaches are made of sand. The words *sand* and *gravel* refer to the size of a grain of mineral or rock. Sand particles are smaller than gravel. Any rock or mineral can be broken into sand-sized or gravel-sized pieces.

The most common sand in the world is quartz sand. Quartz is also one of the most important minerals. It is made of only two elements, silicon and oxygen. The colors of common types of quartz include clear (rock crystal), pink (rose), white (milky), and gray (smoky). Some forms of quartz are semiprecious gem-stones such as amethyst, agate, onyx, and opal.

Native Americans used one form, flint, for tools such as arrowheads.

Building With Quartz

Quartz plays an important role in the building industry. **Concrete**, for example, is a rock material made of sand, gravel, and portland cement.

Portland cement is made by grinding limestone and shale, two kinds of rock, into a powder. This powder is baked until it forms balls called clinker. Cooled clinker is crushed and mixed with gypsum, another mineral. This mixture is then mixed with quartz-rich sand, gravel, and water and allowed to harden to form concrete. How have you seen concrete used in your neighborhood?

Rose quartz ▶

Smoky quartz ▶

Clear quartz ▼

◀ Milky quartz

▲ Concrete, a building material, is made with quartz and other minerals.

▲ Quartz is used to make glass.

Seeing With Quartz

Quartz is also used to make glass. In ancient times, people in the Middle East had a good understanding of quartz and its properties. Glassmaking probably began about 4,000 years ago in Egypt or Mesopotamia. Today the art of glassmaking is a worldwide industry.

Glass is easy to make if you have the proper tools. Powdered quartz is mixed with powdered limestone and soda (not the kind you drink, but a solid substance called sodium carbonate). This mixture is heated to about 1,600°C (2,912°F).

At this temperature the mixture melts. Then it is cooled quickly so that crystals cannot form. Crystals would make objects seen through the glass look wavy and distorted. Look around you. How many ways can you see glass being used?

The Computer Mineral

Quartz can be separated into its two parts, silicon and oxygen. From the silicon, crystals can be grown. Crystals are grown in the activity on pages C22 and C23. Silicon crystals can be cut into thin pieces. These pieces of pure silicon are used in the

◀ Quartz, a compound of silicon and oxygen, is one of the most abundant minerals in Earth's crust.

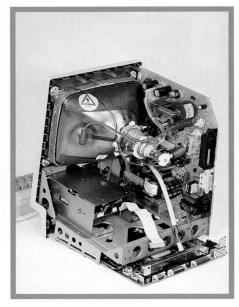

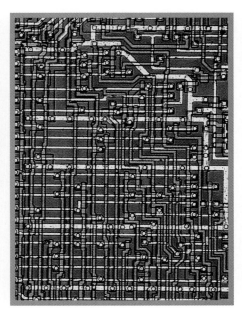

The brain of every desktop computer (left) is a silicon chip. Many chips, each the size of a fingernail, are obtained from silicon wafers (center). Each chip is etched with the electronic circuits (right) that carry out the calculations that make computers such timesavers.

electronics industry, which is a major part of the world's economy. Computer chips, which are the brains of computers, and solar cells, which power solar calculators, are made with silicon.

Perhaps the most amazing thing about quartz crystals is that they generate electricity. If the crystals are squeezed, they bend slightly and produce electricity. In addition, when a small electric current is put through a crystal, the crystal vibrates. The vibrations are very regular, making quartz crystals ideal for keeping time.

Maybe you thought of quartz as something you walked on at the beach. But a world without window glass, transistor radios, CD players, computers, or concrete would be hard to imagine! ■

Internet Field Trip
Visit **www.eduplace.com** to find out more about quartz and other minerals.

◀ **You may be carrying a quartz crystal on your wrist. In a watch with a quartz crystal, the crystal's vibrations keep time more accurately than the spring that is used in other watches.**

How Iron Becomes Steel

Reading Focus Where does iron come from, and how is it made into steel?

In Arizona there is a huge hole in the ground known as the Barringer Meteorite Crater. Scientists hypothesize that the crater formed about 25,000 years ago, when a huge chunk of iron from space collided with Earth. The chunk of iron from space shows that iron isn't found only on Earth. It's all over the universe! Maybe it should be called the universal metal!

Magnetite and hematite are important iron-containing minerals. Minerals from which metals can be removed are called **ores**. An iron ore is made up of iron and other elements.

The most widespread source of iron is hematite, an ore made up of iron and oxygen. Over 2 billion years ago, hematite layers began to build up in the oceans. Over time, the hematite layers were themselves covered over by layers of sediment.

Later, parts of the ocean floor were slowly raised so that they were no longer covered by water. The iron deposits eventually became exposed. Today iron ore is mined all over the world. Most of the iron used in the United States comes from ore mined in Canada and South America.

Iron is used to make many different products such as the blades of skates (*left*), the rails of roller coasters (*center*), and the hulls of ships (*right*).

Magnetite is not as easy to find as hematite, but it's a purer source of iron. The world's largest magnetite mine is in Sweden. Others are located in Wyoming, New York, Utah, South Africa, Austria, Italy, and Russia.

The process of removing metal from ore is called **smelting**. The first smelting of metal may have occurred about 9,000 years ago. Around 3,500 years ago, iron smelting became widespread. Iron was often used in making cooking utensils and weapons. Because the introduction of iron affected world cultures so greatly, that period of time was called the Iron Age. The diagram shows how a type of crude iron, called pig iron, is made.

Smelting Iron

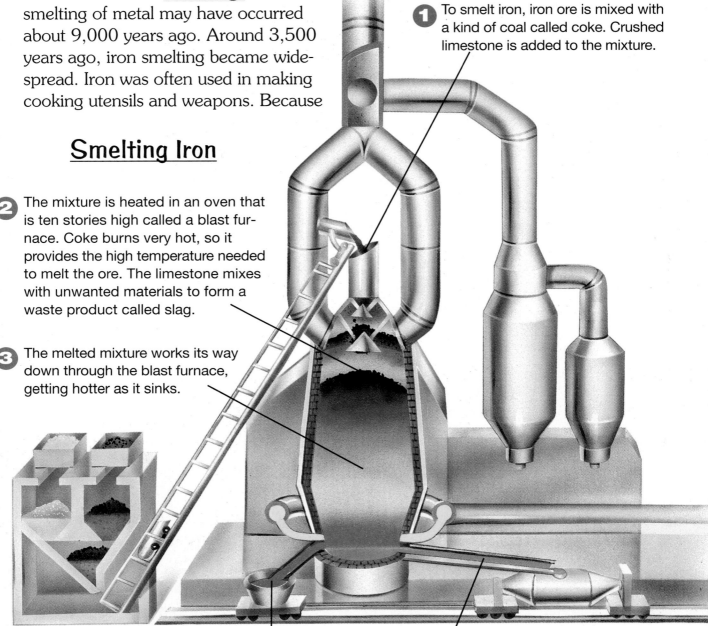

1 To smelt iron, iron ore is mixed with a kind of coal called coke. Crushed limestone is added to the mixture.

2 The mixture is heated in an oven that is ten stories high called a blast furnace. Coke burns very hot, so it provides the high temperature needed to melt the ore. The limestone mixes with unwanted materials to form a waste product called slag.

3 The melted mixture works its way down through the blast furnace, getting hotter as it sinks.

4 Wastes that are less dense separate and float on the molten metal. The slag is then drained off.

5 The remaining melted iron, called pig iron, is drained from the bottom of the blast furnace.

▲ Pig iron is remelted and mixed with a precise amount of carbon, making steel.

Making Steel

Impurities in pig iron make it too brittle to be of practical use. To make pig iron useful, it is remelted and converted into steel. Melted pig iron is poured into a furnace and brought to a high temperature. Air is blown over the iron to increase its temperature and to remove carbon.

▲ The liquid steel is poured into molds and allowed to cool.

Then a measured amount of carbon is mixed back in.

It may seem strange to take carbon out and then put some back. However, an exact amount of carbon is needed to make useful steel. Too much carbon makes steel brittle. Too little carbon makes it weak.

▲ Steel can be produced in a variety of forms, including rolled sheets.

Steel can be rolled into sheets or made into bars, blocks, and other shapes. It can be made as sharp as a razor or as blunt as a hammer. Other metals can be added to steel to make alloys. For example, chromium is added to make steel rust-resistant. Nickel is added to make steel stronger. Tungsten makes steel strong at high temperatures.

How did you get to school today? If you came by public transportation, car, or bike, steel helped you. What other uses for steel can you think of? ■

A World of Minerals

Reading Focus In what ways are Earth's mineral resources valuable?

Mineral resources are in the ground all over the world. But they are not evenly distributed. As the map shows, some countries have more mineral resources than others.

A country can use some of its resources to make products. That country can then sell some of its raw resources and products to other countries. The selling countries are called producers. The buying countries are consumers.

Consumers often buy raw resources to make products. If they sell these products to producers, the producers may actually be buying back their resources in a new form.

For example, iron ore may be shipped from the United States to Japan. A Japanese company turns the ore into steel and the steel into bike frames. Some frames are sold in Japan and some are sold in other parts of the world, including the United States.

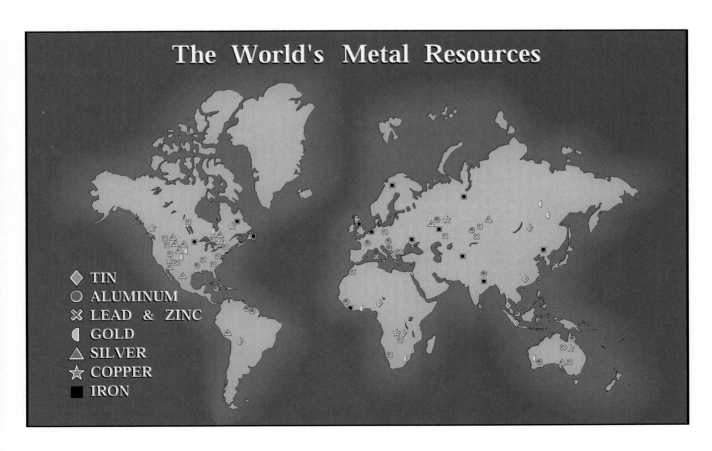

The World's Metal Resources

◇ TIN
○ ALUMINUM
✖ LEAD & ZINC
◖ GOLD
△ SILVER
☆ COPPER
■ IRON

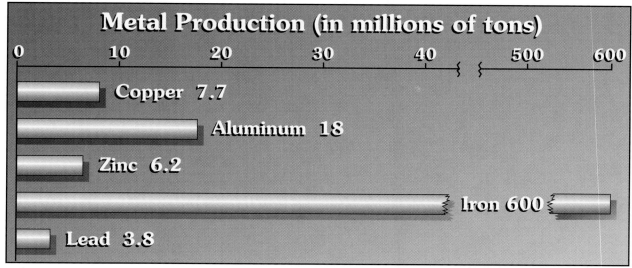

Metal Production (in millions of tons)

| 0 | 10 | 20 | 30 | 40 | 500 | 600 |

Copper 7.7

Aluminum 18

Zinc 6.2

Iron 600

Lead 3.8

Using Math This graph shows the worldwide yearly production of selected metals. How does the amount of aluminum produced in one year compare to the total amount of copper, zinc, and lead produced in a year?

Minerals and mineral products are an important part of the world trading market. There are few places on Earth where iron or steel isn't used in some way. Aluminum is important to the canning and cooking industries. What other ways are mineral resources used in the world?

A Limited Supply

A **natural resource** is any useful material or energy source found in nature. Some natural resources, such as sunlight and wind, are thought of as inexhaustible (in eg zôs′tə bəl). This means that they can never be used up.

Most natural resources are placed in one of two groups—renewable and nonrenewable. A **renewable resource** is one that can be replaced in a fairly short time. Trees are renewable resources. A **nonrenewable resource** is one that cannot be replaced in nature.

Minerals are nonrenewable resources. Supplies of many minerals are limited, and they are being used up fast. However, items made from minerals are not really gone from our environment. The minerals are still here, ready to be recycled.

▲ Much of Earth's mineral wealth ends up in places like this.

C31

In the United States, 1,500 aluminum cans are recycled every second. How could you estimate the number of aluminum cans that are recycled each year?

Recycling Mineral Resources

Many communities in the United States have recycling laws. In addition to nonmineral products like paper and plastic, metals such as copper, steel, brass, and aluminum are recycled. Recycling doesn't solve the problem of using up a mineral resource, but it extends our use of such resources.

World Issues

The way that mineral resources are handled in one country can affect many other countries. Look at the map on page C30 and the bar graph on page C31. Then discuss the following questions with your classmates.

- Which two metals are produced in the largest quantity?

- Do you think the United States has to import such resources?

- What happens when a country holds back on selling resources or products needed by other countries of the world? ■

INVESTIGATE FURTHER!

TAKE ACTION

Research and evaluate services for recycling minerals in your community. Then organize a recycling drive of those materials.

INVESTIGATION 2 WRAP-UP

REVIEW

1. Name six products made from minerals and at least one mineral used to make each product.

2. Where does iron come from, and how is it made into steel?

CRITICAL THINKING

3. List the materials made from minerals that you would use if you were building a house, and explain why you would use them.

4. Describe two ways you can help extend the use of a limited mineral resource.

REFLECT & EVALUATE

Word Power

Write the letter of the term that best completes each sentence. *Not all terms will be used*.

a. cleavage
b. concrete
c. hardness
d. luster
e. mineral
f. ores
g. smelting
h. streak

1. A building material made of sand, gravel, and cement is ___.

2. The color of the powder left by a mineral on a ceramic tile is the mineral's ___.

3. The way a mineral reflects light is known as ___.

4. Metals can be removed from minerals called ___.

5. The way a mineral splits is a property called ___.

6. A measure of how easily a mineral can be scratched is its ___.

Check What You Know

Write the term in each pair that best completes each sentence.

1. The hardest mineral is (diamond, talc).

2. Quartz is made up of silicon and (oxygen, carbon).

3. You can tell gold from pyrite by using (streak, luster).

4. The end product of smelting is (concrete, pig iron).

Problem Solving

1. You are about to take a mineral-collecting field trip. You plan to identify all the minerals you collect. List the materials you will take and explain what property each will be used to identify.

2. What might happen if, from now on, all products made from mineral resources were recycled?

BUILD YOUR PORTFOLIO

Observe the properties of the mineral sample shown. This mineral's streak is gray to black. The mineral cannot be scratched by a fingernail but can be scratched by glass. Make a list of the mineral's properties. Then use the "Properties of Minerals" table on page C19 to identify this mineral.

CHAPTER 2

ROCKS

Rocks are made of minerals, and you find rocks of all kinds and sizes everywhere! Most rocks appear sturdy and unchanging. Actually, natural processes are constantly changing rocks. People too can transform rock.

PEOPLE USING SCIENCE

Stonecutter Edward Torres of Seaside Heights, New Jersey, is a stonecutter. He skillfully turns sheets of white, black, beige, red, or green marble into custom-made items. He crafts such things as fireplace mantels and counter tops.

A typical job for Torres begins when his material is delivered. A huge slab of marble is gently deposited onto his worktable by a forklift! Torres then uses a circular diamond-toothed saw to precisely cut the hard stone to the proper measurements. The fully processed piece, completed and polished, is a beautiful and useful item.

What natural processes change some materials into marble or into other kinds of rocks? What properties distinguish one kind of rock from another? In this chapter you'll explore these and other questions.

◀ Edward Torres, stonecutter

INVESTIGATION ①

HOW ARE ROCKS CLASSIFIED?

Rocks are the "stuff" that makes up Earth. About 4 billion years ago, Earth was a molten ball of rock. Although some of Earth's rock is still molten, the rock in the outer layer is solid. You live on this rocky ball. In this investigation you'll find out how rocks are identified and classified.

Activity
Sort of Rocky

Some rocks are made of only one mineral, but most rocks are made of more than one. In this activity you'll observe some properties of rocks and use properties to classify the rocks.

MATERIALS
- paper punch-outs
- marker
- white glue
- set of rocks
- hand lens
- egg carton
- *Science Notebook*

Procedure

1. Number paper punch-outs from 1 to 12. With white glue, attach one punch-out to each rock specimen.

2. Put all the rocks together on your desktop. Compare the rocks to one another. Classify them by separating them into a dark-colored set and a light-colored set. In your *Science Notebook*, record the numbers for each set.

3. Mineral crystals in rocks are shiny and have flat surfaces that look like tiny mirrors. Place all the rocks together and observe them with a hand lens.

Step 3

4. Classify the rocks into a set with crystals and a set without. Record the numbers for each set.

5. Use the hand lens to study the rocks again. Classify the rocks into two new sets: rocks which appear to be made of more than one mineral and rocks which appear to contain only one mineral. Record the numbers for each set.

6. Classify the rocks with one mineral into two sets: rocks with crystals and rocks without crystals. Do the same for the rocks with more than one mineral. Record your results.

7. Now classify each of the four sets from steps 4 and 5 into sets that contain dark-colored rocks and light-colored rocks. Then use an egg carton to store your rock specimens.

Analyze and Conclude

1. How many sets now contain only one rock?

2. List the properties that you used in this activity to classify rocks. Infer how these properties are used to classify rocks.

UNIT PROJECT LINK

Begin a rock collection. Rocks are easier to find than minerals. Get good, clean rocks that are freshly broken so that you can see what the insides look like. Keep a numbered list of your rocks to tell where they came from. Try sorting them according to their properties.

Technology Link

For more help with your Unit Project, go to **www.eduplace.com**.

Activity

The Rock Key

A key is used to help identify something. The Rock Key will help you use the properties of rocks to find out their names.

MATERIALS

- goggles
- rock set
- square glass plate
- hand lens
- metric ruler
- *Science Notebook*

SAFETY /////

Wear goggles during this activity. When using the glass plate, hold it firmly on the table. Press a point of the rock against the plate and pull the rock toward you. DO NOT HOLD THE GLASS PLATE IN YOUR HAND.

Procedure

1. Choose a rock specimen. Look at the descriptions at the left side of the Rock Key. Observe whether or not your rock has crystals. If it does, follow the line from "Rock has crystals" to the next level in the key. If it does not have crystals, follow the other line. Record all the properties of your rock in your *Science Notebook*.

2. At most levels in the key, two choices are given. Match a choice to your rock and follow the line to your next observation and choice. Eventually, you will arrive at the name of your rock on the right side of the key.

3. To test for hardness use glass, as you did with minerals. Hard rocks scratch glass; soft ones do not.

4. To find out if a rock with crystals is coarse-grained, medium-grained, or fine-grained, observe the size of the crystals. In a coarse-grained rock, most of the rock is made of crystals larger than a grain of rice. In a fine-grained rock, you need a hand lens to see crystals. In a medium-grained rock, you can see the crystals without a hand lens, but they are smaller than rice grains.

Step 4

5. Use the Rock Key to identify your rock. Record this information with your notes on the properties of the rock. Then repeat steps 1 through 5 for each rock in your set.

Analyze and Conclude

1. Which rocks did you find hard to identify?

2. Make an inference about what additional data would have helped you identify them.

THE ROCK KEY

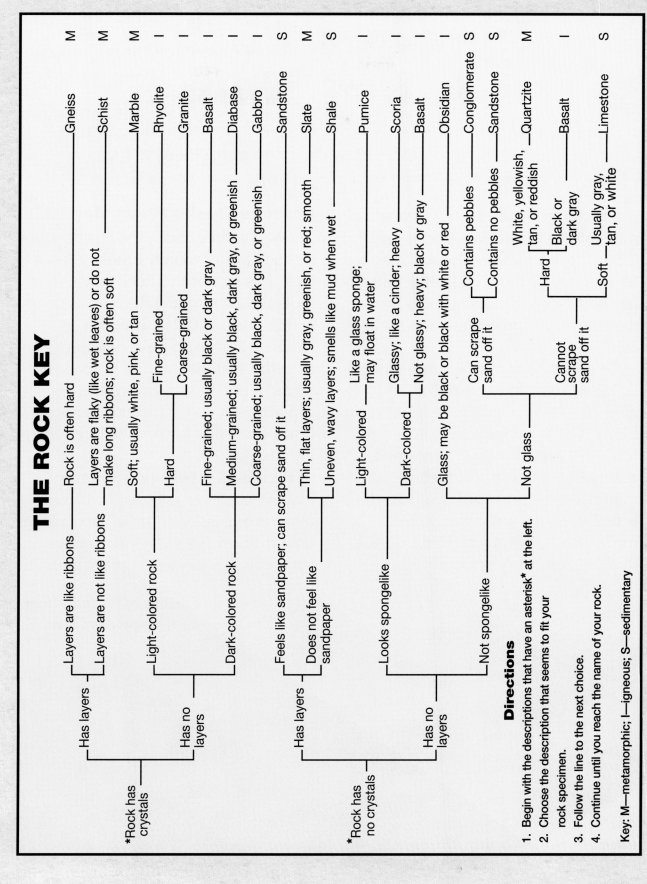

*Rock has crystals

Has layers
- Layers are like ribbons
  - Rock is often hard —————— Gneiss — M
- Layers are not like ribbons — Layers are flaky (like wet leaves) or do not make long ribbons; rock is often soft —————— Schist — M

Has no layers
- Light-colored rock — Soft; usually white, pink, or tan —————— Marble — M
  - Hard
    - Fine-grained —————— Rhyolite — I
    - Coarse-grained —————— Granite — I
- Dark-colored rock
  - Fine-grained; usually black or dark gray —————— Basalt — I
  - Medium-grained; usually black, dark gray, or greenish —————— Diabase — I
  - Coarse-grained; usually black, dark gray, or greenish —————— Gabbro — I

*Rock has no crystals

Has layers
- Feels like sandpaper; can scrape sand off it —————— Sandstone — S
- Does not feel like sandpaper
  - Thin, flat layers; usually gray, greenish, or red; smooth —————— Slate — M
  - Uneven, wavy layers; smells like mud when wet —————— Shale — S

Has no layers
- Looks spongelike
  - Light-colored — Like a glass sponge; may float in water —————— Pumice — I
  - Dark-colored — Glassy; like a cinder; heavy —————— Scoria — I
- Not spongelike
  - Not glassy; heavy; black or gray —————— Basalt — I
  - Glass; may be black or black with white or red —————— Obsidian — I
  - Not glass
    - Can scrape sand off it
      - Contains pebbles —————— Conglomerate — S
      - Contains no pebbles —————— Sandstone — S
    - Cannot scrape sand off it
      - Hard
        - White, yellowish, tan, or reddish —————— Quartzite — M
        - Black or dark gray —————— Basalt — I
      - Soft — Usually gray, tan, or white —————— Limestone — S

Directions

1. Begin with the descriptions that have an asterisk* at the left.
2. Choose the description that seems to fit your rock specimen.
3. Follow the line to the next choice.
4. Continue until you reach the name of your rock.

Key: M—metamorphic; I—igneous; S—sedimentary

C39

Igneous Rocks: A Hot Item

Reading Focus How do igneous rocks form?

Rocks are solid materials made of minerals. In the activities on pages C36 through C39, rocks are classified based on how they are similar and different. Scientists classify rocks into three types based on how the rocks are formed.

One of those types is called igneous (ig′nē əs) rock. Igneous rocks are probably the most common types found on Earth. The word *igneous* comes from the Latin word for "fire." **Igneous rocks** form when hot, melted rock material cools and hardens. Rock that is melted to a liquid form is called molten rock. Where on Earth do you think molten rock is found?

Igneous Rocks From Magma

Deep within Earth, the temperature is much hotter than it is near the surface. It is so hot that rocks melt. The molten rock material that forms deep within Earth is called **magma**. Because it is less dense, or lighter, than the material around it, magma tends to slowly rise toward the surface of Earth. As magma rises, it sometimes cools and hardens before reaching the surface.

Because it is below the surface, magma cools very slowly. As it cools, mineral grains, or crystals, have a long time to form. So the mineral grains are large in rocks formed from magma.

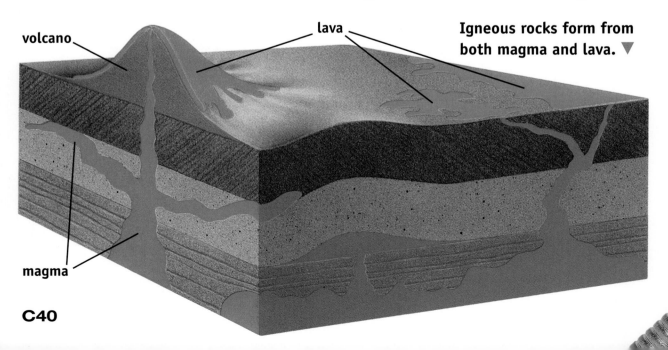

volcano

lava

magma

Igneous rocks form from both magma and lava. ▼

One of the most common rocks formed from magma is granite, shown below. Notice that it consists of different minerals. The grayish mineral is feldspar, the white mineral is quartz, and the black mineral is mica. Notice the size of the mineral grains that make up granite.

Stone Mountain, in the state of Georgia, is a mountain of granite. Where did this rock harden? How do you think this rock became exposed at Earth's surface?

Not all igneous rocks that form from magma are the same. They vary in the kinds of mineral grains that form. The minerals that form depend on what the magma is made up of.

Gabbro is another kind of igneous rock. Like all rocks that cool from magma, it has large mineral grains. But notice that gabbro is mostly made of dark-colored minerals, in this case pyroxene (pī räks'ēn) and olivine. It has few light-colored minerals, such as quartz and feldspar.

▲ **Stone Mountain, in Georgia**

Igneous Rocks From Lava

You know that magma rises toward Earth's surface. Magma that reaches Earth's surface is called **lava**. Look back at the diagram showing lava and magma on page C40. An opening in Earth's surface through which lava flows is called a volcano. When lava cools and hardens at Earth's surface, it forms igneous rock.

Three kinds of rocks formed from lava are shown on page C42. Compare them with the photograph of granite. How do the sizes of the mineral grains compare? Use what you have learned about igneous rocks to explain why the grains differ in size.

▼ **Granite**

Gabbro ▶

▲ **Basalt**

▲ **Obsidian**

Rhyolite ▶

Basalt is an igneous rock that forms when lava rich in dark-colored minerals cools and hardens. Find basalt on the chart below. Note that its makeup is similar to that of gabbro.

Because it flows out onto Earth's surface, lava cools faster than magma. So rocks from cooled lava, such as basalt, have smaller grains than rocks from cooled magma, such as gabbro. Areas in the states of Washington and Oregon are covered by basalt because of past volcanic activity.

Obsidian (əb sid'ē ən), another igneous rock, is often called natural glass. Lava that forms obsidian cools and hardens so quickly that mineral grains have very little time to grow. This rapid cooling gives the rock its glassy look. Native Americans once used obsidian to make cutting tools. That's because obsidian forms sharp edges when broken.

Look at the photograph of rhyolite (rī'ə līt). Find it on the chart. How do you think rhyolite forms? ■

	COMPOSITION	
	Contains more light-colored minerals	Contains more dark-colored minerals
LARGE mineral grains: forms from MAGMA	**Granite**	**Gabbro**
SMALL mineral grains: forms from LAVA	**Rhyolite**	**Basalt**
NO mineral grains: forms from LAVA		**Obsidian**

Sedimentary Rocks: Rocks From Pieces

Reading Focus How do sedimentary rocks form?

Sedimentary (sed ə men′tər ē) **rocks** are rocks that form at Earth's surface when sediments harden into rock. **Sediments** include bits of rock, minerals, and organic materials. As you may know, things that are called organic were once living.

There are many different kinds of sedimentary rocks. In fact, you probably use one sedimentary rock every day in school. You also may have used it to draw on the sidewalk. Chalk is a sedimentary rock.

Animal, Vegetable, or Mineral?

Like igneous rocks, sedimentary rocks can be grouped according to how they form. There are three types of sedimentary rocks: clastic, chemical, and organic.

Clastic sedimentary rocks are made up of pieces of rocks, minerals, and organic materials cemented together. The bits of sediment that make up clastic rocks can be as small as a grain of mud or as large as a boulder! Clastic sedimentary rocks are common on Earth's surface.

Clastic rocks are grouped according to the size of the sediments they contain. Conglomerate (kən gläm′ər it), shale, and sandstone are clastic rocks. Study the photographs of these rocks. How do the size of their sediments compare?

Most clastic rocks form when wind, water, or ice carries and then

◄ **Conglomerate**

Sandstone ►

▲ **Shale**

drops sediments. Over time, these materials become compacted, or squeezed together. Minerals dissolved in water seep into spaces between the materials. As the water evaporates, the minerals are deposited. They bind the loose sediments into solid rock. This binding of sediments is called **cementation** (sē men tā'shən).

Sandstone, as you might have guessed, is made of small, sand-sized rock bits. Sandstone often feels gritty, like sandpaper. Where on Earth might sandstone be forming?

Chemical sedimentary rocks form when water rich in dissolved minerals evaporates, leaving the minerals behind. These rocks also form when chemical changes form new minerals. Rock gypsum, rock salt, and some kinds of limestone are examples of chemical sedimentary rocks.

The type of limestone shown in the photograph below consists mostly of calcite, which formed when sea or lake waters evaporated. Limestone is

▲ **Rock gypsum**

ground and mixed with other materials to make certain kinds of cement.

Rock gypsum forms when water evaporates, leaving behind the mineral gypsum. Gypsum is used in plaster of Paris and plaster walls.

Rock salt, which is almost pure halite, is known as table salt. It does, however, have other uses, as you can see in the photograph below.

Limestone ▼

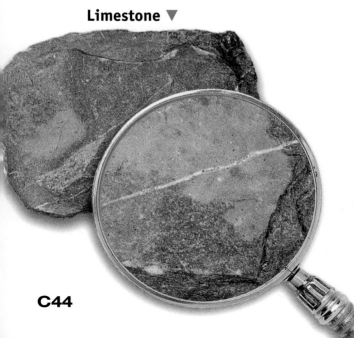

▲ **Rock salt is commonly used to melt ice and snow.**

The third type of sedimentary rock is called organic rock. Organic rocks form from the remains of plants and animals or from parts of organisms, such as shells. One type of coal is an organic sedimentary rock. It forms when bits of dead plants are squeezed together over a long period of time. The squeezing removes water, leaving behind the carbon that forms coal.

Limestones consist mostly of calcite. Some form when sea or lake waters evaporate. Others form when shells of sea animals are cemented together. Fine-grained limestones, like chalk, are the remains of tiny organisms that lived in the ocean.

Sedimentary Rock Features

Scientists can learn about how a sedimentary rock was formed by studying features preserved in the rock. When sediments are dropped by water, wind, or ice, the sediments build up in layers. The layers harden over time. And as more sediments are dropped, more layers are formed, one on top of the other. So most sedimentary rocks are layered. This layering is often called bedding.

Wind, water, ice, and the shape of the land can affect the formation of sedimentary rock beds. Use the chart on page C46 to compare how sediment beds form.

Science in Literature

CLUES TO EARTH'S PAST

"Sedimentary rocks and the fossils they contain provide much information about the climate when the rocks were formed. For example, limestones containing coral remains were formed in warm, shallow seas, while coal was formed in warm swamps."

The sedimentary rocks of places like the Grand Canyon are more than amazing scenery. They also provide a 3-D lesson on the history of Earth! Find out how to "read the rocks" in *Rocks, Minerals and Fossils* by Keith Lye.

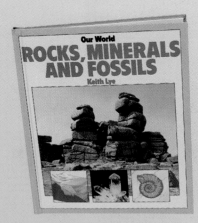

Rocks, Minerals and Fossils
by Keith Lye
Silver Burdett Press, 1991

Sediment Beds

◄ Notice that the surface of this sediment layer looks wavy. These wavy lines are called ripple marks. They are formed by moving water or wind. You may have seen ripple marks near a stream or on a beach. How might they become sedimentary rock?

◄ Most sediment beds, like these in shale, were deposited horizontally, resulting in the characteristic layering of sedimentary rock.

◄ The beds in this sandstone show cross-bedding. They formed when wind dropped sand on the curved slopes of sand dunes. Eventually, the sand beds hardened to form sandstone. What kinds of places can you think of that have sand dunes?

◄ Mud cracks are another feature sometimes preserved in sedimentary rocks. Mud cracks are evidence of wet periods followed by dry periods during the formation of a rock.

If you've ever gone rock collecting or to a natural history museum, you've probably seen fossils. A **fossil** is any remains or evidence of an organism from the past. Sedimentary rocks sometimes contain fossils. The photograph shows a fern fossil. Based on this fossil, what conclusions might you draw about how this rock formed?

The Rock Key on page C39 uses the letter S to show which rocks are sedimentary rocks. Try to classify the sedimentary rocks listed in the Rock Key as clastic, chemical, or organic, based on their properties. ■

Fern fossil ▶

Metamorphic Rocks: A Change of Identity

Reading Focus How do metamorphic rocks form?

The third major group of rocks is the metamorphic (met ə môr′fik) rocks. The word *metamorphic* is made of two word parts that together mean "to change form." In some ways metamorphic rocks are like sedimentary rocks because both kinds form from existing rocks. In other ways, metamorphic rocks are like igneous rocks. Both kinds can form at high temperatures and pressures.

New Rocks

Metamorphic rocks are new rocks that form from existing rocks that are changed by heat, pressure, or chemicals. The rocks that are changed may be sedimentary, igneous, or other metamorphic rocks. The change from one rock type to another is called metamorphism.

Some changes that occur with metamorphism result in changes in texture. *Texture* refers to the size and shape of mineral grains and the way in which they are arranged in a rock. In other cases, changes in chemical makeup take place. The changes that occur during metamorphism can result from three different sets of conditions.

Contact metamorphism occurs when hot magma or lava comes in contact with rock. The rock gets "baked" by the molten material. In

Metamorphic rocks form when existing rocks are changed by heat, pressure, or chemicals. ▼

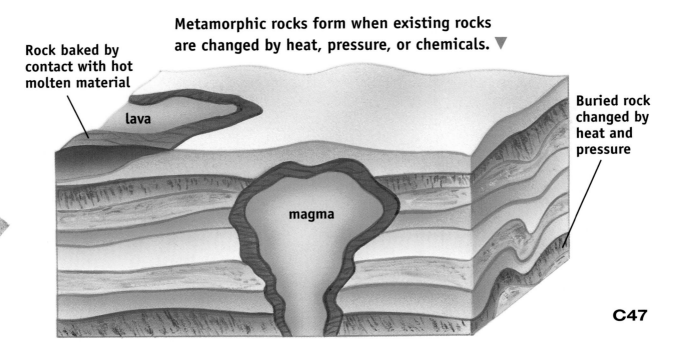

Rock baked by contact with hot molten material

lava

magma

Buried rock changed by heat and pressure

C47

such cases, temperature alone causes the rock to change. Changes can occur in the kinds of minerals present and in the sizes of the grains. Liquids and gases escaping from the magma can also chemically change minerals in the surrounding rocks.

A second type of metamorphism is called regional metamorphism. It occurs in rocks that are buried deep below Earth's surface, where temperature and pressure are high. The texture of the rocks changes, particularly in the way the minerals are arranged. Mineral grains tend to become lined up in the same direction because of high pressures. Also, high temperatures cause changes in the mineral makeup of the rocks.

Burial metamorphism occurs when the weight of rocks and sediments puts pressure on buried rock. With burial metamorphism, temperatures and pressures are not as high as with regional metamorphism. However these conditions are high enough to cause crystals to be altered and rock textures to change slightly. Such changes cause shale, a sedimentary rock, to be changed to slate, a metamorphic rock.

Banded Metamorphic Rocks

Metamorphic rocks are grouped according to their textures as banded or nonbanded. As you would expect, rocks with a banded texture look as if they contain bands, or thin layers. The bands may look wavy or straight. Gneiss (nīs) is a banded metamorphic rock that contains quartz, mica, and feldspar. Which igneous rock is made of these same three minerals? Look at the photograph of gneiss. Note the bands of mineral grains. In which direction do you think the pressure was applied during metamorphism?

Another banded metamorphic rock is slate. Recall that slate forms when shale, a sedimentary rock, is exposed to changes in temperature and pressure. Slate is used as a roofing material. Some chalkboards are made of slate. When exposed to more extreme heat and pressure, shale can be changed to the banded metamorphic rock called phyllite (fil′īt).

Gneiss ▼

Phyllite ▶

Slate ▶

▲ Marble

▲ Quartzite

Nonbanded Rocks

In nonbanded metamorphic rocks the mineral grains have not been lined up by pressure. The texture of these rocks is described as massive because the grains are so tightly packed. Look at the photographs of the nonbanded rocks above. Contrast them with the photographs of banded rocks.

Marble is a nonbanded metamorphic rock. Marble forms when limestone is changed by metamorphism. Marble can be white, black, pink, gray, or green with colored streaks.

Another nonbanded metamorphic rock is quartzite (kwôrts′īt). Quartzite forms when sandstone is exposed to high pressures and temperatures. ■

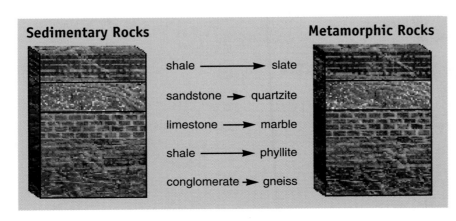

Sedimentary Rocks

shale ⟶ slate

sandstone ⟶ quartzite

limestone ⟶ marble

shale ⟶ phyllite

conglomerate ⟶ gneiss

Metamorphic Rocks

◀ **The drawing shows some different parent rocks of metamorphic rocks.**

INVESTIGATION 1 WRAP-UP

THINK IT WRITE IT

REVIEW

1. Name the three basic types of rocks and describe how each forms.

2. Name the three basic types of sedimentary rock and describe how each forms.

CRITICAL THINKING

3. How are rocks that form from magma and lava alike and different?

4. Fossils are found almost exclusively in sedimentary rocks. Suggest a hypothesis to explain this observation.

HOW DO THE PROPERTIES OF ROCKS MAKE THEM USEFUL?

Make a rock! Punch a few holes in the bottom of a paper cup. Pour in some sand and white glue mixed with water. After the mixture has dried, tear off the paper and behold your "rock." What are its properties?

Activity

Comparing Properties of Rocks

Different kinds of rocks have different properties, which make the rocks useful in different ways.

- -

Procedure

1. Look at the Rock Key on page C39. In your *Science Notebook*, **make a chart** like the one shown. Include one row for each rock listed in the Rock Key.

Name of Rock	Group (I, S, or M)	Predictions	Observations

See SCIENCE and MATH TOOLBOX page H11 if you need to review **Making a Chart to Organize Data.**

2. **Classify** your rocks into three groups so that the first group has all the igneous rocks (I), the second group has all the sedimentary rocks (S), and the third group has all the metamorphic rocks (M). In the chart, **record** the names of all the rocks in each group.

3. **Predict** which groups will have layered rocks. Look for layered rocks and **record** your observations.

4. **Predict** which groups will have crystalline rocks (rocks with crystals). Look for crystalline rocks and **record** your observations.

5. **Predict** which rocks will be made of particles or fragments. Look for rocks that are made of particles or fragments. **Record** your observations.

6. **Compare and contrast** the rocks in your collection. **Record** as many properties as you can for each rock.

Analyze and Conclude

1. In which group(s) of rocks do you find layers, and in which do you not find layers?

2. In which group(s) of rocks do you find crystals, and in which do you not find crystals?

3. In which group(s) do you find particles or fragments, and in which do you not find particles or fragments?

4. Consider the properties of the rocks in your collection. Then **make inferences** about some uses for the rocks.

INVESTIGATE FURTHER!

RESEARCH

How's your Unit Project rock collection coming? Do some research to find out how the types of rocks in your collection are used by people.

Rock Quarries

Reading Focus What are two kinds of rock removed from quarries, and how are these rocks used?

Have you ever seen a fireplace built of rocks? How about a rock wall or a path lined with stones? Chances are, the rocks that make up these things came from a quarry (kwôr′ē). A rock **quarry** is an open pit at Earth's surface from which certain rocks are removed. Billions of tons of rock, such as granite, slate, and marble are removed each year from quarries all over the world.

Rock is removed from quarries in two forms. Dimension stones are slabs of rock that are removed from quarries in specific shapes and sizes. Most dimension stones are used to build structures that will last and look decorative.

Most of the rock removed from quarries is in a form called crushed stone. Crushed stone consists of bits and pieces of rock. These rock pieces are primarily used in concrete and other construction materials.

The method used to mine rocks depends on how the rocks will be used. Most crushed stone gets blasted from solid rock. Explosives are placed in holes drilled into the solid rock. Then the explosives are set off causing the rock to break up. Of course, this wouldn't be a great way to mine dimension stones, unless you are planning to cement the pieces back together!

Marble being cut at a quarry ▼

Marble slab being lifted by a crane ▼

Transporting marble slabs ▼

In most quarries, dimension stones are cut from solid rock by using either a drill or a torch. Air moving through the drill makes the drill bit, or tip, spin rapidly. As it spins, the bit cuts away at the rock. A torch, on the other hand, cuts the rock by melting it. When cut with a torch, the edges of the slabs are smooth.

Once the dimension stones are cut, a huge crane is used to move them. The blocks of rock, which can weigh several tons each, are secured with hooks and chains. Then the crane is used to slowly lift the stones and carry them away.

From the quarry, loose slabs are taken to a processing mill. Many quarries that mine dimension stones have their own processing mills. At these mills the rock slabs are cut to size using steel wires and rock saws. The saw blades are often made with diamonds. As you learned in Chapter 1, diamond is the hardest mineral. Diamonds can cut through even the hardest rocks.

Once the rocks are cut and sized, they may be polished. Polishing gradually smooths out any wire or saw marks left from the cutting stage. When the dimension stones are highly polished, they are ready to be shipped around the corner, around the country, or around the world.

The table shows some common dimension stones, where they come from, and what they are used for. Do any quarried rocks come from your state? What states might produce the marble for a counter top? Which stones are used in monuments? ■

Dimension Stones

Rock	Where From	Uses
Granite	Vermont, Massachusetts, Maine, New Hampshire, Rhode Island, Minnesota, Wisconsin	monuments, buildings, grave markers
Sandstone	New York, Ohio, Pennsylvania, Kentucky, Connecticut	buildings, trim
Marble	Vermont, Georgia	monuments, buildings, flooring, counter tops, kitchen items
Limestone	Texas, Utah, Indiana, Missouri, Florida, Minnesota	decorative trims, buildings, monuments, park benches

A Ton of Bricks!

Reading Focus How are bricks made?

Although they are hard like most rocks and are made from minerals, bricks aren't actually rocks. Rocks are made of one or more minerals, and they form naturally. Since rocks are formed by nature, bricks cannot be rocks because bricks are made by people!

Brick Making Today

What, then, are bricks? Bricks are small, rectangular blocks made from a mixture of clays and other sediments. To make bricks, different kinds of clay are dug from river bottoms or other places on Earth's surface. These materials are then taken to a factory where they are graded and crushed into a fine powder.

Water is added to the powder to make a thick, gooey paste. The paste is pressed into molds that are coated with sand or water. The coating helps to prevent the mixture from sticking to the molds, much as butter helps to keep cake batter from sticking to a pan.

Next, molds are placed in a kiln, or drying oven. When the clay mixture is completely dry, the molds are fired in another kiln. Firing chemically changes the clay blocks by heating them for up to 12 hours at temperatures above 800°C (1,500°F). Once fired and cooled the bricks are ready to be packed and shipped.

Brick Making in the Past

People have used bricks for at least 60 centuries! The first bricks were probably simple mud blocks dried in the sun. Adobe (ə dō'bē), or sun-dried brick, is thought to have first been made in dry areas of the world.

Adobe bricks are made with a mixture of clay, sand, and sometimes, straw. The materials are mixed by hand, with bare feet, or with a simple tool. The mixture is then put into molds and allowed to dry for at least two weeks. When dry, the bricks are removed from the molds and used.

▲ **This structure is made from adobe.**

Making Bricks

1. Clays and sediments are removed from Earth.

2. They are ground into powder in a factory.

3. The powder is mixed with water to form a paste.

4. The mixture is put into molds.

5. The molds are placed in ovens, called kilns, in which the mixture dries and changes.

6. The hardened brick is cooled.

INVESTIGATION 2 WRAP-UP

THINK IT WRITE IT

REVIEW

1. How are rocks mined in quarries?

2. What are four common types of dimension stones?

CRITICAL THINKING

3. Identify some ways in which rocks differ.

4. Suppose you were asked to select a type of rock that could be used to make a strong but attractive building. What rock would you choose? Use the Rock Key on page C39 for help. Give reasons to support your choice.

HOW DO ROCKS CHANGE OVER TIME?

It may seem that rocks last forever, but they don't. They change, just like everything else. Unwrap some broken crayons and set them on wax paper in the hot sunlight. What happens? What rock-forming change have you just modeled?

Activity

'Round and 'Round She Goes

It may take hundreds of thousands of years, even millions of years, but Earth materials go through changes called the rock cycle. In this activity you'll investigate this cycle.

Procedure

1. Place the Rock Cycle diagram on your desk.

2. Granite, sandstone, sand, and quartzite form part of a loop in the rock cycle. Use samples of these from your rock set to **make a model** of the rock cycle. Arrange the sand and rocks in their correct places on the Rock Cycle diagram. Then, in your *Science Notebook*, **draw** the part of the loop they make. **Label** your drawing to show the kinds of materials or rocks and the processes they undergo in changing from one to another.

3. Gneiss, sandstone, and sand make a complete loop in the rock cycle. Arrange those samples in order on the diagram. **Draw** and **label** this loop.

4. Basalt, slate, shale, and clay make another part of a loop. Arrange your samples in order on the diagram. **Draw** and **label** this loop.

5. Another part of a loop in the rock cycle is made by seashells, marble, and limestone. Get samples of these materials and arrange them on your rock cycle. **Draw** and **label** this loop.

Step 2

Analyze and Conclude

1. Explain why the loop in step 3 is a complete cycle that could happen over and over again.

2. In step 2, why don't the materials listed form a complete loop? What is needed to make this a complete loop in the rock cycle?

3. **Suggest a definition** of the rock cycle, based on how you think it works.

Technology Link CD-ROM

INVESTIGATE FURTHER!

Use the **Science Processor CD-ROM**, *The Solid Earth* (Investigation 2, Recycling Rocks) to explore the rock cycle.

Fossil Fuels

Reading Focus What are fossil fuels, and how do they form?

How many ways did you use energy today? Most energy comes from fossil fuels. As you might suspect from its name, a fossil fuel is a material formed from plant or animal remains that can be burned for the energy they contain.

Over millions of years, pressures and temperatures have squeezed and changed the remains. Left behind are substances that are rich in carbon and hydrogen that were once parts of organisms. When these substances burn, energy is released.

Coal is one kind of fossil fuel. The drawings show the different stages in the formation of different types of coal. Peat and all types of coal are used as fuel. In the United States, coal provides about 20 percent of our energy needs.

Millions of years ago

PEAT
60% Carbon
Coal begins to form when swamp plants die and are quickly buried beneath sediments and other plants. Tiny organisms called bacteria cause organic material to decay and change. Over time, a dark, watery organic material called peat forms.

peat layer

LIGNITE
70% Carbon
With time, the peat gets buried by more sediments. The weight of these sediments compacts the peat and squeezes water out. Eventually, the percent of carbon present increases and a sedimentary rock called lignite, a type of coal, forms.

lignite layer

Two other kinds of fossil fuel are oil and natural gas. Oil and natural gas form when ocean plants and animals die and their remains settle to the ocean floor. Over time these remains become buried by sediments.

Over time, heat, pressure, and the action of bacteria change the organic remains into oil and natural gas. The oil and natural gas seep through cracks and spaces in the rocks. When they reach a rock layer that doesn't have cracks or spaces, the oil and gas become trapped. The oil collects in a layer of rock and the gas collects in a pocket above the oil. ■

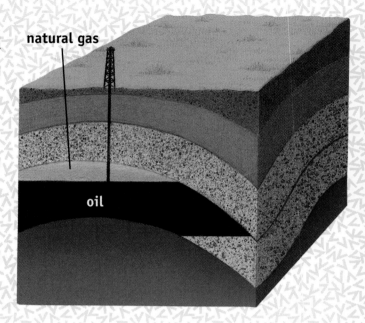

natural gas

oil

▲ **Oil and natural gas are often found trapped below the surface.**

Present Day

BITUMINOUS COAL
80% Carbon
As the rock becomes buried deeper, temperature and pressure increase. Nearly all of the water that was once in the plant parts gets forced out and bituminous (bi tŏŏ′ mə nəs) coal forms. Bituminous coal, or soft coal, is a sedimentary rock that is mostly carbon.

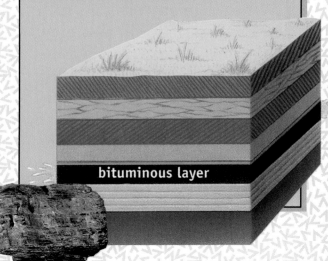

bituminous layer

ANTHRACITE
95% Carbon
With deep burying and great temperature and pressure, bituminous coal becomes metamorphosed to form anthracite (an′thrə sīt). Anthracite is a metamorphic rock. It has the highest percent of carbon of all the forms of coal.

anthracite layer

C59

Rocks in Circles

Reading Focus How do rocks change over time?

You learned that high temperatures and great pressures can change any rock into a metamorphic rock. But any kind of rock—igneous, sedimentary, or metamorphic—can be changed into another kind of rock, not just by metamorphism but also by other processes. The series of changes that rocks undergo in nature is called the **rock cycle**.

Notice the ovals in the diagram of the rock cycle on the next page. They represent five kinds of rock materials: igneous rock, sedimentary rock, metamorphic rock, sediments, and molten rock (magma and lava). Between the ovals are factors that cause rocks to change. Among these factors are compacting, cementing, heat, pressure, melting, and cooling.

When you play most board games, you can move in only one direction around the board. But the rock cycle follows many paths. Use the diagram to see how one type of rock changes into another. Start at any oval. Then move in the direction of any arrow coming out of the oval. Follow the arrows, and you can't go wrong.

Sedimentary to Metamorphic

As you can see from the diagram, there are many factors in the rock cycle that cause change. Find the words *Sedimentary Rock* on the diagram. You know that sedimentary rocks form near Earth's surface. What do you think happens when these rocks become buried? High temperatures and pressures deep below the surface change sedimentary rocks into metamorphic rocks. Follow this change on the diagram.

Metamorphic to Igneous

What do you suppose happens when temperatures deep below the surface become very high? Melting, or the changing of a solid to a liquid, occurs. Melting changes metamorphic rock into molten rock. Find *Melting* on the diagram.

As magma or lava cools, minerals form. When different minerals, such as quartz and mica, form, they grow into different-sized crystals. So this step is sometimes called crystallizing.

Notice in the rock cycle diagram that when magma and lava cool, they crystallize to form igneous rock. On the diagram, follow the change from metamorphic rock to igneous rock.

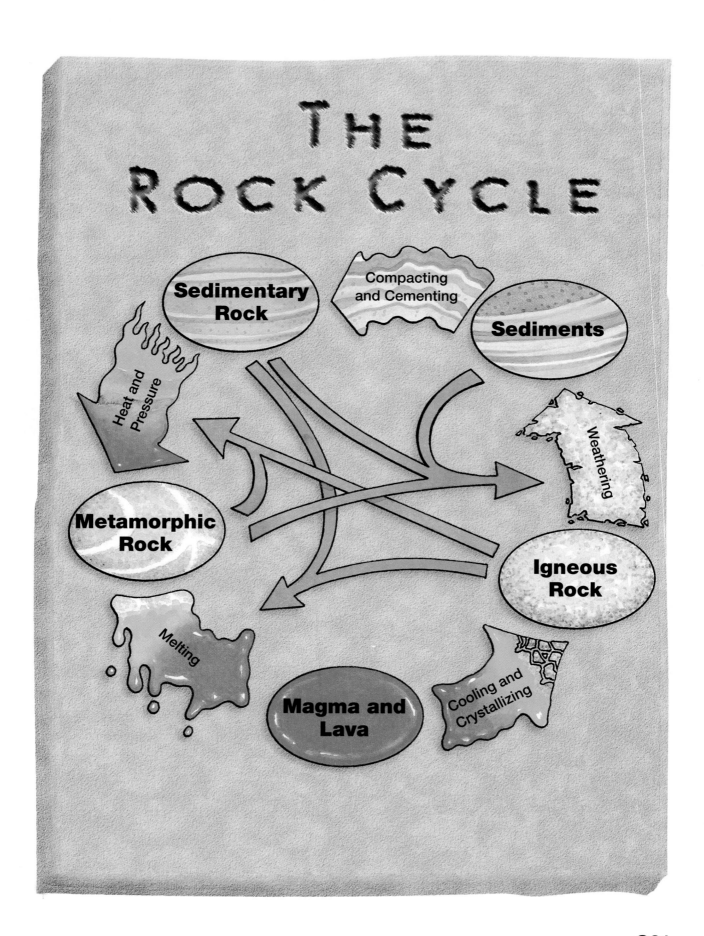

THE ROCK CYCLE

Sedimentary Rock

Compacting and Cementing

Sediments

Heat and Pressure

Weathering

Metamorphic Rock

Igneous Rock

Melting

Magma and Lava

Cooling and Crystallizing

Igneous to Sedimentary

Any rock at Earth's surface is exposed to conditions that cause the rock to break into small rock bits, or sediments. **Weathering** is the breaking up of rocks into sediments. Through weathering, an igneous rock can eventually become sediment bits.

Find the arrow labeled *Compacting and Cementing* in the diagram on page C61. Recall that when sediments are compacted, they are squeezed together. Cementing bonds sediments together. Compacting and cementing of sediments changes them into sedimentary rock. So, as you can see in the diagram, igneous rock must first weather to become sediment. Then the sediment is compacted and cemented and changed into sedimentary rock.

There are many other paths of change in the rock cycle. For example, how might sedimentary rock change into igneous rock? How might metamorphic rock become sediment?

▲ When water mixes with hot lava that flows from a volcano, the lava cools, forming igneous rock, as the water becomes steam.

By using the diagram on page C61, you can follow these changes. What other changes in rocks and rock materials can you find? ■

INVESTIGATION 3 WRAP-UP

REVIEW

1. What is the rock cycle?

2. Describe four ways rocks can change over time.

CRITICAL THINKING

3. Sand in a riverbed can become sandstone, and sandstone can become sand in a riverbed. Is this statement true or false? Explain your answer.

4. Describe how granite might become obsidian.

REFLECT & EVALUATE

Word Power

Write the letter of the term that best matches the definition. *Not all terms will be used.*

1. An open pit from which rocks are removed
2. Series of changes that rocks undergo
3. Rocks that form when sediments harden
4. Rocks that form from existing rocks
5. Bits of rocks, minerals, and organic materials
6. Rocks that form when melted rock material cools and hardens

a. fossil
b. igneous rocks
c. metamorphic rocks
d. quarry
e. rock cycle
f. sedimentary rocks
g. sediments

Check What You Know

Write the term in each pair that best completes each sentence.

1. Granite forms when (lava, magma) cools.
2. Sandstone is an example of a (clastic, chemical) sedimentary rock.
3. Mineral grains of a rock tend to become lined up during (contact, regional) metamorphism.
4. Rocks are changed into sediments through (weathering, compacting).

Problem Solving

1. You observe that a rock has large crystals and is unlayered. What type of rock would you infer it to be? Explain your inference.

2. Watch TV commercials or read advertisements of companies that provide coal, oil, or natural gas for heating homes. What can you infer about the safety of each product and the service offered by the companies?

Explain how the cycle shown could be never-ending. Then describe an event that could break the cycle.

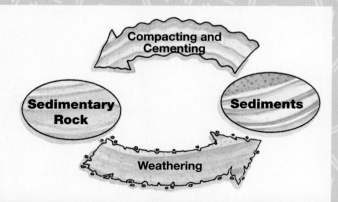

CHAPTER 3

EARTH'S STRUCTURES

Did you know that the solid ground under your feet is drifting on a layer of hot, gooey rock? This rock is only one of the remarkable materials that make up Earth. Sometimes the drifting movement leads to earthquakes.

PEOPLE USING SCIENCE

Geophysicist Scientists who study the physics of Earth are geophysicists (jē o fiz' i sists). Some geophysicists, such as Dr. Rufus D. Catchings, study earthquakes and their effects. Dr. Catchings works for the United States Geological Survey. He is mapping the underground rock formations where earthquakes are likely to be felt.

Dr. Catchings is coordinating a project that "shoots" sound into the ground in order to find places where rock sections are likely to move. His team has mapped the area around the 1994 earthquake site in Northridge, California. On the opposite coast, his team is mapping an area in northern Delaware. In this chapter you'll learn more about where and why earthquakes occur.

Coming Up

◀ Dr. Catchings and a coworker in earthquake territory

INVESTIGATION 1

WHAT IS EARTH'S STRUCTURE?

How do rocks make up the sphere called Earth? What's at the center of that sphere? This investigation will help you answer such questions about Earth's structure by looking at what's inside as well as outside Earth.

MATERIALS

- wax paper
- apple
- plastic knife
- *Science Notebook*

Activity

A Model Earth

An apple makes a good model of Earth's structure. Sometimes a model helps scientists to ask better questions. In this activity you'll use an apple as a model of Earth.

Procedure

1. Place a piece of wax paper on your desktop. Put an apple on the wax paper.

2. Use the apple to model the interior of Earth. Cut the apple in half. Carefully observe the cut surface from the skin to the center of the apple. In your *Science Notebook*, sketch and describe what you see.

Step 2

3. Cut both halves in half again. The skin represents Earth's **crust,** or surface layer. The skin on three of the pieces is a model for the amount of Earth's crust that is covered by oceans.

Step 3

 Math Hint *Recall that one half of one half is one fourth, so the apple is now divided into fourths.*

4. Examine one of the pieces of apple carefully. Compare the thickness of the skin to the thickness of the rest of the piece.

Analyze and Conclude

1. Based on your model, how much of Earth's crust is covered by oceans? How much of the crust is land?

2. Earth has a layer below its crust called the **mantle**. The mantle covers a ball, called the **core**, in the middle of Earth. Infer which parts of the apple are models for the mantle and the core.

3. Compare the thicknesses of the crust, mantle, and core in your model. Based on your model, what can you hypothesize about the depths, or thicknesses, of the layers of Earth?

 Technology Link
CD-ROM

INVESTIGATE FURTHER!

Use the **Science Processor CD-ROM**, *The Solid Earth* (Unit Opening Investigation, Down to Earth) to find out what it would be like to dig a hole through Earth's center.

The Sphere We Live On

Reading Focus What is the interior of Earth like?

When you hear the word *model*, what do you think of? You may picture a model airplane or a fashion model. In science, a **model** is something used to represent an object or an idea. In the activity on pages C66

Using Math *The thicknesses of Earth's layers add up to the radius of Earth. What is a reasonable estimate of Earth's radius in kilometers?*

and C67, an apple is used as a model of Earth. What would happen if you took a huge knife and sliced right through Earth instead of through an apple? You'd see four layers instead of three—so the apple model is a bit too simple. Now take a look at another Earth model, shown below.

The Crust

Earth's outer layer is called the **crust**. It is the thinnest layer, and it varies in thickness around Earth. It can be as thin as 10 km (6 mi) under the oceans and as thick as 65 km (40 mi) below the continents. The crust is made up of solid rock. It is mostly granite, gabbro, and basalt, but it also includes all the igneous, sedimentary, and metamorphic rocks you have learned about. Much of the crust is covered by oceans, lakes, rivers, sediments, plants, and soil. The crust is broken into several

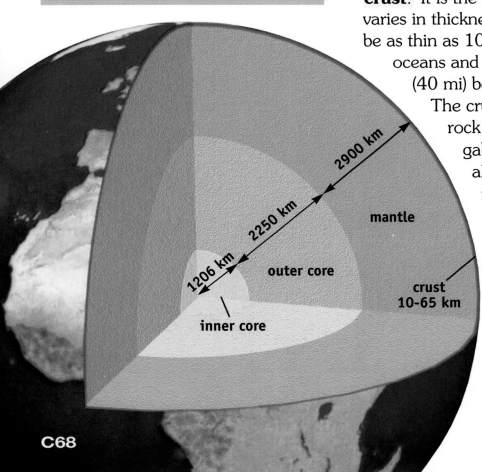

2900 km

2250 km

1206 km

mantle

outer core

inner core

crust 10-65 km

sections called plates. These plates float like rafts on the layer below the crust. They move very slowly around Earth's surface, carrying the continents and oceans with them.

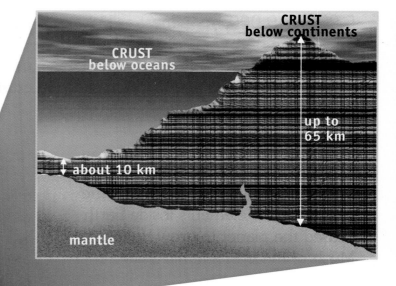

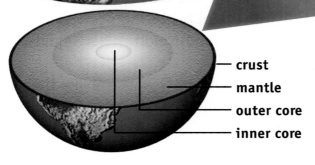

— crust
— mantle
— outer core
— inner core

▲ Earth's crust is thicker beneath continents than beneath oceans.

The Mantle

Below the crust is the **mantle**, Earth's thickest layer. It makes up about 84 percent of Earth's volume. The part of this layer that is closest to the crust is made of solid rock. However, much of this solid rock has some properties of liquids. It can flow like syrup or be stretched out like putty. Much of the mantle is composed of an igneous rock called peridotite (per-ə dō′tīt). This dark-colored rock is rich in iron, magnesium, and silicon.

When you studied metamorphic rocks, you found out that temperature and pressure increase as you go deeper below Earth's surface. Temperature and pressure are greater in the mantle than in the crust. As a result, some rock in the mantle melts. This molten rock sometimes makes its way to the surface.

The Inner and Outer Core

The **core** is the innermost layer of Earth. It is made up of a solid inner layer and a molten outer layer. The outer core is made of molten iron, silicon, and carbon. Scientists think the boundary between the outer core and the mantle is wavy. The hills and valleys in this boundary are likely caused by the movement of molten rock between the outer core and the mantle.

At Earth's center is the inner core, which is made of solid iron and nickel. Temperatures here may exceed

HOW CAN FOSSILS HELP TELL US HOW OLD A ROCK IS?

Think of Earth as a book, with layers of rock stacked on top of one another like pages. How can you use the fossils in rocks to number the pages and read the book?

Activity
Layering Fossils

Scientists study rock layers and the fossils in them to learn about ancient forms of life. Find out what scientists can learn by doing this activity.

MATERIALS

- 3 different colors of modeling clay
- shell
- leaf
- twig
- *Science Notebook*

Procedure

1. Flatten three pieces of clay, each a different color.

2. Make a model of a fossil imprint by making an impression of a shell in one piece of clay. Make an impression of a leaf in a second piece of clay and a twig in a third piece of clay. Set aside the shell, leaf, and twig.

Step 2

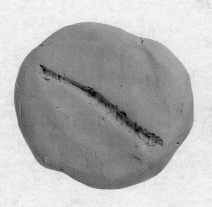

3. Each piece of clay represents a layer of sedimentary rock. Stack your layers one on top of the other. In your *Science Notebook*, **record** the order from top to bottom.

Analyze and Conclude

1. Based on what you know about how sedimentary rock forms, **infer** which of your "fossils" would be the oldest and which would be the youngest. Explain your reasoning.

2. Suppose that the twig is from a bush that lived after the shellfish died but before the tree from which the leaf was taken lived. Which fossil would be on the top of the stack? Which fossil would be on the bottom?

3. **Compare** your stack of fossils with those of other students. Are the fossils in the same order? If not, **infer** the relative ages of the fossils in each of the other stacks.

UNIT PROJECT LINK

Find out about fossils that have been collected in your community or that were discovered in your state. If possible, obtain examples of such fossils for your collection. Be sure to note the exact location where each fossil was found. If you can't get examples, make drawings of the fossils.

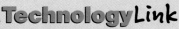 **Technology Link**

For more help with your Unit Project, go to **www.eduplace.com**.

Sorting Through Time

Reading Focus What did William Smith use to identify rock layers of the same age?

People have been digging up fossils for centuries. But the idea that fossils were the remains of creatures from the past was not accepted until the 1700s. You can bet that William Smith, an English geologist, didn't realize that his hobby of fossil collecting would show a way of matching rock layers by age!

While surveying land in England, Smith observed many rock layers and collected fossils. He noticed that rock layers lie stacked in a set order. Next, he saw that each layer of sedimentary rock contained different types of fossils. He soon realized that fossils could be used to recognize rock layers of the same age in different places. Scientists today use fossils to do just that!

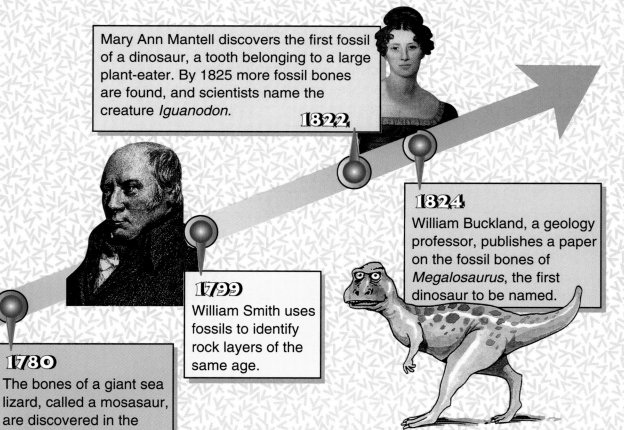

Mary Ann Mantell discovers the first fossil of a dinosaur, a tooth belonging to a large plant-eater. By 1825 more fossil bones are found, and scientists name the creature *Iguanodon*. **1822**

1824
William Buckland, a geology professor, publishes a paper on the fossil bones of *Megalosaurus*, the first dinosaur to be named.

1799
William Smith uses fossils to identify rock layers of the same age.

1780
The bones of a giant sea lizard, called a mosasaur, are discovered in the Netherlands.

Fossils Tell Tales!

Reading Focus What clues do fossils provide about Earth's history?

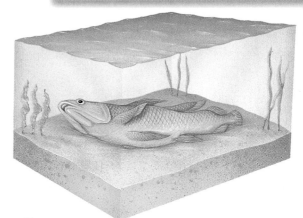

1 An organism dies.

2 The remains get buried quickly by sediment. The soft parts decay.

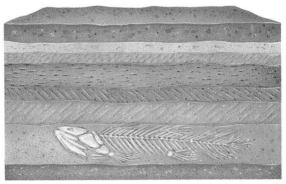

3 Over time, the hard parts get replaced with minerals. The sediment layer gets buried deeper and is compacted and cemented to form sedimentary rock.

There aren't many things more exciting than coming face to face with a dinosaur—a dinosaur skeleton, that is. Our knowledge of dinosaurs has come from studying fossils. Recall from Chapter 2 that fossils are remains or traces of living things from the past. A fossil can give clues about the environment where an organism once lived, how it may have moved, what it ate, what it looked like, and the age of the rock it was found in.

You Old Fossil!

Many fossils form when plants and animals die and are quickly buried by clay, sand, and other sediments. Look at the drawings to see how a fossil might form. In some cases, bone and other hard materials are replaced by minerals.

Other fossils form when plants and animals leave imprints in soft sediment.

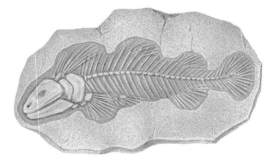

4 A fossil is later exposed due to the carrying away of weathered rock.

A cast ▶

A mold ▼

Over time, the organic material dissolves and the imprint gets filled with minerals or sediments. The imprint, or hollow part of the fossil, is called a mold. The material that fills in the imprint is called a cast. In the activity on pages C72 and C73, the imprints left in modeling clay by a shell, a leaf, and a twig are all examples of molds.

Relative Age

Scientists began studying fossils partly in the hope that fossils would help them estimate the age of Earth's rocks. There are many clues, including fossils, that you can use to learn about the ages of the rocks you see.

One clue to look for is the position of the rock layers. Recall that most sedimentary rocks begin as horizontal sediment layers. Think about books you might stack before putting them away. The first book you put down is on the bottom of the stack. It's the

same with rock layers. The oldest rock layer was laid down first and is on the bottom. The youngest rock layer was laid down last and is on the top.

When you can say that one rock is older than another, you have found its relative age. A rock's **relative age** is how old it is compared to other rocks.

In addition to a rock's position, scientists also use certain kinds of fossils, called **index fossils**, to help them tell the relative ages of rock. Plant and animal species that lived for only a short time (perhaps only a few million years) but that could be found in large numbers over much of Earth make very helpful index fossils.

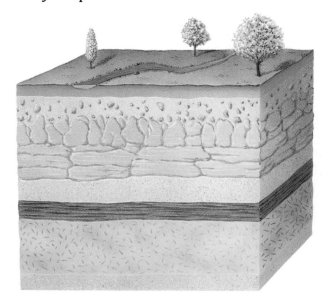

▲ **The sequence of rock layers can be used to determine the relative ages of rocks.**

The fossil shown here is a trilobite (tri′lō bīt). Many kinds of trilobites lived in oceans all over the world. Since certain kinds lived only at certain times in the past, they make good index fossils. When scientists find rocks in two different places that contain the same kind of trilobite fossils, they know that both rocks are about the same age.

Trilobites are common index fossils. ▶

Absolute Age

When someone asks how old you are, you probably say, "I'm 11 years old," rather than "I'm older than my sister." At times, scientists need to know more than a rock's relative age. They need to know its **absolute age**, or how old the rock really is.

Some elements found on Earth are not stable. These elements decay, or break down, into other elements at a known rate. Scientists measure how much of a decaying element is present in a rock layer. They also measure how much of the new element, into which it decays, is present. The time required for this level of decay provides the rock's absolute age.

Potassium is an element found in rocks. Potassium found in some igneous and metamorphic rocks breaks down to form the element argon. Scientists have used the amount of potassium and argon in rocks to find their absolute age. Some are as old as a few billion years! ■

Technology Link
CD-ROM

INVESTIGATE FURTHER!

Use the **Science Processor CD-ROM**, *The Solid Earth* (Investigation 3, Can You Dig It?) to dig for and identify fossils.

INVESTIGATION 2 WRAP-UP

THINK IT WRITE IT

REVIEW

1. How do fossils form?

2. How are index fossils used to date rocks?

CRITICAL THINKING

3. Suppose you find fossils in different layers of sedimentary rock. What can you infer about which fossil formed first? Explain.

4. A layer of shale is 3 million years old, and a layer of sandstone below it is 4 million years old. What can you conclude about the relative and absolute ages of each layer?

HOW DO ROCKS BEND?

Tonight, before you get into bed, place your hands flat on top of your covers. Then push the covers 20 cm (8 in.) across the bed. Make them push up into folds. How are these folds, or bends, like mountains?

Activity
Big Wrinkles

The Appalachian Mountains in the eastern United States are folded mountains that are worn down. Geologists "read" these mountains as they would a book. Here's how.

MATERIALS

- 3 different colors of modeling clay
- metric ruler
- plastic knife
- *Science Notebook*

Procedure

1. Flatten three pieces of clay, each a different color, into slabs about 2 cm thick. Each slab represents a layer of rock. Stack the layers. In your *Science Notebook*, **make a sketch** to show the order of the layers by color, from top to bottom.

2. Gently press the ends of the stack together, folding the layers upward into a mountain. Continue pressing until the sides come together.

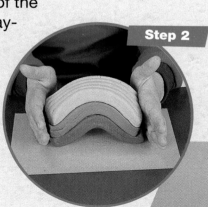

Step 2

3. In step 4 you will cut off the top of your mountain. **Predict** what the cut surface will look like. **Make a sketch** of your prediction.

4. In the process of **erosion**, weathered rock materials are carried away. **Model** erosion by cutting the top off your mountain. Use a plastic knife and cut so that you can see all three layers in the cut surface. **Observe** the cut surface and **compare** it with your prediction. **Draw** the eroded top. **Label** the layers by color. Title your drawing "Upward Fold."

5. Separate the three layers of clay. Flatten each lump again and make another stack. Keep the order of the layers the same as in step 1.

6. Fold the left and right ends of the stack upward until they meet, forming a mountain.

7. **Model** erosion by cutting the top off your mountain. **Draw** the eroded top. **Label** the layers and title your drawing "Downward Fold."

Analyze and Conclude

1. Where was the oldest layer of rock in the stack in step 1? in the upward fold (step 4)? in the downward fold (step 7)?

2. Suppose you know the relative ages of rock layers on an eroded surface. Explain how you can tell if an upward folding of rocks or a downward folding of rocks has occurred.

UNIT PROJECT LINK

Walk around your community to observe natural landforms. A landform is a feature of Earth's surface, such as a hill, a valley, or a plain. Make a list of the landforms you observe. Try to identify the types of rocks that make up the different landforms. Can you tell which rock layers are oldest?

 **Technology Link**

For more help with your Unit Project, go to **www.eduplace.com**.

Activity

Dome Questions

Some rocks get pushed up to form a geologic structure called a dome. Investigate how bending rocks can form this structure.

MATERIALS

- 3 different colors of modeling clay
- small ball (table-tennis or golf ball)
- plastic knife
- *Science Notebook*

Procedure

1. Flatten and stack three layers of clay, each a different color. Then press the stack down over a small ball to make a dome.

Step 1

2. Predict what the pattern of layers will be when you cut the top off the dome. In your *Science Notebook*, make a sketch of your prediction.

3. Model erosion by cutting the top off the dome, but do not cut so deep that you can see the ball. Observe the pattern of layers and compare it to your prediction. Make a sketch of the pattern and title it "Dome." Label the layers in order.

Analyze and Conclude

1. What does the pattern of layers in a dome look like?

2. Infer what forces could cause a dome to form. Explain your inference.

INVESTIGATE FURTHER!

RESEARCH

With a model dome made of clay, it takes only a short time to model erosion. But in nature, erosion can take a very long time. Research how long it took for the Appalachian Mountains to weather and erode from jagged peaks to smooth-topped mountains.

All Bent Out of Shape

Reading Focus What processes caused the Appalachian Mountains to form?

No matter how hard you try, you will probably never be able to bend a rock. But mountains all over the eastern United States formed because rocks can and do bend. Explore how this comes about.

Forces Bend Rocks

Every time you push a swing or pull a wagon, you apply a force. A force is a push or a pull. In the activity on pages C78 and C79, forces are applied to layers of clay, pushing on the clay layers in different directions.

Sometimes forces in nature push on rocks in the same way. If the forces are strong enough and are applied long enough, they can cause rock layers to bend. A bend in a rock layer is called a **fold**.

Most forces that bend rock layers are caused by moving plates. Recall that Earth's crust consists of huge slow-moving plates. When two plates come together, their edges may become folded. Over millions of years the folds become higher and form mountains.

Folded mountains form as rock layers bend and are pushed upward. ▼

The Appalachian Mountains

The Appalachian Mountains formed from folded rock. This mountain range stretches from Newfoundland in Canada to Alabama in the United States. The Appalachians formed about 250 million years ago as the plate carrying Africa collided with the plate carrying North America. Over time, the folded rock formed high hills and deep valleys.

When rock layers bend, some layers fold up and some layers fold down. An **anticline** is an upward fold of rock layers. A **syncline** is a downward fold of rock layers. An anticline and a syncline are modeled in the activity on pages C78 and C79.

The process of weathering wears rocks at Earth's surface into sediments. The carrying away of these weathered rock materials is called **erosion**. Wind, moving water, ice, and gravity all erode rocks. Since the Appalachians were formed, it has taken millions of years for them to weather and erode to their present height and shape.

Notice in the diagram on page C83 that the oldest rock layers of an anticline are found near the center of the fold. The layers get younger and younger as you move away from the center of the anticline. Now compare this to an eroded syncline. When a syncline is eroded, where is the youngest rock located?

Science in Literature

A MOUNTAIN ADVENTURE

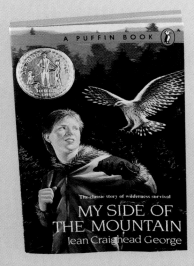

My Side of the Mountain
by Jean Craighead George
Puffin Books, 1991

"I landed with an explosion on my seat. The jolt splintered the ice and sent glass-covered limbs clattering to earth like a shopful of shattering crystal. As I sat there, and I didn't dare to move because I might get hurt, I heard an enormous explosion. It was followed by splintering and clattering and smashing."

In *My Side of the Mountain* by Jean Craighead George, Sam Gribley escapes his city home to find a new life on a mountain. This exciting tale tells how Sam survives the dangers he faces.

The Appalachian Mountains are made up of many anticlines and synclines. All areas do not weather and erode at the same rate. Rocks such as sandstone and conglomerate resist weathering. Where they are exposed at the surface, these rocks form ridges. Rocks such as limestone and shale wear away easily. These rocks form valleys. The combination of folding, weathering, and erosion has made the Appalachian Mountains a varied and beautiful landscape. ■

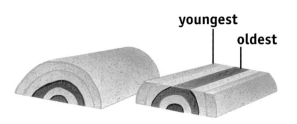

youngest

oldest

▲ **The oldest rock layers of a weathered and eroded anticline are near the center.**

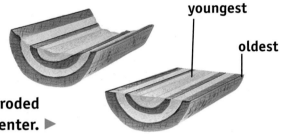

youngest

oldest

The oldest layers of a weathered and eroded syncline are farthest from the center. ▶

▲ **The Appalachian Mountains have a varied landscape because of folding, weathering, and erosion.**

The Black Hills

Reading Focus How do dome mountains form?

Forces pressing on rock from opposite sides can cause rock layers to fold. Over time, the folds may form mountains such as the Appalachians. Dome mountains can also form from folded rock layers. The Black Hills of South Dakota and Wyoming are an example of dome mountains.

A dome mountain forms when forces deep within Earth push rock layers upward. Recall that magma can flow into existing rock. Sometimes the magma pushes the rock layers above it upward, creating a dome.

The wearing down of a dome exposes other rock layers. In the Black Hills the magma that created the domes is now granite and is exposed at the surface. The center of the dome is granite surrounded by schist. How do you think the schist formed? Around the center are rings of sedimentary rock, including limestone and sandstone. The sandstone is very hard and resists weathering, forming steep ridges called hogbacks. People have also shaped the Black Hills—by carving the faces of four presidents into Mount Rushmore!

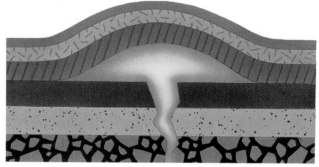

1 A dome forms when a vertical force, such as rising magma, pushes up.

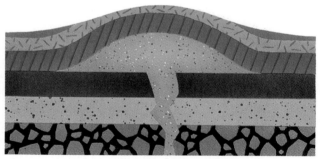

2 In a dome, the youngest rock is the igneous rock formed from the magma.

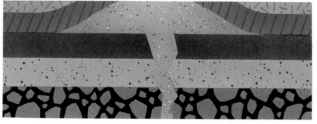

3 Weathering and erosion of a dome may expose the igneous rock formed from the magma.

MOUNT RUSHMORE

Mr. President...
How many of the likenesses of former presidents carved into this mountain's granite wall can you identify? The national memorial on Mount Rushmore's northeastern side is just over 1800m high. Each head is about 30m tall.

JEWEL CAVE

A Real Jewel...
Jewel Cave National Monument is a 100-km long maze of underground rooms and passageways. Its caves formed long ago when water seeped underground and eroded the limestone rock layers.

INVESTIGATION 3 WRAP-UP

THINK IT
WRITE IT

REVIEW

1. How did the Appalachian Mountains form?

2. How do dome mountains form?

CRITICAL THINKING

3. How are folded mountains different from dome mountains? How are they alike?

4. Suppose you see some folded rock layers exposed by weathering and erosion. How would knowing the ages of the layers help you tell if the folding was an anticline or a syncline?

WHAT IS A FAULT, AND HOW CAN IT MAKE MOUNTAINS?

Mountains are big blocks of rock. You already know that rock can be bent to make mountains. In this investigation you'll find out about another way that mountains are made.

Activity

It's Your Fault

Cracks and breaks in sidewalks are common. Sometimes a section of sidewalk is thrust up above nearby sections. Sometimes sections of rock are also thrust up to make mountains!

MATERIALS

- goggles
- wooden meterstick
- 2 pairs of identical books
- *Science Notebook*

SAFETY

Wear goggles during this activity.

Procedure

1. A place where rock has moved on one or both sides of a crack is called a **fault**. To model how a fault starts to form, have a partner hold one end of a meterstick down on a table, with most of the stick extending off the table.

2. Apply a gentle downward force to the free end of the meterstick. In your *Science Notebook*, describe what you observe. Predict what would happen if you used more force.

Step 2

3. Make two identical stacks of books, each consisting of two books of different sizes. The book stacks are models of rock layers.

4. Hold one stack on your right hand and the other stack on your left hand. Hold the books so that the top surfaces are level. The open sides of the books should face each other.

5. Move the books so that the edges of the covers in your left hand are just under the edges of the covers in your right hand.

6. The separation between the two stacks of books represents a fault. To **model** the motion along a fault, slowly raise your left hand a distance equal to the thickness of one book. **Observe** what happens, especially to the covers. **Record** your observations.

Analyze and Conclude

1. The meterstick in step 2 represents rock in Earth's crust. What happens to rock if a force strong enough to bend it is applied?

2. After you raised the books in step 6, which books were beside each other on opposite sides of the fault? **Infer** what happens as layers of rock move vertically along a fault.

3. In step 6, did the covers of the books catch on each other? How might this be like the rocks along a fault?

INVESTIGATE FURTHER!

RESEARCH

The mountain ranges in the Great Basin of the western United States were created by faults in blocks of rock. In which states are these mountains located? What mountain ranges are part of the Great Basin?

It's So Grand

Reading Focus What forces created the Grand Canyon?

Name the natural wonder that is 446 km (268 mi) long, up to 29 km (17 mi) wide, and more than 1.6 km (1 mi) deep. If you guessed the Grand Canyon, you're right! The Grand Canyon is cut into thousands of meters of rock! What forces could have created this amazing place?

If you could peer over the edge of the canyon rim, you would see layer upon layer of rock. These rock layers were formed long before the canyon existed. Recall that when rock layers form, the oldest layers are on the bottom. The oldest rocks exposed at the very bottom of the Grand Canyon are metamorphic and igneous rocks that formed as many as 1.5 billion years ago. The youngest rocks at the top of the rim are limestone that formed on an ocean floor 225 million years ago.

The Grand Canyon ▼

◀ **A normal fault**

◀ **A reverse fault**

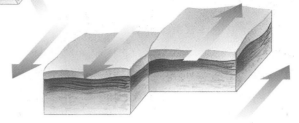

A strike-slip fault ▼

The Rocks' Fault

After the rock layers in the Grand Canyon formed, a variety of events caused them to change. One such event involved forces applied to rock, causing it to break. A break in rock along which movement has occurred is called a **fault**. As with folded rock, the forces that form faults usually are caused by Earth's moving plates.

Forces acting in different directions cause different kinds of faults to form in rock. In a game of tug of war, you pull on a rope in one direction and your friend pulls in the opposite direction. When forces pull on rock in opposite directions, a break called a normal fault can form. Notice in the diagram that rock layers on one side of the break move down in relation to those on the other side.

When moving plates caused rock in the Grand Canyon area to be stretched, many normal faults formed. Some of these faults have been given magical names such as the Crystal, Dragon, and Phantom faults. Tipoff Fault cuts right across the canyon.

Recall that forces can fold rock layers into anticlines and synclines. When such pushing forces cause rock to break, a reverse fault forms. In this type of fault, rock layers on one side of the fault are pushed up in relation to those on the other side. Use the diagram above to compare movement along a reverse fault with the movement along a normal fault.

In the activity on pages C86 and C87, two stacks of books are used to model movement of rock along a fault. When rock layers move along normal and reverse faults, older rocks can end up next to, or even above, younger rocks. For example, there is a reverse fault just west of Las Vegas, Nevada, called the Keystone Thrust.

▲ **Butte Fault is one of many faults that cut through the Grand Canyon.**

Along this fault, limestone layers were pushed up so that they sit above sandstone layers. But the sandstone is about 300 million years younger than the limestone above it!

When blocks of rock move along normal and reverse faults, special kinds of mountains called fault-block mountains can form. Several ranges of fault-block mountains occur throughout the states surrounding the Grand Canyon.

Not all movement along faults is up and down. Plate movements sometimes cause rock layers to break and slide past each other. Look back at the diagram on page C89. Notice that in a strike-slip fault, rock on either side of the fault moves horizontally in opposite directions. The San Andreas Fault in California is an example of this type of fault.

Carving a Canyon

Millions of years ago, the Colorado River flowed through northwestern Arizona just as it does today. Because it was a powerful fast-flowing river, it cut down into the rock over which it flowed. The river carried away billions of tons of sediment. Even today the Colorado River continues to transport thousands of tons of rock material each day!

Although erosion accounts for how the Grand Canyon became so deep, the process of weathering accounts for how it became so wide. Recall that weathering is the breaking up of rock. Over time, bits of rock wore off the canyon sides and fell to the bottom. There they were carried away by the river. The more rock that weathered from the canyon walls, the wider the canyon became. ■

Using Math

The power of the Colorado River carved the Grand Canyon and today propels these rafters. The river is 2,333 km (1,450 mi) long. Is it shorter or longer than the Grand Canyon? How much shorter or longer is it?

Earthquake!

Reading Focus What causes earthquakes?

▲ **Bridge damaged by the 1994 Los Angeles earthquake**

Can you imagine how scary it must be to wake up with the room shaking around you? That's what happened to millions of people around Los Angeles in 1994. The ground was shaking because an earthquake was occurring along a fault in California.

Why did this happen? As you have learned, forces within Earth can cause rock to break and move. When this occurs, energy is released. As a result, the ground shakes. This shaking of the ground is called an earthquake.

The place where movement first occurs along a fault is below Earth's surface and is called the focus. The place on Earth's surface above the focus is called the epicenter. Find the fault, the focus, and the epicenter in the drawing.

Have you ever struck a bell to make it ring? If so, you know it starts to vibrate, sending out waves of sound energy. In the same way, waves of energy move out from the focus of an earthquake and start the ground shaking. These waves damage land and buildings. In general, the deeper the focus, the greater the area that will be damaged by earthquake waves.

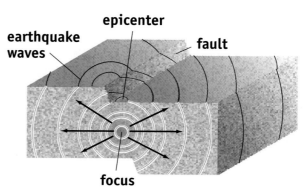

▲ **Earthquakes occur when there is movement along a fault.**

▲ **Signs of movement along the San Andreas Fault**

Why do you think earthquakes don't occur all the time along the system of faults under California? As plates move, sections of rock on either side of the fault lock together. Eventually enough force builds up so that the rocks unlock and slip past each other, causing an earthquake.

Most earthquakes occur at depths less than 650 km (390 mi). Below this depth, temperature and pressure are so high that all rock bends and flows rather than breaks. Along the famous San Andreas Fault, most earthquakes occur at depths less than 30 km (18 mi).

There have been major earthquakes along the San Andreas Fault. In 1857 a section of the fault 120 km (72 mi) from Los Angeles moved 9 m (30 ft). In 1906 the fault shifted 6 m (20 ft), and the resulting earthquake destroyed San Francisco. Over the past 20 million years, there have surely been many major earthquakes along the same fault.

Slow movement occurs along the San Andreas Fault all the time. Each year, crust along the fault moves several centimeters. Scientists believe that in about 10 million years, Los Angeles will have moved so far north that it will sit just across the fault from San Francisco! In about 60 million years, Los Angeles will be completely separated from the rest of California. As long as the crust along the San Andreas Fault continues to move, earthquakes will happen. ■

Internet Field Trip
Visit **www.eduplace.com** to explore earthquakes.

INVESTIGATION 4 WRAP-UP

REVIEW

1. What are the three types of faults?

2. How do faults result in the formation of mountains?

CRITICAL THINKING

3. Along what type of fault is a mountain not likely to occur? Explain your answer.

4. You find a 6-million-year-old conglomerate above a 4-million-year-old shale. Explain this arrangement of rock layers.

REFLECT & EVALUATE

Word Power

Write the letter of the term that best matches the definition. *Not all terms will be used.*

1. A bend in a rock
2. Earth's thickest layer
3. A break in rock along which movement has occurred
4. A downward fold of rock layers
5. Actual age of an object
6. Earth's outer layer

a. absolute age
b. anticline
c. core
d. crust
e. fault
f. fold
g. mantle
h. syncline

Check What You Know

Write the term in each pair that best completes each sentence.

1. Extreme pressure keeps the inner core (molten, solid).
2. An imprint of a trilobite is called a fossil (mold, cast).
3. In a weathered and eroded anticline, the center contains the (oldest, youngest) rock layers.
4. When forces on rock pull in opposite directions, a break known as a (reverse, normal) fault can form.

Problem Solving

1. Compare and contrast folding and faulting.

2. Make a sketch of a syncline and an anticline. Then make a sketch showing the weathered and eroded top of each formation. Label the rock layers from oldest to youngest in each sketch.

3. How could folding make it hard to find the relative ages of rock layers?

Copy the drawing of the model of Earth. Then label the layers on your drawing. For each layer, write a short paragraph that describes its thickness, the kind of material it contains, and any other information that interests you.

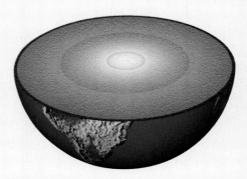

Detecting the Sequence

Sequence is the order in which things happen. To keep track of the sequence, look for signal words such as *first*, *then*, *next*, and *later*. When a passage doesn't contain signal words, look for other clues, such as numbers in the text or numbered steps in a diagram.

Look for these clues to detect the sequence.

• Signal words: *first, then, next, later*

• Numbers in the text

• Numbered steps in a drawing

Read the following paragraph. Then complete the exercises that follow.

A Cut Above

After grading, diamonds are sent to a gem cutter. Gem-quality diamonds are cut because doing so shows off their brilliant nonmetallic luster. Next, the diamond is shaped. Finally, it is polished by holding it at an angle to a spinning disk coated with diamond dust. This step creates the sparkling facets highly prized in gemstones.

1. **Which statement tells what happens to a diamond just before it is finally polished? Write the letter of that statement.**

    a. It is sent to a gem cutter.

    b. It is cut to show off its brilliant nonmetallic luster.

    c. It is shaped.

    d. It is polished by holding it at an angle to a spinning disk coated with diamond dust.

2. **List each clue that helped you keep track of the sequence.**

Using Math Volume

Volume is the amount of space something takes up. You can measure the volume of both liquids and solids.

You can measure the volume of liquids by using liters (L) and milliliters (mL).

$1 L = 1,000$ mL

1 liter

Use these containers to answer the questions that follow.

1. Which container has about 750 mL of water in it?

2. What fraction tells how much water is in container *C*?

 A B C D E

You can measure the volume of solids by using cubic units.

Volume = length × width × height

$3 \times 3 \times 3 = 27$

The volume of the cube is 27 cubic centimeters (cm³).

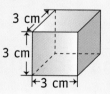
3 cm
3 cm
3 cm

Find the volume of each in cubic centimeters.

3.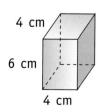
4 cm
6 cm
4 cm

4.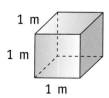
1 m
1 m
1 m

5.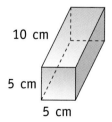
10 cm
5 cm
5 cm

6. These containers hold the same amount of sand. Explain.

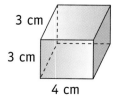
3 cm
3 cm
4 cm

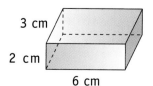
3 cm
2 cm
6 cm

WRAP-UP!

On your own, use scientific methods to investigate a question about Earth's materials, structure, or changes.

THINK LIKE A SCIENTIST

Ask a Question

Pose a question about Earth's materials that you would like to investigate. For example, ask, "How can freezing water break down, or weather, rocks?"

Make a Hypothesis

Suggest a hypothesis that is a possible answer to the question. One hypothesis is that freezing water can crack rocks, weathering them.

Plan and Do a Test

Plan a controlled experiment to find out if freezing water can weather, or break down, rocks. You could start with four pieces of limestone or four other rocks that have cracks, four sealable plastic bags, water, and a freezer. Develop a procedure that uses these materials to test the hypothesis. With permission, carry out your experiment. Follow the safety guidelines on pages S14–S15.

Record and Analyze

Observe carefully and record your data accurately. Make repeated observations.

Draw Conclusions

Look for evidence to support the hypothesis or to show that it is false. Draw conclusions about the hypothesis. Repeat the experiment to verify the results.

WRITING IN SCIENCE
Interview

To learn about valuable gems, interview an expert such as a gemologist or a jeweler. Write up your interview as an article for a class newsletter. Follow these guidelines.

- Prepare questions before the interview.
- Take notes and, with permission, record the interview.
- Use a question-and-answer format in writing up the main points of the interview.

D

Magnetism and Electricity

Theme: Models

THINK LIKE A SCIENTIST

POLAR LIGHT SHOW

This photo shows an aurora seen from Denali National Park, in Alaska. At certain times, auroras such as this one light up the sky in brilliant displays of color over Earth's poles. What causes auroras? Scientists have learned that Earth is a giant magnet that attracts particles of matter streaming from the Sun. The displays of color result from these particles colliding with particles in the atmosphere. Although scientists know what causes auroras, they can't fully explain what causes Earth to be a magnet.

THINK LIKE A SCIENTIST

Questioning In this unit you'll study magnetism and electricity. You'll investigate questions such as these.

- What Are Magnetic Force Fields?
- What Is Current Electricity?

Observing, Testing, Hypothesizing In the Activity "A Magnet's Ends," you'll make observations about how magnets react with each other. You'll test a magnet and infer which end is its north pole.

Researching In the Resource "Properties of Magnets," you'll gather more information about magnets, including kinds of magnets and some uses for magnets.

Drawing Conclusions After you've completed your investigations, you'll draw conclusions about what you've learned—and get new ideas.

MAGNETISM

Where do you find magnets? Perhaps your refrigerator door at home has small magnets that are holding up papers. You may have seen pictures of a giant magnet lifting tons of junked cars in the air. How do these magnets work?

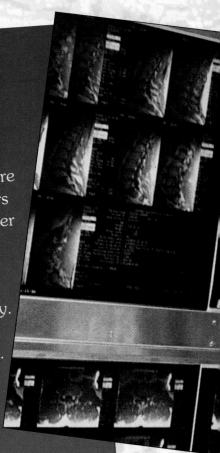

PEOPLE USING SCIENCE

Radiologist The rear doors of an ambulance open. Quickly, Pat is wheeled into the hospital. There are bandages around her head and arm. The doctors need to make sure there are no serious injuries to her head and spine.

Pat is taken to the Magnetic Resonance Imaging (MRI) center. MRI is a technology that uses powerful magnets to produce pictures of the inside of the body. Dr. Ray Cobb, a radiologist, gives Pat the MRI. A radiologist is trained to understand MRI pictures. The pictures help Dr. Cobb identify injuries to muscles and tissues. He can even find problems with blood circulation. In this chapter you'll find out about other ways that magnets help people.

◀ Dr. Ray Cobb studies MRI pictures to identify injuries.

INVESTIGATION 1

WHAT ARE MAGNETS?

Think about where you might find magnets in each room of your house. But keep in mind that many magnets are out of sight. Just what is a magnet, and what can it do? In Investigation 1 you'll find out.

Activity

Make a Magnet

Make your own magnet. Then find out what kinds of objects it pulls on, or sticks to.

MATERIALS
- bag of small objects
- bar magnet
- nail
- *Science Notebook*

SAFETY
Be careful when handling the nail.

Procedure

1. Open the bag of small objects and spread them on a table. Have each group member collect two other small objects. Include things made of many different materials.

2. In your *Science Notebook,* make a chart like the one shown to record your observations.

Attracted by Magnet or Sticks to Magnet		
Object	Prediction	Actual

Step 3

See **SCIENCE** *and* **MATH TOOLBOX** page H10 if you need to review *Making a Chart to Organize Data*.

3. **Talk with your group** and together **predict** which objects will stick to a magnet. **Record** your predictions in your chart. Then move a magnet close to each object. **Record** your observations in your chart.

4. **Make a chart** like the one you made in step 2. **Predict** whether a nail will attract any of the objects. Then move a nail close to each object. **Record** your observations.

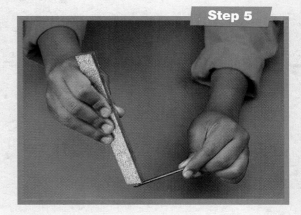

Step 5

5. Stroke the nail with the end of the magnet 30 times. *Stroke in one direction only*.

6. Repeat step 4, using the stroked nail. Make a set of predictions about the stroked nail. **Record** your predictions and, after testing the objects, **record** your observations.

Analyze and Conclude

1. **Compare** your predictions about which objects would be attracted to a magnet with your results.

2. **Compare** your predictions about the nail before you stroked it with a magnet with your results.

3. Explain your observations about the stroked nail. **Hypothesize** how stroking the nail with the magnet affects the nail.

4. What can you **infer** about the objects that were attracted by the magnet and the stroked nail?

INVESTIGATE FURTHER!

EXPERIMENT

Hold the nail that you stroked with a magnet near a pile of paper clips. If nothing happens, stroke the nail with the magnet 30 times. How many paper clips does the nail pick up?

Suppose you stroke the nail with the magnet 40 times and then 50 times. Will the nail be able to pick up more paper clips? Find out. Make a chart of your results.

Activity

A Magnet's Ends

Both ends of a magnet have "pull." But are both ends of a magnet alike in every way? Find out in this activity.

MATERIALS
- string
- 2 bar magnets
- meterstick
- 2 chairs
- *Science Notebook*

Procedure

1. Tie a string to a bar magnet on which one end is marked *N* and the other is marked *S*. Tie the string to a meterstick placed between two chairs, as shown.

2. **Predict** what will happen if you move the end of another bar magnet marked *N* and *S* close to the hanging magnet. Think about the ways you might arrange the ends of the magnets. **Record** each arrangement and what you **predict** for each arrangement in your *Science Notebook*.

3. **Make a plan** with your group to test your predictions. Then **test** your plan and **record** your observations.

Step 2

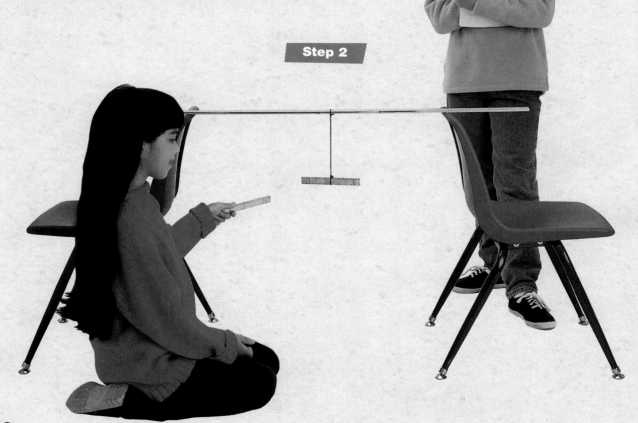

4. Now **test** a bar magnet on which one end is marked *X* and the other end is marked *Y*. Hold one end and then the other end of this magnet near one end of the hanging magnet. **Infer** which end of the magnet you're holding is really *N* and which is really *S*. **Record** your inference and state your evidence. Remove the tape. **Record** whether your inference was correct.

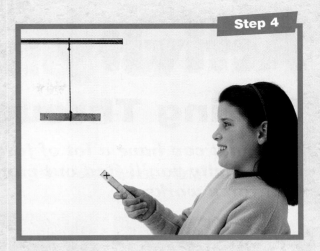

Step 4

Analyze and Conclude

1. The *N* on the end of a magnet marks its north-seeking pole, or north pole. The *S* on the other end of a magnet marks its south-seeking pole, or south pole. From your observations, **conclude** which poles attract, or pull toward, each other.

2. Conclude which poles repel, or push away from, each other. How do you know?

UNIT PROJECT LINK

For this Unit Project you'll invent games, fun devices, and machines. You'll use magnets or electricity in all your inventions. Your first challenge is to invent a magic trick that makes use of magnets. Think about a trick that works because the force of a magnet can be "felt" through various materials. Build a model of your magic trick. Include instructions for others to follow.

TechnologyLink
For more help with your Unit Project, go to **www.eduplace.com**.

Two Kinds of Magnets

Magnets made in factories, including toy magnets, are permanent magnets. A permanent magnet is not easy to make, but it keeps its magnetism for a long time. It may be made from steel that contains iron as well as other metals.

Some objects, such as iron nails, are easy to make into magnets. For example, the activity on pages D6 and D7 shows that you only have to stroke a nail with a permanent magnet to magnetize the nail. But magnets made in this way are temporary magnets. A temporary magnet is one that doesn't keep its magnetism for very long.

▲ Are the magnets on this refrigerator door likely to be temporary or permanent?

Science in Literature

MIND YOUR MAGNETS

"Magnetize a needle by allowing it to lie on a magnet for two minutes. Tie a thread to the center of the magnetized needle and suspend it inside a glass jar. Use a compass to determine which end of the needle points toward the north. Once you have identified the polarity of the needle, it can be used as a compass."

To learn more about this and other magnet activities, read *Magnets: Mind-boggling Experiments You Can Turn Into Science Fair Projects* by Janice VanCleave.

Magnets: Mind-boggling Experiments You Can Turn Into Science Fair Projects
by Janice VanCleave
John Wiley & Sons, 1993

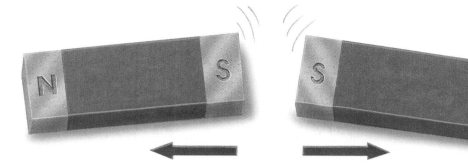

▲ The south poles or north poles of two magnets repel each other.

▲ The south pole of one magnet attracts the north pole of another magnet.

North and South Poles

When a magnet is hung so that it can move freely, one end of it always points toward the north. This is the magnet's north-seeking pole, or **north pole**. If one end points north, you know what direction the other end points toward. It points south. This is the magnet's south-seeking pole, or **south pole**.

What happens if you move the north pole of one magnet near the south pole of another magnet? If both magnets are free to move, they move closer together, and the north and south poles may stick to each other.

What happens if you bring the north pole of one magnet near the north pole of another? The two magnets move farther apart. Here is a rule to remember about how magnets behave. The unlike poles of magnets attract, or pull toward, each other. The like poles of magnets repel, or push away from, each other. In the activity on pages D8 and D9, the taped-over poles of a magnet can be determined from the way a second magnet moves. ■

Technology Link
CD-ROM

INVESTIGATE FURTHER!

Use the **Science Processor CD-ROM**, *Magnetism and Electricity* (Unit Opening, Shocking Behavior!) to see how objects react when they are charged and to test objects for magnetism.

Maglev Trains

RESOURCE

Reading Focus In what ways is a maglev train different from other forms of transportation?

Can a train fly? The maglev train does, in a way. If you visit Europe or Japan, you might ride on a maglev. It may look as if this train runs on a track, but it doesn't. The maglev train floats about 1 cm (0.4 in.) above the track!

It Flies and It's Fast

The maglev's full name tells something about how it works. *Maglev* is short for "magnetic levitation" (lev ə-tā'shən). *Levitation* means "rising into the air." The maglev uses magnetic force to rise into the air.

Ordinary trains are slowed by friction, the force caused by the wheels rubbing on the track. Because the maglev doesn't touch its track, there's no friction. This means that it can go as fast as 500 km/h (310 mph)!

Ordinary trains go "clackety-clack" along the rails. But speeding on air makes a maglev train ride very quiet, as well as smooth and superfast. What if maglev trains were everywhere? How might this affect people where you live?

This maglev train can travel about 500 km/h. An ordinary train can travel 300 km/h. How long would it take a maglev train to reach a city 1,500 km away? An ordinary train?

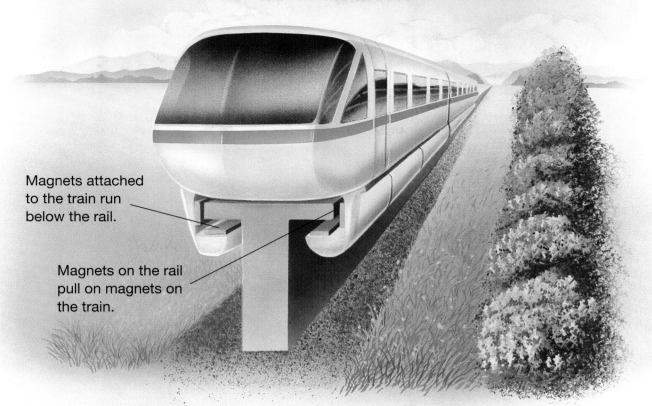

Magnets attached to the train run below the rail.

Magnets on the rail pull on magnets on the train.

▲ **Maglevs are lifted into the air by magnetic forces. There are powerful magnets on both the train and the rails.**

It's Clean

Most buses and cars run by burning oil or gasoline. So do most trains. When oil and gasoline burn, they pollute the air. That means those vehicles make the air dirty by giving off harmful substances.

The maglev runs on electricity. Power plants that produce electricity do burn fuels that pollute the air. But the train itself doesn't pollute the air because it doesn't burn fuels. Would you call the maglev an environmentally friendly train? Explain your answer. ■

═══ INVESTIGATION 1 WRAP-UP ═══

REVIEW

1. What happens when you put the unlike poles of two magnets together?

2. What general types of materials are attracted to magnets?

CRITICAL THINKING

3. Suppose that a rock sample from Mars is brought to Earth. Pieces of the rock can be picked up by a magnet. What metal may be present in the rock?

4. Two doughnut-shaped magnets are placed on a pencil. One of the magnets floats above the other one. What makes this happen?

WHAT ARE MAGNETIC FORCE FIELDS?

You can't see, hear, or smell a magnetic force field. But bring a magnet near an iron object and you can *feel* the force. In Investigation 2 you'll explore the patterns of magnetic force fields.

Activity

Getting Directions

Earth has a magnetic force field around it. In this activity you'll make a magnet and use it to detect Earth's magnetic force field.

Procedure

1. Magnetize a needle by stroking it 30–40 times with one end of a bar magnet. Stroke the needle in the same direction each time.

2. Stick the needle through the center of a plastic-foam ball, as shown.

MATERIALS

- goggles
- bar magnet
- needle with blunt end
- plastic-foam ball
- small bowl
- water
- *Science Notebook*

SAFETY //////

Wear goggles during this activity. Clean up spills immediately.

Step 2

D16

3. Half-fill a bowl with water. Carefully place the foam ball and needle on the water. **Observe** what happens. **Record** your observations in your *Science Notebook*.

Step 3

4. Wait until the foam ball is still. **Talk with your group** and together **predict** what will happen if you move the bar magnet near the bowl. **Test** your prediction and **record** your observations.

5. Take away the bar magnet. Give the bowl a quarter turn. Make sure that the foam ball is free to move. Keep turning until you complete a full circle. **Record** your observations.

Math Hint *Remember that a quarter turn measures 90°.*

6. Then repeat steps 4 and 5 to check your results.

Analyze and Conclude

1. Find out from your teacher which direction is north. In which directions did the ends of the needle point?

2. **Compare** your prediction with your observation of what happened when you moved a bar magnet near the bowl.

3. One end of a compass always points in the direction of north. From your observations, **infer** whether or not you have made a compass. Give reasons for your inference.

INVESTIGATE FURTHER!

RESEARCH

When you magnetize an object, the particles that make up the object become tiny magnets called domains. Find out more about magnetic domains at a library. One book you might read is *Magnets: Mind-boggling Experiments You Can Turn Into Science Fair Projects* by Janice VanCleave. Write a report and illustrate it with a drawing of magnetic domains.

Activity

Picture a Magnet's Force

Even though you can't see a magnet's force, you can make a picture of it. In this activity you'll find out how.

Procedure

1. Place a bar magnet on a sheet of newspaper. Put a sheet of white cardboard on top of the magnet.

2. Hold a jar of iron filings over the cardboard. Carefully sprinkle the filings on the cardboard over the magnet.

3. Gently tap the cardboard. Look for a pattern of lines of iron filings. In your *Science Notebook*, **draw** the pattern the lines form.

4. Put a clean sheet of cardboard over a horseshoe magnet. **Talk with your group** and together **predict** the pattern that will form if you sprinkle iron filings on the cardboard. Then **make a drawing** to show your prediction.

5. **Test** your prediction. Then **draw** what you see.

6. Put the iron filings back into the jar. Repeat the experiment to check your results.

Step 1

Analyze and Conclude

1. **Compare** your predictions with your observations of the patterns of the iron filings.

2. The lines made by the iron filings are a picture of **lines of force**. The space in which the lines of force form is a **magnetic field**. What do the magnetic fields you observed tell you about where the magnetic force is greatest?

Force Fields

Reading Focus What is a magnetic field, and what evidence shows it exists?

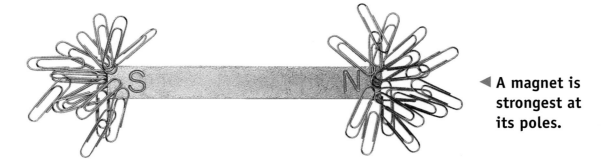

◄ **A magnet is strongest at its poles.**

What happens if you dip a bar magnet into a pile of paper clips and then hold the magnet up? Look at the picture. A lot of clips stick to the magnet. Notice where the clips stick—at the magnet's two poles. Why does this happen?

Lines of Force

The activity on page D18 shows pictures of the force fields of bar and horseshoe magnets. When iron filings are sprinkled on cardboard over a magnet, the iron filings form a pattern.

The pattern of filings shows how the force field spreads between the poles of the magnet and around it. The filings are thickest and closest together where the force is strongest.

These lines formed by the iron filings are called **lines of force**. The picture below shows a bar magnet that was sprinkled with iron filings. Actually, it's the same magnet that was used with paper clips in the picture above. Notice how the lines of force are heaviest at the poles, where the magnet also picked up the paper clips.

Pattern formed by lines of force of a bar magnet ►

A Magnet's Force Field

The space in which the force of a magnet can act is called a **magnetic field**. You can't see a magnetic field. But you have seen some evidence that it exists.

For example, suppose you want to use a magnet to pick up a paper clip. You know that you have to move the clip and the magnet close enough together for the magnet to attract the clip. That's because a magnet attracts only those paper clips—or other objects that contain iron—that come into its magnetic field.

You can see in the photos on pages D19 and D20 that iron filings can make pictures of the lines of force around a magnet. The photos make it seem that the magnetic field is flat. But is the magnetic field really flat?

▲ The pattern of the iron filings around the magnet in this jar of oil shows how a magnetic field spreads out all around a magnet.

The magnetic field actually spreads out in all directions throughout the space around the magnet.

Comparing Force Fields

You've found out about several properties of magnets.

- A magnet attracts objects made of iron.
- The force of a magnet is greatest at its poles.
- Like poles of two magnets repel each other.
- Unlike poles of two magnets attract each other.

How are the force fields of magnets related to those properties? Use the pictures on the next page to find out. As you look at each picture, read the description below it.

INVESTIGATE FURTHER!

EXPERIMENT

Make a permanent display of one or more patterns made by magnets as shown in the pictures on page D21. Use the procedure in the activity on page D18 to make the patterns you choose. Then put on goggles and spray white vinegar over the filings. Let them stand overnight. Brush off the rusted filings and observe what remains. Write captions for your pictures and put the pictures on display.

MAGNETIC FIELDS

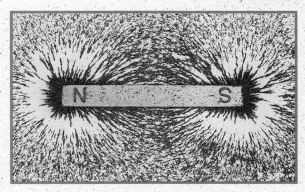

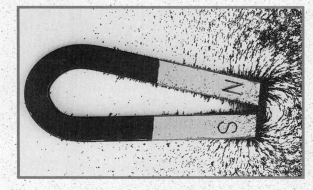

▲ This picture shows the magnetic field of a bar magnet. With your finger, trace the lines of force as they come out of the north pole, curve around the magnet, and enter the south pole.

▲ This picture shows the magnetic field of a horseshoe magnet. Notice how the strongest lines are closer together than they are for the bar magnet. Infer why this is so.

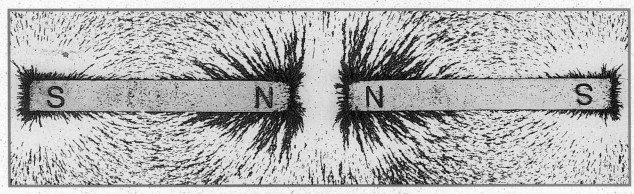

▲ The north poles of these two magnets are facing each other. What do you observe about the lines of force between the two magnets? If you hold two magnets with their north poles together like this, what will you feel?

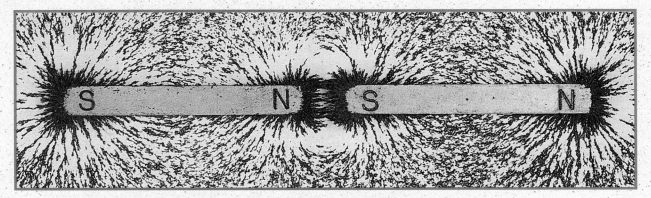

▲ The north pole of the magnet on the left is facing the south pole of the magnet on the right. Notice that the lines of force seem to move straight from one magnet to the other. If you hold two magnets like this, what will you feel?

Earth as a Magnet

Reading Focus What makes a compass show direction on Earth?

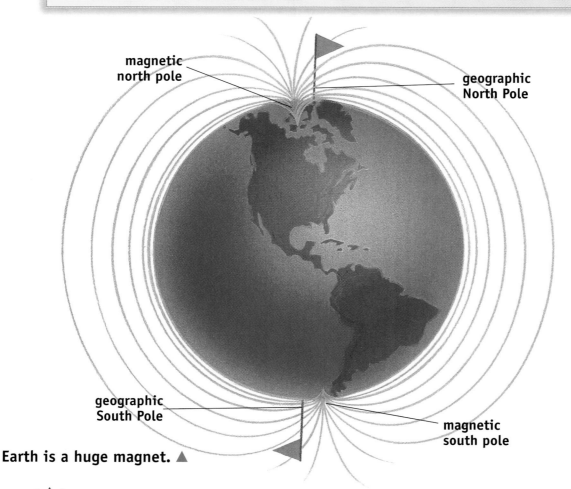

magnetic north pole

geographic North Pole

geographic South Pole

magnetic south pole

Earth is a huge magnet. ▲

Today scientists know that Earth is a giant magnet. However, long before scientists knew anything about Earth's magnetism, they knew about lodestone (lōd′stōn).

Lodestone is a naturally magnetic rock found at or near Earth's surface. The first lodestone was discovered by a sheepherder in Turkey more than 2,000 years ago. The stone attracted iron nails in the sheepherder's shoes. Almost 1,000 years later the Greeks made a discovery. They found that when hung from a string, lodestone always lined itself up in a north-south direction. The same end of the lodestone always pointed north.

A Stone Leads the Way

Chinese sailors found a practical use for lodestone. They floated a small piece of lodestone on some straw in a bowl of water. Since one end of the stone always pointed toward the north, the sailors always knew in which direction they were sailing.

The device used by the Chinese sailors is easy to make. In the activity on pages D16 and D17, a similar device is made with a magnetized needle and a foam ball. The device is a simple compass. A **compass** is a magnetized needle that is allowed to swing freely.

Earth's Magnetism

Since the discovery of lodestones, scientists have learned that Earth's center is made up mostly of iron. They know that the spinning of Earth on its axis has magnetized this iron, turning Earth into a giant magnet. But they can't explain how the spinning causes this.

The "Earth magnet" has poles. It is surrounded by a magnetic field with lines of force like those that can be seen in the activity on page D18. Magnets are affected by Earth's magnetic field. The north-seeking pole of a magnet is attracted to Earth's magnetic north pole. This attraction is what makes a compass work.

Why Two Sets of Poles?

As the drawing on page D22 shows, Earth has two sets of poles—geographic and magnetic. The geographic poles mark the ends of the imaginary line, or axis, around which Earth rotates.

When the first explorers set out for the North Pole, they expected their compass to lead them to the geographic North Pole. But it didn't. Their compass led the explorers to a spot more than 1,600 km (1,000 mi) from the geographic North Pole. This spot marks the location of Earth's magnetic north pole.

A piece of lodestone ▼

▲ **This ancient Chinese compass is a spoon that turns so that its handle points south.**

▲ An aurora in the northern sky

Magnetism Lights Up the Sky

At certain times of the year, people living in regions near the poles get a special treat. They get to see the northern or southern lights. During these times, the sky above the poles lights up in a display of brilliant colors. The times when these displays occur are also marked by disturbances of radio signals.

These displays, called auroras (ô rôr'əz), are produced when particles of matter from space are captured by Earth's magnetic field. Why are these displays brightest near Earth's magnetic poles? ■

Internet Field Trip

Visit **www.eduplace.com** to find out more about Earth's magnetism.

INVESTIGATION 2 WRAP-UP

REVIEW

1. What is a magnetic field?

2. Compare Earth to a magnet.

CRITICAL THINKING

3. When a circular magnet is dipped into a pile of paper clips, about the same number of clips sticks to the top as to the bottom. What does this tell you about the magnetic field of that magnet?

4. How could you make a compass with a magnetized nail, a string, a plastic jar with a lid, and some tape?

REFLECT & EVALUATE

Word Power

Write the letter of the term that best completes each sentence. *Not all terms will be used*.

a. compass
b. lines of force
c. lodestone
d. magnetic field
e. magnetism
f. north pole
g. south pole

1. A magnet's property of attracting iron is called ___.

2. The end of a magnet that seeks north is its ___.

3. The space in which the force of a magnet can act is called a ___.

4. A magnetized needle that swings freely is a ___.

5. A naturally magnetic rock is called ___.

6. The end of a magnet that seeks south is its ___.

Check What You Know

Write the term in each pair that best completes each sentence.

1. Lines formed by iron filings near a magnet are (lines of force, poles).

2. The force of a magnet is greatest at its (center, poles).

3. A magnet can be used to pick up (wood, iron).

4. If the south poles of two magnets are brought near each other, the poles (attract, repel) each other.

Problem Solving

1. Suppose that you are lost in the woods. You do not have a compass, but you do have a bar magnet and some string. How can you use the magnet and string to find your way?

2. You have two magnets—one strong and one weak. How could you use paper clips to find out which magnet is stronger?

Study the photograph. Explain whether the magnetic poles that are closest together are like or unlike. In your own words, write how you know this.

CHAPTER 2

ELECTRICAL ENERGY

What does a comic-book artist show by drawing a zigzag line? How can you tell that a character in a cartoon is having a bright idea? Think of some other signs and symbols that stand for electrical energy in action.

Connecting to Science

ARTS

Electric Art Artist David Archer creates pictures with an electric paintbrush. This device produces lightninglike arcs of electricity. Archer uses a wand to direct the arcs so that they hit large blobs of wet paint. The paint forms cloudy shapes on large glass plates. The artist calls these shapes art storms.

Most often, David Archer paints pictures of planets and other bodies in space as he imagines them. His work has appeared in magazines and even in the movies. You may have seen some of this artist's works on a television science-fiction show.

To run his electric paintbrush, David Archer uses household electricity. In this chapter you'll find out more about why electricity is such hot stuff!

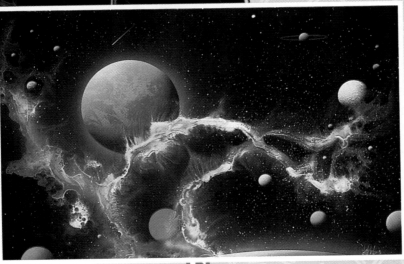

David Archer (*top*) uses an electric paintbrush; one of Archer's paintings (*bottom*).

WHAT IS STATIC ELECTRICITY?

Your clean hair clings to your comb. A shirt you take out of the dryer has socks stuck to it. As you pull up a blanket on a chilly night, you see sparks and feel a slight shock. In Investigation 1 you'll find out how all these events are related.

Activity

Charge!

Sometimes a balloon will stick to another balloon; other times it won't. Try this activity and see if you can figure out why.

MATERIALS

- 2 balloons
- 2 strings (30 cm each)
- metric tape measure
- wool cloth
- plastic wrap
- *Science Notebook*

Procedure

1. Have two members of your group blow up balloons. Tie each balloon tightly with a string.

2. Have two other group members hold the strings so that the balloons hang about 10 cm apart. **Observe** any movement. **Record** your observations in your *Science Notebook*.

 See **SCIENCE** and **MATH TOOLBOX** page H6 if you need to review *Using a Tape Measure or Ruler.*

Step 1

3. Rub each balloon with a wool cloth. **Predict** what will happen now if you repeat step 2. **Talk with your group** and **record** your prediction. Then repeat step 2.

4. Repeat step 3, but this time rub each balloon with plastic wrap instead of a wool cloth.

5. With your group, **predict** what will happen when a balloon rubbed with wool is brought near a balloon rubbed with plastic wrap. **Test** your prediction and **record** your observations.

Step 3

Analyze and Conclude

1. Rubbing a balloon with wool or plastic wrap gives the balloon an electric charge. From observing the behavior of the balloons, **infer** whether there is more than one kind of electric charge. Explain how you made your inference.

2. **Compare** your prediction about the balloons with your observations after they were rubbed with the wool cloth.

3. **Compare** your prediction about the balloons with your observations after they were rubbed with the plastic wrap.

4. Like charges repel, or push away from, each other. Unlike charges attract, or pull toward, each other. How do your results support these statements?

INVESTIGATE FURTHER!

EXPERIMENT

How does a balloon that has been charged interact with objects that have not been charged? Bring a charged balloon close to some puffed-cereal grains. Then bring another charged balloon near a wall. What can you conclude about the effect of a charged balloon on uncharged objects?

Static Electricity

Reading Focus What is static electricity, and how do objects become charged with static electricity?

You're combing your clean, dry hair. Strands of your hair fly away from each other. At the same time, the strands also stick to your comb. In the activity on pages D28 and D29, rubbing balloons with a wool cloth or plastic wrap causes the balloons to be attracted to or repelled by each other. Why does rubbing materials together cause these effects?

Hair, combs, balloons, wool, and plastic are kinds of matter. All matter is made up of tiny particles. Some of these particles carry units of electricity called **electric charges**.

Positive and Negative Charges

An electric charge can be positive or negative. A plus sign (+) stands for a positive charge, and a minus sign (−) stands for a negative charge. Most matter is neutral. A neutral object has the same number of positive charges as negative charges.

Only negative charges can move from one material to another. If negative charges move from one neutral object to another, the first object then has an overall positive charge. The second one has an overall negative charge. Look at the pictures

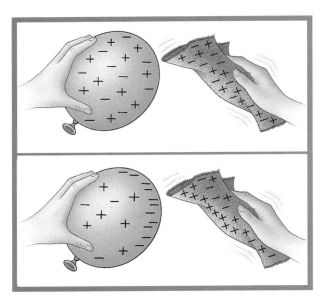

▲ Rubbing a balloon with wool (*top*) gives a negative charge to the balloon (*bottom*). What is the charge on the wool?

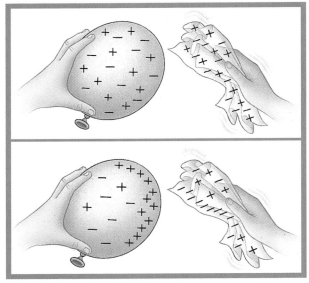

▲ Rubbing a balloon with plastic (*top*) gives a positive charge to the balloon (*bottom*). What is the charge on the plastic?

on page D30. They show balloons becoming charged.

The form of energy that comes from charged particles is called electrical (ē lek′tri kəl) energy. Negative electric charges can move from one object to another. When this happens, an electric charge builds up on both objects. One object will have a positive charge; the other will have a negative charge.

This buildup of electric charges is called **static electricity**. An object charged with static electricity has a buildup of electric charges on its surface. Objects with a buildup of like charges repel, or push away from, each other as shown in the top picture below.

Recall that when you comb your freshly washed and dried hair, your hair sticks to the comb. When the comb is removed, some of the hairs move away from each other. You're rubbing hair, which is one kind of matter, with plastic, which is another kind of matter.

If the air is dry enough, negative charges move from the hair to the comb, giving the comb an overall negative charge. Since the hair loses negative charges, it now has an overall positive charge. As the bottom picture of the balloons shows, objects having unlike charges attract, or pull toward, each other.

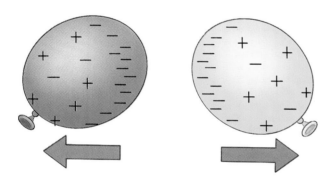

▲ A balloon that has a negative charge repels another one that has a negative charge.

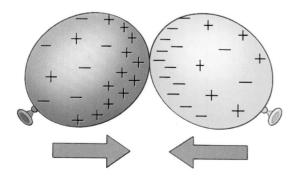

▲ A balloon that has a positive charge attracts one that has a negative charge.

Why do separate strands of the girl's hair repel each other? Why does the comb attract each strand of hair? ▼

You're taking the laundry out of the dryer, and your socks are stuck to your shirt. This is a case of static cling. Why does this happen?

As the dryer whirls, the clothes rub together. When different materials rub together, negative charges move from some materials to others. So the clothes become charged with static electricity. Your wool socks may have a positive charge and your cotton shirt may have a negative charge. So they attract one another.

When cotton is rubbed with wool, negative charges move from the wool onto the cotton. The cotton then has more negative charges than positive charges. And the wool has more positive charges than negative charges. So both socks and shirt become charged with static electricity.

Attracting Neutral Objects

If you charge a balloon by rubbing it with wool, the balloon may stick to a wall. But the wall is neutral. In the

Why is static cling called "static"? ▼

▲ **What evidence is there that the charge on the balloon is the opposite of the charge on the wall?**

activity on pages D28 and D29, the balloons that stick together are both charged. Why does a charged balloon stick to a neutral wall?

The rubbed balloon has extra negative charges that repel the negative charges in the wall. As a result, that part of the wall has extra positive charges. These charges attract the negative charges of the balloon. So the balloon sticks to the wall.

Shock, Spark, and Crackle

Do you want to shock a friend? Walk across a rug and touch your friend's hand. Your friend may get a mild electric shock. There's a catch, though. You'll feel the shock, too.

You may even see a spark and hear a slight crackling sound.

What causes the shock, the spark, and the crackle? When you rub your shoes against the rug, negative charges move from the rug onto your shoes. The charges move from your shoes onto your body. Your body is now charged with static electricity.

Charges that build up in this way don't stay on the charged object. Sooner or later the charges move away. Charges may leak harmlessly into the air. Or the charges may "jump" when static electric charges move off a charged object. When that happens, an **electric discharge** takes place. ■

In an electric discharge, negative electric charges move from a charged object to another object. ▼

Technology Link
CD-ROM

INVESTIGATE FURTHER!

Use the **Science Processor CD-ROM**, *Magnetism and Electricity* (Unit Opening, Shocking Behavior!) to watch a video about the nature of electric charges and static electricity. See what happens when everyday objects become charged.

Lightning

Reading Focus How do electric charges cause lightning?

Using Math *A flash of lightning contains enough electricity to light a 100-watt light bulb for three months. How many flashes would be needed to light a 100-watt bulb for one year?*

Zap! Boom! Lightning flashes across the sky. Then thunder cracks. The wind is strong and rain starts pouring down—it's a thunderstorm. You may know that lightning causes thunder. But what causes lightning?

During a thunderstorm, positive charges can build up at the top of a cloud. Negative electric charges build up at the bottom of the cloud. These negative charges at the bottom of a cloud repel negative charges in the ground below. That causes the ground, and objects on the ground, to be positively charged.

When negative charges jump between the cloud and the ground, there's a giant electric discharge, or spark. This spark is lightning.

Lightning Safety

Lightning often strikes the tallest object on the ground. That is why you should never stand under a tree during

1 Negative charges on a cloud cause positive charges to build up on the ground and the tree.

2 Lightning strikes when negative charges jump from the cloud to the ground or to the tree.

a lightning storm. Also, you should not play in an open field or swim. Take shelter in a building or an enclosed car.

Using lightning rods is another way to increase lightning safety. A lightning rod is a metal rod about 20 cm (8 in.) long. It is attached to the highest point of a structure. Heavy wires connect the rod to the ground. If lightning strikes the rod, electric charges move through the wires safely to Earth. ■

Internet Field Trip
Visit **www.eduplace.com** to see how scientists are studying lightning.

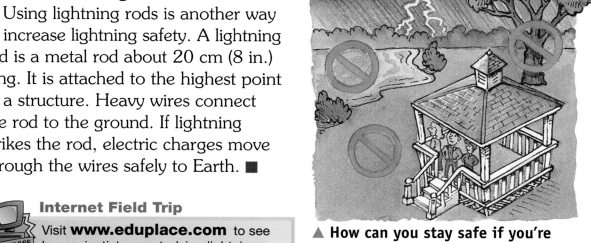

▲ **How can you stay safe if you're outdoors when lightning starts?**

INVESTIGATION 1 WRAP-UP

REVIEW

1. What is static electricity?

2. How does a neutral object become positively charged?

CRITICAL THINKING

3. How might you use a balloon with a negative charge to find out whether the charge on another balloon is positive or negative?

4. Explain why playing in an open field during a lightning storm is unsafe.

WHAT IS CURRENT ELECTRICITY?

In Investigation 1 you saw that electric charges can move from place to place. In Investigation 2 you will find out how this flow of electricity can be controlled.

Activity

On or Off?

You usually take for granted that flipping on a light switch will turn on a light. What else has to happen for the light to go on? Find out in this activity.

MATERIALS

- dry cell (size D) in holder
- light bulb in holder
- 3 insulated wires (stripped on ends)
- thick cardboard
- 2 brass paper fasteners
- paper clip
- *Science Notebook*

Procedure

1. Place all the materials listed above on your desk. With your group, **hypothesize** ways you can connect some of the parts to make the bulb light. **Draw** pictures of these ways in your *Science Notebook*.

Step 1

2. **Test** each idea that your group has drawn. Circle the drawings you made that make the bulb light.

3. When the bulb lighted, you had made an electric circuit (sʉr′kit). An **electric circuit** is a path through which electricity can flow.

4. Use the round picture as a guide to arrange a paper clip, two brass fasteners, and two wires on a piece of thick cardboard.

Step 4

5. You have made a switch, which you can use to turn the bulb on or off. **Make a drawing** to **predict** how you can connect the switch to the circuit. **Test** your prediction. Make sure your drawing shows how the parts are connected when the switch works.

Analyze and Conclude

1. **Compare** your predictions about how to light the bulb—with and without the switch—with your results.

2. An electric circuit through which electricity moves is called a closed circuit. When you disconnect a part of a closed circuit, the circuit is called an open circuit. When you flip a switch to turn on a light, are you opening a circuit, or closing it? Explain your answer.

INVESTIGATE FURTHER!

RESEARCH

What are some different types of switches? How do the switches on electric devices and on the wall work in your home? Why do some switches click and others not click when you turn them on or off? Use resources in a library to find the answers.

Activity

Stop or Go?

Does electricity flow easily through all materials? Try some tests to find out.

- -

Procedure

1. With your group, use a wire to connect a light-bulb holder to a dry-cell holder. Attach a second wire to the light-bulb holder only. Attach a third wire to the dry-cell holder only. *Do not allow the two wires that are attached to the dry cell to touch.*

2. Predict what will happen if you touch the free ends of the wires together, as shown. **Record** your prediction in your *Science Notebook*. **Test** your prediction and **record** your results.

3. A material that allows electricity to flow through it is called a **conductor** (kən duk′tər). **Infer** whether the wires in your circuit are conductors. **Record** your inference.

MATERIALS
- goggles
- 3 insulated wires (stripped on ends)
- light bulb in holder
- dry cell (size D) in holder
- copper wire
- plastic straw
- penny
- toothpick
- paper clip
- rubber band
- cardboard strip
- aluminum foil strip
- *Science Notebook*

SAFETY
Wear goggles during this activity.

Step 2

4. A material that does not allow electricity to flow through it easily is called an **insulator** (in′sə lāt ər). **Make a chart** like the one shown. **Predict** which objects in the Materials list are conductors and which are insulators. **Record** your predictions in the chart. Then **test** them and **record** your results.

Step 4

Conductor or Insulator		
Object or Material	**Prediction**	**Result**

See **SCIENCE** and **MATH TOOLBOX** page H10 if you need to review *Making a Chart to Organize Data.*

Analyze and Conclude

1. **Compare** your predictions about which materials electricity would flow through with your results.

2. Which of the objects or materials that you tested are conductors? How do you know?

3. Which of the objects or materials that you tested are insulators? How do you know?

UNIT PROJECT LINK

Invent a way to use the opening and closing of circuits to make a quiz board. Work with your group to write a set of questions and answers. Then decide how to place dry cells, wires, and light bulbs. Test your invention by trying it in front of members of other groups in your class.

TechnologyLink

For more help with your Unit Project, go to **www.eduplace.com**.

Electric Current

Reading Focus What are the parts of an electric circuit?

You press a switch and your flashlight lights or your radio plays music. Electrical energy powers your flashlight and radio. You depend on electricity in hundreds of other ways, too. The picture below shows some ways that electricity works for the members of one family.

Charges in Currents

In Investigation 1 you found out about static electric charges. The charges collect on objects and may jump quickly between objects. But these charges can't be used to run electric devices. For electric charges to be useful, they have to flow.

Using Math *This home has four different electric circuits. Each circuit has six outlets, or places to plug in appliances. How many outlets are in the home?*

In the form of electricity used in homes and businesses, electric charges flow steadily, somewhat like currents of water in a stream. An **electric current** is a continuous flow of negative charges. An **electric circuit** is a path along which negative charges can flow. The activity on pages D36 and D37 shows how to put together the parts of an electric circuit.

A simple electric circuit starts with a source of electric charges, such as a dry cell. A wire connects the source to a light bulb or another device. A second wire connects the bulb or the other device back to the source of negative charges.

Open and Closed Circuits

When a circuit is closed, or complete, there is no break in the pathway of negative charges. The charges can flow through a closed circuit. In a closed circuit containing a light bulb, the bulb lights.

When a circuit is open, or incomplete, there's a break in the pathway. Charges can't flow through an open circuit. If you disconnect a wire in a simple circuit, the bulb can't light.

A **switch** is a device that opens or closes a circuit. When you turn a switch to *on*, you close a circuit so it is complete. When you turn a switch to *off*, you open a circuit so it is incomplete. If you add a switch to a circuit, you don't have to disconnect a wire to open the circuit.

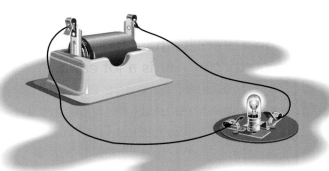

▲ Trace the path of electric charges in this circuit. Start and end at the dry cell. Why does the bulb light?

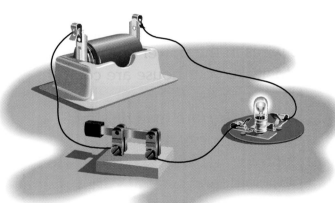

▲ This circuit contains a closed switch. Trace the path of the charges through this circuit. Why does the bulb light?

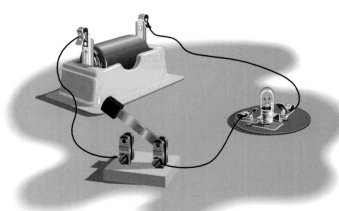

▲ How is this circuit the same as the one in the middle picture? How is it different? Why doesn't the bulb light?

The Light Bulb

Reading Focus In what ways are incandescent bulbs different from fluorescent bulbs?

What everyday object turns electrical energy into light? It's a light bulb, of course. Light bulbs come in a number of different sizes, shapes, and colors.

There are bulbs for ceiling fixtures and for table lamps. There are bulbs for street lights, for headlights, and even for growing plants.

Many light bulbs are incandescent (in kən des'ənt) bulbs. Look at the diagram of this type of bulb. As electric current passes through the **filament** (fil'ə mənt), the filament gets so hot that it begins to glow, or give off light.

Now look at the fluorescent (floo-ə res'ənt) bulb. In this bulb, ultraviolet light is changed into white light.

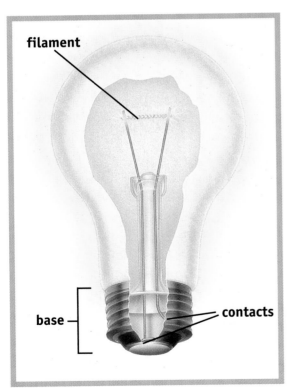

filament

base — contacts

▲ **INCANDESCENT BULB** The filament is a long, thin wire coil made of the metal tungsten (tuŋ'stən). It glows when electricity passes through it. The contacts at the base conduct electricity.

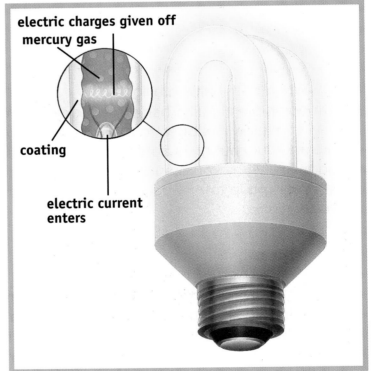

electric charges given off
mercury gas

coating

electric current enters

▲ **FLUORESCENT BULB** As electricity enters the bulb, electric charges bump into particles of mercury gas. The gas gives off ultraviolet light. This light strikes the coating, which gives off white light.

Using Math

Thomas Edison (top) and Lewis Latimer (bottom) are shown with an early incandescent bulb invented in the 1870s. About how many years ago was the incandescent bulb invented?

INVESTIGATE FURTHER!

RESEARCH

Count the number of incandescent light bulbs in your house. Estimate how long they are used each day. Add together the number of watts for each bulb. Then contact your electric company or an electrical supply store in your community.

Get information about fluorescent bulbs that could replace the incandescent bulbs in your home. Based on the information you obtain, figure out how much money your family could save by switching to fluorescent bulbs.

Bulbs and Energy

In incandescent bulbs, electrical energy changes to heat and light. These bulbs produce much more heat than light, so they get very hot. All the heat that incandescent bulbs produce is wasted energy.

In fluorescent bulbs, electricity is used to change one type of light to another. These bulbs produce much less heat and cost less to operate than incandescent bulbs do. Fluorescent bulbs are good for the environment because they don't waste energy.

Invention of the Light Bulb

Thomas Edison, who headed a team of scientists called the Edison Pioneers, invented the light bulb. Edison's first bulb used a filament made of scorched thread. But this bulb was costly and didn't last long.

Lewis Latimer was a member of the Edison Pioneers. Latimer made a greatly improved bulb that used a carbon filament. This bulb cost less and lasted longer than Edison's bulb. Carbon was later replaced by tungsten, which is used in bulbs today. ■

Series and Parallel Circuits

Reading Focus How do series circuits and parallel circuits differ?

You've seen how electricity flows along paths called circuits. You can compare a circuit's path to a path in a maze. In the two mazes shown below, you start at point A, follow some paths, and come back to A. You can turn right or left, but you must move only in the direction of the arrows.

In the first maze there is only one path you can follow. You can move from A to B and then through C to get back to A. In the second maze there are two paths you can follow to make a round trip. Use your finger to trace these paths.

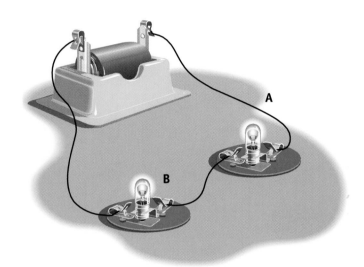

▲ **Trace the path of current through this series circuit.**

Just One Path

In the activity on pages D44 and D45, a series circuit is made. A **series circuit** is one that has only a single path for current to follow. In a series circuit, all of the parts are connected one after the other in a single loop, or path, as shown in the drawing above.

In this circuit, charges flow from the dry cell through bulb A and bulb B and back to the dry cell. If either bulb is removed from the circuit, the circuit is broken and the current stops.

Mazes that are like two kinds of circuits ▼

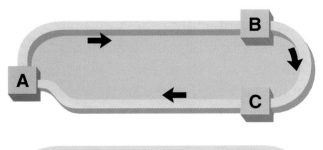

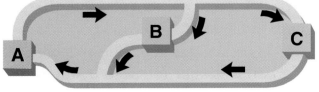

More Than One Path

In the activity on pages D46 and D47, a parallel circuit is made. A **parallel circuit** is one that has more than one path for an electric current to follow, as shown in the picture on the right.

Notice that in path 1, negative charges can flow from the dry cell through bulb A and back to the dry cell. In path 2, negative charges can flow from the dry cell through bulb B and back to the dry cell.

When both bulbs are in place, current will follow both paths, and both bulbs will be lighted. However, if either bulb is removed, current will still

There are two paths a current can follow in this parallel circuit. ▼

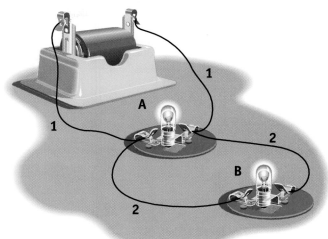

follow the path through the other bulb. So the bulb in this part of the circuit will remain lighted.

Science in Literature

YOUR ELECTRIC VOICE

"When you talk into your phone, your words zip through the telephone wires in electrical form. They travel across the streets all the way to your friend's house. Here, your friend's phone changes the electric signals back into sound waves. And, presto, your friend is listening to the sounds of your voice."

**Hello! Hello!
A Look Inside the Telephone**
by Eve and Albert Stwertka
Illustrated by Mena Dolobowsky
Julian Messner, 1991

This description comes from *Hello! Hello! A Look Inside the Telephone* by Eve and Albert Stwertka. If you like amusing and unusual stories, this book is for you.

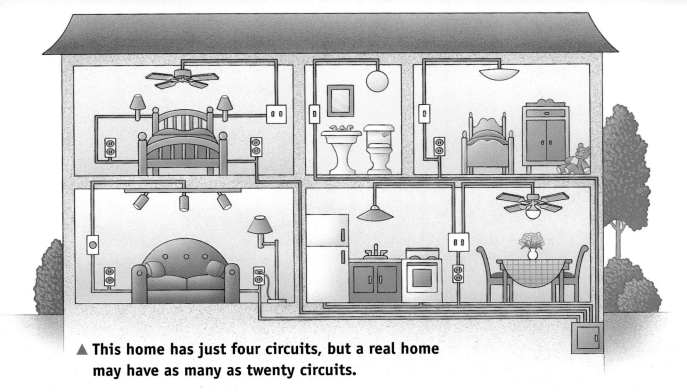

▲ This home has just four circuits, but a real home may have as many as twenty circuits.

How Homes Are Wired

All of the lights and electric appliances in your home are linked in circuits. Lamps, toaster ovens, stereo systems, hair dryers, and refrigerators are parts of the circuits. The circuits in home wiring are parallel, not series. Why, do you think, is this so?

Different circuits control electrical outlets in different parts of a home. Each of these circuits is connected to an outside source of electric current.

One circuit in the house shown above controls the outlets in the kitchen. Trace the circuit that controls the outlets in a child's bedroom.

Every home circuit has a fuse or a circuit breaker. These safety devices open circuits that overheat when too much electricity flows through them. A **fuse** contains a metal strip that melts when overheated. A **circuit breaker** is a switch that opens a circuit by turning itself off. ■

INVESTIGATION 3 WRAP-UP

THINK IT WRITE IT

REVIEW

1. Compare a series circuit with a parallel circuit.

2. Why do circuits in homes have fuses or circuit breakers?

CRITICAL THINKING

3. Explain why you can open a series circuit, but not a parallel circuit, by removing one bulb.

4. You want to make a parallel circuit with two light bulbs, a dry cell, and two switches. Draw the way you would connect the parts so that each switch can turn off one bulb at a time.

REFLECT & EVALUATE

Word Power

Write the letter of the term that best matches the definition. *Not all terms will be used.*

1. Circuit that has only one path for electricity to follow
2. Buildup of electric charges on objects
3. Material that lets electricity flow easily
4. A thin wire inside a light bulb
5. Circuit that has more than one path for electricity to follow
6. Safety device that opens a circuit by melting

a. circuit breaker
b. conductor
c. filament
d. fuse
e. insulator
f. parallel circuit
g. static electricity
h. series circuit

Check What You Know

Write the word in each pair that best completes each sentence.

1. A switch that opens a circuit by turning itself off is a (fuse, circuit breaker).
2. A continuous flow of negative charges is an (electric current, electric discharge).
3. A path through which electricity can flow is (a conductor, an electric circuit).
4. A device that opens or closes a circuit is a (switch, cell).

Problem Solving

1. You and a friend are trying to shock each other by rubbing your feet on the carpet. Your friend can shock you, but you aren't able to shock him. Give a reason why this might be so.

2. Suppose that all of the outlets in a room are part of the same circuit. Why is it better to have the outlets wired in a parallel circuit than in a series circuit?

Study the drawing. Explain on paper why the drawing is incorrect. Then make a drawing of a circuit that is correct.

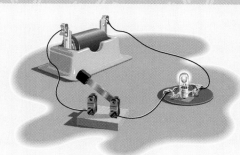

CHAPTER 3

ELECTRICITY
AT WORK

You turn on the TV set and the picture appears. Where does the electricity come from to make this happen? How does electricity get to your home? What produces this electricity? In this chapter you'll find out the answers to these questions as you explore the story of electricity.

PEOPLE USING SCIENCE

Electrical Engineer Have you ever wondered what makes your telephone work? When Adelina Mejia-Zelaya was a child, she wondered about such things. She wondered how, by just pressing a button, she could make an elevator or a calculator work. Since that time she has studied much about all kinds of electronic equipment.

Today Adlina Mejia-Zelaya is an electrical engineer. Designing tiny electric circuits is part of her everyday work. Explaining her work, she says, "I design circuits for the computers that make your phone work."

In this chapter you'll learn more about electricity. And you'll explore some of the many ways that electricity can be useful.

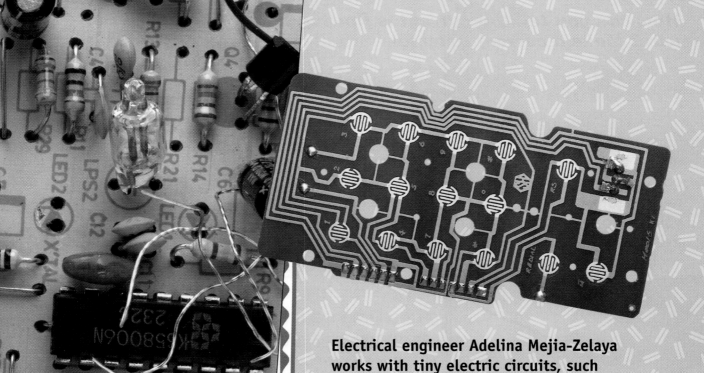

Electrical engineer Adelina Mejia-Zelaya works with tiny electric circuits, such as these.

Producing Electric Current

Reading Focus How do generators and electric cells produce electrical energy?

Where do you get the energy to kick a soccer ball? You get energy from food. Suppose you eat a peanut butter sandwich. The sandwich—and everything else you eat—has chemical energy stored in it. Your body can change that chemical energy into energy of motion.

Electricity From Magnetism

Energy of motion can change to electrical energy. In the activity on page D57, moving a magnet inside a wire coil produces an electric current in the wire. Moving a wire coil in a magnetic field will also produce a current in the coil.

A device in which a wire coil and a magnet are used to produce electricity is called a **generator**. A generator is a device that changes energy of motion into electrical energy.

Getting a Strong Current

The magnet used in the activity is not very strong. And not many turns of wire are used to make the coil. With a current detector you can detect a current produced by such a generator.

But the current isn't even strong enough to light a bulb. How can a stronger current be made?

The stronger the magnet in a generator, the stronger the current produced. Adding more turns of wire to the coil also strengthens the current. So you could make your generator stronger by using a strong magnet and many coils of wire.

Giant generators produce the electricity that flows to the electrical outlets in homes and schools. These generators also produce the electricity that lights cities, powers machinery, and works in other ways. The generators have powerful magnets and huge coils of wire.

Where does the energy of motion that turns large generators come from? The energy may come from a power plant that uses coal or nuclear fuel to heat water. The heated water makes steam, which turns the generator. Sometimes the energy comes from water falling over a dam such as the one shown on the next page. Or the energy may come from wind turning the blades of a windmill.

Hoover Dam is 201 m (660 ft) thick at its base and 14 m (45 ft) thick at its top. How much thicker is Hoover Dam at its base than at its top?

Hoover Dam stands in the Black Canyon of the Colorado River. Water falling over the dam provides energy to turn large generators.

▲ Power plant at Hoover Dam

▲ Generators inside the power plant at Hoover Dam

Chemicals and Currents

Batteries are another source of useful electrical energy. A battery is made up of one or more smaller parts called **electric cells**. Energy is stored in chemicals used in an electric cell. When an electric cell is connected to a circuit, this stored chemical energy changes into electrical energy.

There are two basic types of electric cells—wet cells and dry cells. The drawing below shows the operation of a simple wet cell. In this wet cell, strips of the metals copper and zinc hang from the wires of a current detector into a liquid chemical. The zinc metal reacts with substances in the liquid to produce a chemical change. This change separates negative charges from zinc atoms.

The negative charges move through the zinc strip, which then becomes the negative end of the cell. These charges then move through the wire around the current detector to the copper strip. This strip has become the positive end of the cell. As the charges move back into the liquid, the circuit is completed.

A WET CELL

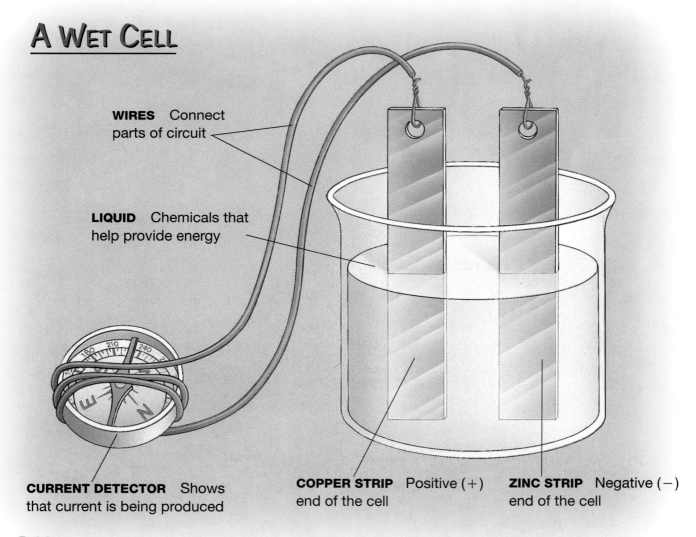

WIRES Connect parts of circuit

LIQUID Chemicals that help provide energy

CURRENT DETECTOR Shows that current is being produced

COPPER STRIP Positive (+) end of the cell

ZINC STRIP Negative (−) end of the cell

A dry cell like the one used in the activity on page D56 is shown below. Trace the path of charges through the cell and around the current detector.

A zinc case is the negative end of the cell. A chemical paste inside the case has a carbon rod in its center. The carbon rod is the positive end of the cell. Zinc reacts with substances in the paste, separating negative charges from the zinc atoms. These charges move through the wire around the current detector to the carbon rod and back to the paste, completing the circuit. ■

Technology Link
CD-ROM

INVESTIGATE FURTHER!

Use the **Science Processor CD–ROM**, *Magnetism and Electricity* (Investigation 3, Power Play) to experiment with an on-screen magnet and coil. From the same program, you can learn more about the parts of a genera-tor and how a generator works.

A DRY CELL

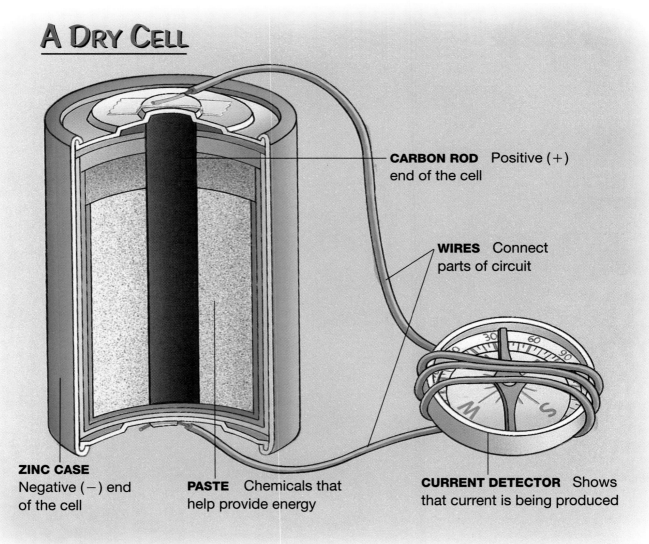

CARBON ROD Positive (+) end of the cell

WIRES Connect parts of circuit

ZINC CASE Negative (−) end of the cell

PASTE Chemicals that help provide energy

CURRENT DETECTOR Shows that current is being produced

From Power Plant to You

Reading Focus How does the electricity from a power plant reach your home?

Most of the electricity you use is as near as a wall switch or an outlet. When you flip a switch or plug in a cord, the electric current is right there. But the generators in the power plant that make this current may be very far away from your home. How does electricity from power plants get to other places where it's used? Study the drawing below to find out.

The Force of Electricity

The generators in power plants push the electricity through heavy-duty power lines that leave the plant.

WHERE YOUR ELECTRICITY COMES FROM

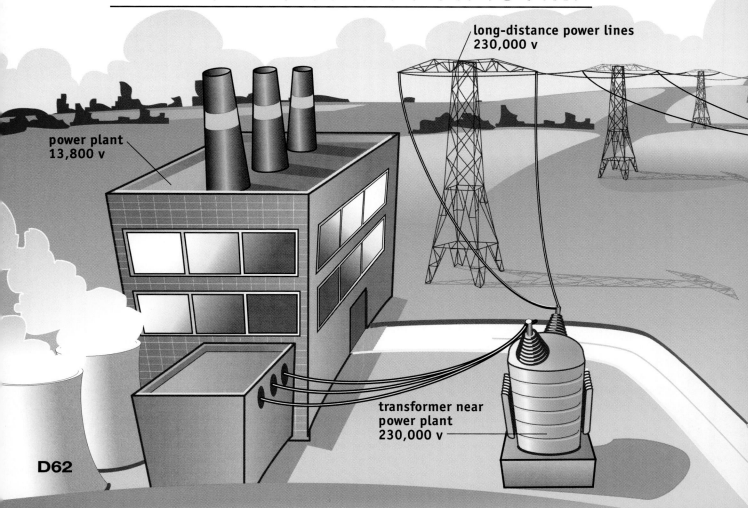

long-distance power lines
230,000 v

power plant
13,800 v

transformer near
power plant
230,000 v

The force that pushes electricity along wires is called **voltage** (vōl′tij). This force is measured in units called volts. The letter v is the symbol for volts.

You can compare voltage to the pressure, or pushing force, of water in a hose. Water can rush from a hose, or flow gently, depending on the pressure. The current in a wire can also be strong or weak, depending on the voltage.

Raising and Lowering Voltage

A transformer (trans fôrm′ər) is a device that changes the voltage of a current. The voltage of the current coming from a power plant is too low to send long distances. A transformer raises the voltage, sending it cross-country to users.

After current makes a long journey from a power plant, its voltage must be lowered. It is too high for use in homes and in most other buildings. So the current is sent through another transformer. Study the drawing to see how voltages are changed as current travels from a power plant to you and to other users of electricity. ■

Using Math *How much greater is the voltage at the transformer near the power plant than the voltage at the substation transformer?*

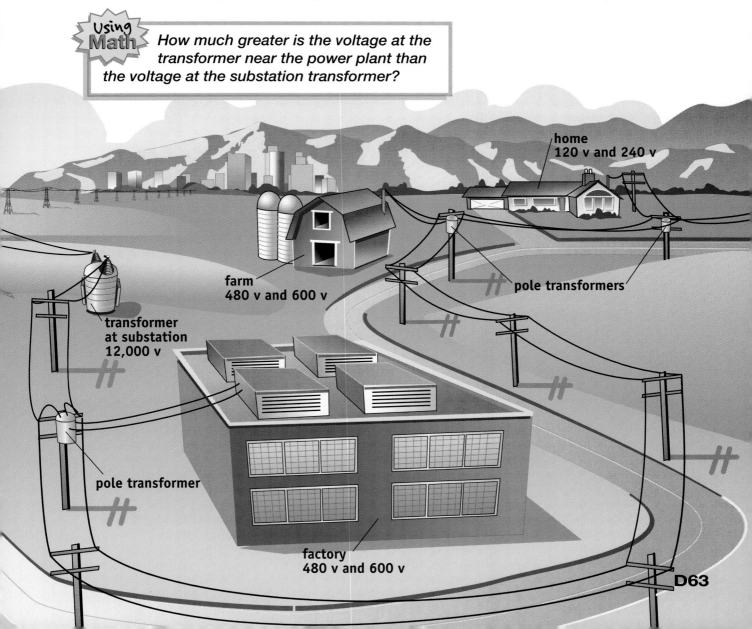

home
120 v and 240 v

pole transformers

farm
480 v and 600 v

transformer
at substation
12,000 v

pole transformer

factory
480 v and 600 v

Electricity From Sunlight

Reading Focus What is a solar cell, and how is it used in a solar panel?

SCIENCE
TECHNOLOGY
& SOCIETY

Did you ever use a solar calculator? **Solar energy**, or the energy of the Sun, powers the calculator. Inside solar calculators are solar cells. A **solar cell** is a device that changes light into electrical energy. Solar cells are so sensitive they even work on overcast days.

Solar Cells, Clean Energy

About 25 power plants in the United States use solar cells to produce electricity. Solar cells produce electricity in a way that helps keep the environment clean. Burning coal or oil to produce electricity can pollute the air. Using nuclear energy can create toxic wastes that pollute water and land.

Another advantage of using solar energy is that it helps to save fossil fuels. The amount of solar energy Earth receives in 12 hours is equal to the energy produced from burning fossil fuels in one year! Look at the photographs to see some uses of solar cells.

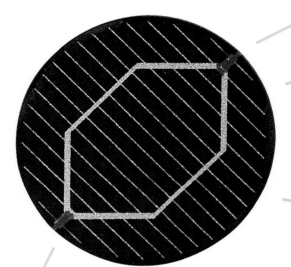

▲ One solar cell produces a tiny amount of electricity. Because of this, many cells are connected in panels.

Solar-powered airplane ▼

▲ Solar-powered car

◀ Solar-powered watch

▲ Solar-powered toy

Solar-powered home ▶

INVESTIGATION 1 WRAP-UP

REVIEW

1. What energy change takes place in a generator? in a dry cell? in a solar cell?

2. Compare how electricity is produced by a generator with how it's produced by an electric cell.

CRITICAL THINKING

3. List and discuss at least two advantages of using solar energy over energy from burning fossil fuels.

4. Certain electric devices, such as cordless telephones, have small transformers that plug into a wall. What do the transformers do?

Long Distance, Short Time

Reading Focus What types of devices help us communicate with one another?

How do you communicate (kə myōō'ni kāt) with friends over long distances? Do you talk on the phone? Do you use electronic mail, or E-mail, on a computer? If so, then you use telecommunication (tel i-kə myōō ni kā'shən). This is using electricity for almost instant communication over a long distance.

Electricity has made telecommunication possible, beginning with the invention of the telegraph. Today people link television, telephones, and computers all over the world. These devices work together in a system that provides information, communication, and entertainment. The time line shows some highlights in the field of telecommunication since the 1840s.

Radio first sends voices and music. Radio waves carry sounds through air without wires. **1906**

Telegraph is first used. Telegraph messages are sent over wires from city to city in a code of dots and dashes. **1845**

1876 Telephone is first used. People use the telephone to talk over wires.

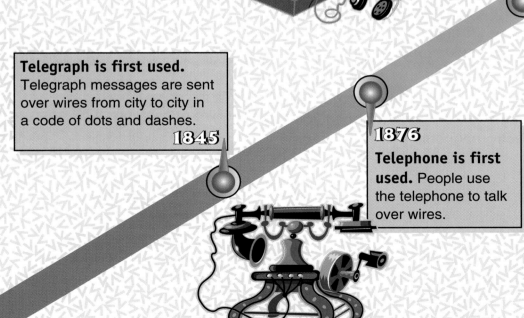

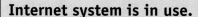

Internet system is in use.
People use the Internet to send information from computer to computer. They use this system to communicate almost instantly throughout the world.

1990s

Communications satellite *Telestar* is sent into space.
Satellites carry live television, radio, telephone calls, and computer data all over the world.

1962

2000
Video phones are used. Users can see the person they're talking to on a video screen.

1980s
Cellular (sel′yo͞o lər) **phones and fax machines are in use.** Cellular phones allow people to talk on the phone as they travel. Facsimile (fak sim′ə lē), also called fax, machines are used to send written messages over telephone lines.

1936
Television programs are broadcast.
Television sends clear pictures and sound.

INVESTIGATE FURTHER!

RESEARCH

Analyze television commercials for three phone companies. Infer and then determine which company would save you the most money if you talked to a friend in another state for 17 minutes.

Electric Magnets

Reading Focus What are some uses of electromagnets?

Did you ever flip a coin? When the heads side of the coin is up, you can't see the tails side. But you know the tails side is there. In a way, electricity and magnetism are like the two sides of a coin.

In Investigation 1 you found one way that magnetism and electricity are related. Moving a coil of wire in a magnetic field produces electric current. In this way, magnetism produces electricity.

Electricity and magnetism are also related in another way. In the activity on pages D66 and D67, a dry cell and a nail are used to make an electromagnet. An **electromagnet** is a magnet made when electric charges move through a coil of wire wrapped around an iron core, or center. In an electromagnet, electricity is used to produce magnetism.

Properties of Electromagnets

Electromagnets are like natural magnets in some ways. Like natural magnets, they attract materials that contain iron. Electromagnets have a north pole and a south pole. An electromagnet also has a magnetic field, as the drawing above shows.

This electromagnet makes it easy to separate steel from other materials. The magnet is turned on in order to lift the steel. ▶

How are electromagnets different from other magnets? In Chapter 1, a temporary magnet is made by stroking a nail with a bar magnet. Recall that a temporary magnet slowly loses its magnetism over time. An electromagnet is a different kind of temporary magnet. It acts like a magnet only while electric current flows through it. As soon as you turn off the current, it loses its magnetism. As a result, an electromagnet can be turned on or off.

Using Electromagnets

Imagine that you're in charge of a collection center for recycling. People dump bags of cans made of different metals in one big pile. But the cans made of steel and those made of aluminum have to be sent to different places to be recycled. This means that you have to separate the two kinds of cans. One way to do this job is by using a large electromagnet, as the pictures below show.

After the crane swings away from the pile of mixed materials, the magnet is turned off. Then the steel objects fall into a separate pile. ▶

When you push a doorbell, a circuit closes and the electromagnet pulls on the hammer, which strikes the bell. ▶

Many objects in your home have electromagnets in them. These electromagnets are hidden inside loudspeakers, telephones, VCRs, cassette players, and doorbells. All electric motors contain electromagnets, too. Electric motors run refrigerators, clocks, hair dryers, vacuum cleaners, and ceiling fans.

Take another look at the pictures on page D40 in Chapter 2. Electric motors drive many of the devices shown there, too. What other things can you think of that are run by electric motors? ■

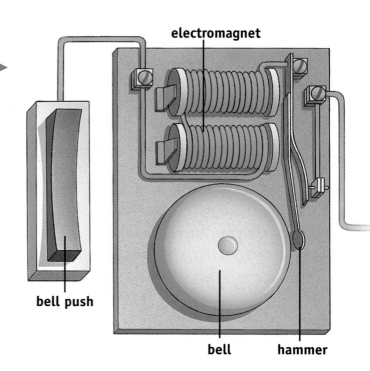

electromagnet

bell push

bell   hammer

Science in Literature

STATION, PLEASE?

"Today the telephone no longer has to depend on wires strung across mountains or under large bodies of water. Because sound waves can now be changed into radio signals, part of the wire circuit can be replaced by radio."

This quotation from *Hello! Hello! A Look Inside the Telephone* by Eve and Albert Stwertka helps you realize how phones have changed communication. Read this book to find out how the first telephones were different from the one you may have today.

Hello! Hello!
A Look Inside the Telephone
by Eve and Albert Stwertka
Illustrated by Mena Dolobowsky
Julian Messner, 1991

A Car That Plugs In

Reading Focus What are some advantages and disadvantages of using electric cars?

Do you live in or near a large city? In many cities, air pollution is a serious problem. As you read in Chapter 1, cars that run on gasoline pollute the air. Many cars crowded together can make the air unhealthy. Using electric cars may be one way to solve this problem. These cars run on batteries, which results in less pollution.

Have you ever used a rechargeable battery? Electric cars have rechargeable batteries. As you know, batteries are made up of electric cells. The cells in the batteries of electric cars lose energy, or run down, and stop working after being used a certain length of time. When the batteries run down, they have to be recharged.

Electric cars aren't used much today. Their batteries must be recharged about once every 96 km (60 mi). Their top speed is about 80 km/h (50 mph). And electric cars cost more to operate than most gas-powered cars.

In the future, many people may drive cars that won't rely only on gasoline. Why? Gasoline is made from oil, and the need to conserve oil is great. The need to clean up the air is just as important.

Internet Field Trip

Visit **www.eduplace.com** to find out more about electric cars.

Using Math *Suppose you traveled 8 km to school each day in an electric car. The car can travel 96 km (60 mi) on one charge of its batteries. How many trips could you make to school on one charge?*

Safety Around Electricity

Reading Focus What are some ways to be safe around electricity?

In the activities, electric current is sent through wires. But why are those wires safe to touch? The activities use size D dry cells that are marked 1.5 v, which stands for 1.5 volts. A current with such a low voltage has very little energy. But the voltage of the current in the wiring of a house is 110 volts or more. This electric current is dangerous. But you can be safe if you follow certain safety rules.

DON'T use any appliance that has a torn cord or a cord that is worn out. If two bare wires of a cord touch each other while the cord is in use, current will go to the crossed wires and back to its source. This is an example of a short circuit. In a short circuit, wires overheat. Overheated wires can cause a fire. ▶

◀ **NEVER** stick your finger or anything else except an electrical plug into an electrical outlet. Be sure any electrical plug you use is in good condition. Also, always hold a cord by its plug when you pull it from an outlet. What do you think is the reason for this rule?

DON'T overload circuits. Plugging too many appliances into one circuit can overload the circuit. Wires in overloaded circuits can become hot enough to start fires. ▶

◀ **STAY AWAY** from anything with a sign that says "High Voltage." Voltages in electric power lines and electric rails are even higher, and more dangerous, than they are in house current.

NEVER touch an electrical cord, appliance, or light switch when you are wet. Unless water is pure, it is a conductor. Electric current can pass through the water and your body more easily than through an appliance. Any water that's in contact with a person's body is not pure. ▶

Have you ever had a power failure in your home? This can happen if a fuse blows or a circuit breaker switches off. As you read in Chapter 2, page D52, fuses and circuit breakers are safety devices. They open circuits when wires get too hot.

What should be done when a fuse blows or a circuit breaker trips, or switches off? First, it's important to find out the cause. Is there an overloaded circuit? Is there a short circuit somewhere? The cause of the overheating should be corrected. Then an adult in your home should replace the fuse or turn the circuit breaker back on. ■

▲ **A home circuit-breaker box**

▲ **A good fuse**

▲ **A blown fuse**

INVESTIGATION 2 WRAP-UP

REVIEW

1. What is an electromagnet?

2. List at least six devices that contain electromagnets.

CRITICAL THINKING

3. What are some advantages of an electric-gasoline combination car? What might the disadvantages be?

4. How would you explain to a group of first graders why radios used in a bathroom should be battery-powered?

REFLECT & EVALUATE

Word Power

Write the letter of the term that best matches the definition. *Not all terms will be used.*

1. A device that uses a wire coil and a magnet to produce electricity
2. A device that produces electric current from energy stored in chemicals
3. A device that changes sunlight into electrical energy
4. A magnet made from a wire wrapped around iron
5. The force that pushes electricity through wires

a. electrical cell
b. electromagnet
c. generator
d. solar cell
e. solar energy
f. voltage

Check What You Know

Write the word in each pair that best completes each sentence.

1. Solar energy is changed to electricity by (an electric cell, a solar cell).
2. When wires get too hot, circuit breakers (close, open) circuits.
3. Doorbells and telephones contain (generators, electromagnets).
4. Electric current can be produced by a (generator, transformer).

Problem Solving

1. A magnet passing through a coil of wire does not produce enough electric current to light a bulb. What are two ways to increase the amount of current?

2. How do you think the energy of the Sun might be used to power a motorcycle?

BUILD YOUR PORTFOLIO

Study the photograph. Name the device shown and describe how it works. Explain how the usefulness of the device would change if it could not be turned on and off.

Drawing Conclusions

Often writers imply, or hint at, more information than they actually state. They give clues and expect readers to figure out the rest, using what they already know. Suppose an author writes, "The children stared out the window." A reader can conclude that something interesting was happening outside—or that the children were bored by what was happening inside.

Consider these questions as you draw conclusions.

- What did the author write?
- What do I know?
- What is my conclusion?

Read the paragraphs. Then complete the exercises that follow.

Invention of the Light Bulb

Thomas Edison, who headed a team of scientists called the Edison Pioneers, invented the light bulb. Edison's first bulb used a filament made of scorched thread. But this bulb was costly and didn't last long.

Lewis Latimer was a member of the Edison Pioneers. Latimer made a greatly improved bulb that used a carbon filament. This bulb cost less and lasted longer than Edison's bulb. Carbon was later replaced by tungsten, which is used in bulbs today.

1. **Which statement is a conclusion you can draw from the paragraphs? Write the letter of that statement.**

   a. Edison was jealous of Latimer's success.

   b. Carbon lasts longer than tungsten and costs less.

   c. People will someday invent a better way to make electric light.

   d. Edison and Latimer should share the credit for the invention of the light bulb.

2. **What was the most important clue in helping you draw that conclusion?**

Using Math — Bar Graph

The graph below shows the estimated life span, in hours, of light bulbs of different wattages.

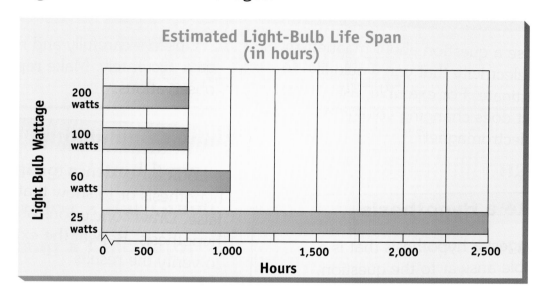

Use the data in the graph to complete the exercises that follow.

1. Which light bulb should last the longest?

2. About how many times longer will a 25-watt light bulb last than a 60-watt bulb?

3. Which bulb, if left on continuously, will last for about one month?

4. Estimate the life span, in days, of a 60-watt light bulb.

5. Estimate the number of months a 100-watt light bulb will last if it is left on for 8 hours a day.

6. Estimate the life span, in hours, of a 150-watt light bulb. Explain your answer.

7. Estimate the life span of a 75-watt light bulb in hours. Explain your answer.

Using a Hand Lens

A hand lens is a tool that magnifies objects, or makes objects appear larger. This makes it possible for you to see details of an object that would be hard to see without the hand lens.

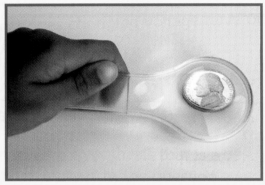

▲ Place the lens above the object.

▲ Move the lens slowly toward you.

Look at a Coin or a Stamp

1. Place an object such as a coin or a stamp on a table or other flat surface.

2. Hold the hand lens just above the object. As you look through the lens, slowly move the lens away from the object. Notice that the object appears to get larger.

3. Keep moving the lens until the object begins to look a little blurry. Then move the hand lens a little closer to the object until the object is once again in sharp focus.

If the object starts to look blurry, move the lens toward the object. ▶

Making a
Bar Graph

A bar graph helps you organize and compare data.

Make a Bar Graph of Animal Heights

Animals come in all different shapes and sizes. You can use the information in the table to make a bar graph of animal heights.

Heights of Animals	
Animal	**Height (cm)**
Bear	240
Elephant	315
Cow	150
Giraffe	570
Camel	210
Horse	165

1. Draw the side and the bottom of the graph. Label the side of the graph as shown. The numbers will show the height of the animals in centimeters.

3. Choose a title for your graph. Your title should describe the subject of the graph.

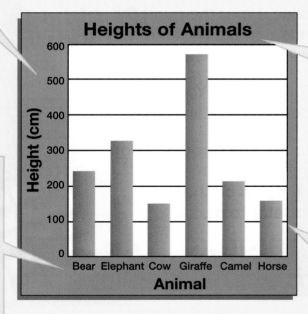

2. Label the bottom of the graph. Write the names of the animals at the bottom so that there is room to draw the bars.

4. Draw bars to show the height of each animal. Some heights are between two numbers.

$$\begin{array}{r} -\ 42 \\ \hline 12 \\ -\ 12 \\ \hline 0 \end{array}$$

3. The average rainfall per month for the first six months was 72 mm of rain.

Using a
Calculator

After you've made measurements, a calculator

Using a
Tape Measure
or Ruler

Tape measures and rulers are tools for measuring the length of objects and distances. Scientists most often use units such as meters, centimeters, and millimeters when making length measurements.

Use a Tape Measure

1. Measure the distance around a jar. Wrap the tape around the jar.

2. Find the line where the tape begins to wrap over itself.

3. Record the distance around the jar to the nearest centimeter.

Use a Metric Ruler

1. Measure the length of your shoe. Place the ruler or the meterstick on the floor. Line up the end of the ruler with the heel of your shoe.

2. Notice where the other end of your shoe lines up with the ruler.

3. Look at the scale on the ruler. Record the length of your shoe to the nearest centimeter and to the nearest millimeter.

Measuring Volume

A graduated cylinder, a measuring cup, and a beaker are used to measure volume. Volume is the amount of space something takes up. Most of the containers that scientists use to measure volume have a scale marked in milliliters (mL).

Measure the Volume of a Liquid

1. Measure the volume of juice. Pour some juice into a measuring container.

2. Move your head so that your eyes are level with the top of the juice. Read the scale line that is closest to the surface of the juice. If the surface of the juice is curved up on the sides, look at the lowest point of the curve.

3. Read the measurement on the scale. You can estimate the value between two lines on the scale.

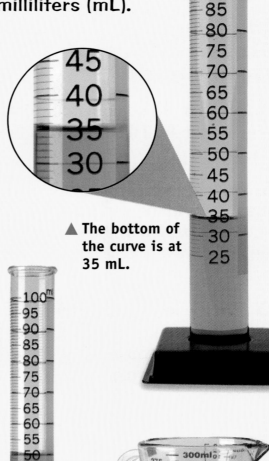

▲ The bottom of the curve is at 35 mL.

This beaker has marks for each 25 mL. ▶

This graduated cylinder has marks for every 1 mL. ▶

▲ This measuring cup has marks for each 25 mL.

Using a
Thermometer

A thermometer is used to measure temperature. When the liquid in the tube of a thermometer gets warmer, it expands and moves farther up the tube. Different scales can be used to measure temperature, but scientists usually use the Celsius scale.

Measure the Temperature of a Cold Liquid

1. Take a chilled liquid out of the refrigerator. Half fill a cup with the liquid.

2. Hold the thermometer so that the bulb is in the center of the liquid. Be sure that there are no bright lights or direct sunlight shining on the bulb.

3. Wait a few minutes until you see the liquid in the tube of the thermometer stop moving. Read the scale line that is closest to the top of the liquid in the tube. The thermometer shown reads 21°C (about 70°F).

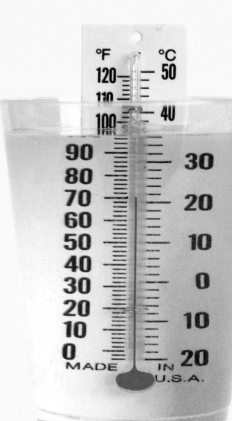

Using a
Balance

A balance is used to measure mass. Mass is the amount of matter in an object. To find the mass of an object, place it in the left pan of the balance. Place standard masses in the right pan.

Measure the Mass of a Ball

1. Check that the empty pans are balanced, or level with each other. When balanced, the pointer on the base should be at the middle mark. If it needs to be adjusted, move the slider on the back of the balance a little to the left or right.

2. Place a ball on the left pan. Then add standard masses, one at a time, to the right pan. When the pointer is at the middle mark again, each pan holds the same amount of matter and has the same mass.

3. Add the numbers marked on the masses in the pan. The total is the mass of the ball in grams.

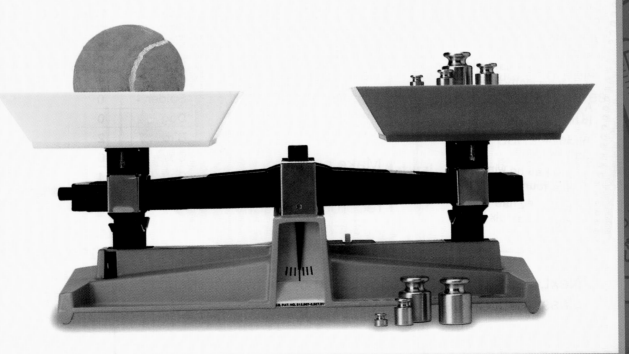

MEASUREMENTS

Volume
1 L of sports drink is a little more than 1 qt.

Area
A basketball court covers about 4,700 ft^2. It covers about 435 m^2.

Mass and Weight
A basketball has a mass of about 650 g. It weighs about $1\frac{1}{2}$ lb.

Metric Measures

Temperature
Ice melts at 0 degrees Celsius (°C)

Water freezes at 0°C

Water boils at 100°C

Length and Distance
1,000 meters (m) = 1 kilometer (km)

100 centimeters (cm) = 1 m

10 millimeters (mm) = 1 cm

Force
1 newton (N) =
    1 kilogram x meter/second/second
    (kg x m/s^2)

Volume
1 cubic meter (m^3) = 1 m x 1 m x 1 m

1 cubic centimeter (cm^3) =
    1 cm x 1 cm x 1 cm

1 liter (L) = 1,000 milliliters (mL)

1 cm^3 = 1 mL

Area
1 square kilometer (km^2) = 1 km x 1 km

1 hectare = 10,000 m^2

Mass
1,000 grams (g) = 1 kilogram (kg)

1,000 milligrams (mg) = 1 g

Temperature
The temperature at an indoor basketball game might be 25°C, which is 77°F.

Length/ Distance
A basketball rim is about 10 ft high, or a little more than 3 m from the floor.

Customary Measures

Temperature
Ice melts at 32 degrees Fahrenheit (°F)
Water freezes at 32°F
Water boils at 212°F

Length and Distance
12 inches (in.) = 1 foot (ft)
3 ft = 1 yard (yd)
5,280 ft = 1 mile (mi)

Weight
16 ounces (oz) = 1 pound (lb)
2,000 pounds = 1 ton (T)

Volume of Fluids
8 fluid ounces (fl oz) = 1 cup (c)
2 c = 1 pint (pt)
2 pt = 1 quart (qt)
4 qt = 1 gallon (gal)

Metric and Customary Rates
km/h = kilometers per hour
m/s = meters per second
mph = miles per hour

GLOSSARY

Pronunciation Key

Symbol	Key Words
a	c**a**t
ā	**a**pe
ä	c**o**t, c**a**r
e	t**e**n, b**e**rry
ē	m**e**
i	f**i**t, h**e**re
ī	**i**ce, f**i**re
ō	g**o**
ô	f**a**ll, f**o**r
oi	**oi**l
ൊo	l**oo**k, p**u**ll
o̅o̅	t**oo**l, r**u**le
ou	**ou**t, cr**ow**d
u	**u**p
ʉ	f**u**r, sh**i**rt
ə	**a** in **a**go
	e in ag**e**nt
	i in penc**i**l
	o in at**o**m
	u in circ**u**s
b	**b**ed
d	**d**og
f	**f**all

Symbol	Key Words
g	**g**et
h	**h**elp
j	**j**ump
k	**k**iss, **c**all
l	**l**eg
m	**m**eat
n	**n**ose
p	**p**ut
r	**r**ed
s	**s**ee
t	**t**op
v	**v**at
w	**w**ish
y	**y**ard
z	**z**ebra
ch	**ch**in, ar**ch**
ŋ	ri**ng**, dri**n**k
sh	**sh**e, pu**sh**
th	**th**in, tru**th**
th	**th**en, fa**th**er
zh	mea**s**ure

A heavy stress mark (′) is placed after a syllable that gets a heavy, or primary, stress, as in **picture** (pik′chər).

absolute age (ab′sə lо̄о̄t āj)
The actual age of an object. (C77)
The *absolute age* of this rock is
3,500 years.

adaptation (ad əp tā′shən) A
structure or behavior that enables
an organism to survive in its environment. (B9) The thick fur of
some animals is an *adaptation* to
cold environments.

anticline (an′ti klīn) An upward
fold of rock layers. (C82) Bending
layers of rock formed an *anticline*.

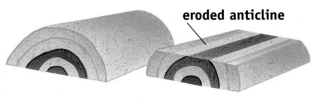

eroded anticline

bay (bā) Part of a sea or lake
extending into the land. (A14) The
ship anchored in the *bay*.

biodiversity (bī ō də vur′sə tē)
The variety of organisms that live
in Earth's many ecosystems; the
variety of plants and animals that
live within a particular ecosystem.
(B56) The *biodiversity* of an
ecosystem quickly changes after a
natural disaster.

biome (bī′ōm) A major land
ecosystem having a distinct combination of plants and animals. (B46)
Some *biomes*, such as tundra, and
deserts do not easily support
human populations.

carbon dioxide–oxygen cycle
(kär′bən dī äks′īd äks′i jen
sī′kəl) A natural cycle in which
plants and other producers use carbon dioxide and produce oxygen,
and animals, plants, and other living things use oxygen and produce
carbon dioxide. (B32) The *carbon
dioxide–oxygen cycle* must be
duplicated in space if humans wish
to make long voyages to other
planets.

carnivore (kär′nə vôr) A consumer that eats only other animals.
(B16) Lions are *carnivores* that
prey on zebras and other large
plant-eaters.

cell respiration (sel res pə-
rā′shən) The process of using oxygen to release energy from food.
(B32) Animals and plants release
energy from food and produce
carbon dioxide gas as a waste
product of *cell respiration*.

cementation (sē men tā'shən)
A process in which minerals,
deposited as water evaporates,
bind sediments into solid rock.
(C44) Sandstone is a sedimentary
rock formed by *cementation*.

circuit breaker (sʉr'kit brāk'ər)
A switch that opens or closes a
circuit by turning off or on. (D52)
When a circuit overheats, the *circuit breaker* switches off and the
lights go out.

cleavage (klēv'ij) The tendency
of some minerals to split along flat
surfaces. (C15) Salt, or halite,
shows *cleavage* in three planes.

coastal ocean (kōs'təl ō'shən)
A saltwater ecosystem close to the
shoreline that supports an abundance of life. (B52) The *coastal
ocean* is an ecosystem that lies
beyond the shoreline.

commensalism (kə men'səl iz-
əm) A close relationship between
two kinds of organisms that benefits one of the organisms while neither benefiting nor hurting the
other. (B20) The way that some
insects use their resemblance to
plants to hide from predators is an
example of *commensalism*.

community (kə myoo'nə tē) All
the organisms living together in a
particular ecosystem. (B8) Deer,
raccoons, and trees are part of a
forest *community*.

compass (kum'pəs) A device
containing a magnetized needle
that moves freely and is used to
show direction. (D23) The north
pole of the needle in a *compass*
points toward Earth's magnetic
north pole.

concrete (kän'krēt) A mixture of
rock material and cement that is
used as a building material. (C24) .
Many sidewalks are made of *concrete* because it is strong.

condensation (kän dən sā'shən)
The process by which a gas
changes to a liquid. (B34)
Condensation can occur on a
glass containing ice cubes as water
vapor in the air changes to liquid
water.

conductor (kən duk′tər) A material through which electricity moves easily. (D42) Copper wire is a good *conductor* of electricity.

conservation (kän sər vā′shən) The preserving and wise use of natural resources. (A31) The *conservation* of forests is important to both humans and wildlife.

consumer (kən sōōm′ər) A living thing that obtains energy by eating other living things. (B16) Meat eaters and plant eaters are *consumers*.

controlled experiment (kəntrōld′ ek sper′ə mənt) A test of a hypothesis in which the setups are identical in all ways except one. (S7) In the *controlled experiment*, one beaker of water also contained salt.

core (kôr) The innermost layer of Earth, which consists of a molten outer part and a solid inner part. (C69) Temperatures inside Earth's *core* are nearly as hot as those on the Sun's surface.

crust (krust) The outer layer of Earth. (C68) Earth's *crust* is a thin layer of rock.

deciduous forest (dē sij′ōō əs fôr′ist) A biome that contains many trees and in which rainfall is moderate. (B49) *Deciduous forests* support a great variety of animal life.

decomposer (dē kəm pōz′ər) A living thing that breaks down the remains of dead organisms. (B16) *Decomposers,*such as fungi, get their energy from the remains of dead plants they break down.

delta (del′tə) A flat, usually triangular plain formed by deposits of sediment where a river empties into the ocean. (A12) The largest *delta* in the United States is at the mouth of the Mississippi River.

desert (dez′ərt) A biome in which plant life is not abundant and rainfall is low. (B48) Plants that live in a *desert* have adaptations to conserve water.

ecosystem (ek'ō sis təm) An area in which living and nonliving things interact. (B8) An oak tree and the organisms that inhabit it can be thought of as a small *ecosystem*.

electric cell (ē lek'trik sel) A device that changes chemical energy to electrical energy. (D60) A battery in a flashlight consists of one or more *electric cells*.

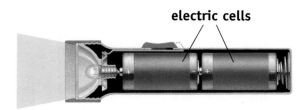

electric cells

electric charge (ē lek'trik chärj) The electrical property of particles of matter; an electric charge can be positive or negative. (D30) Rubbing a balloon with a wool cloth causes *negative electric charges* to move from the wool to the balloon.

electric circuit (ē lek'trik sʉr'kit) A path along which an electric current can move. (D41) We made an *electric circuit*, using a battery, wires, and a light bulb.

electric current (ē lek'trik kʉr'ənt) A continuous flow of electric charges. (D41) *Electric current* in wires allows you to run electric appliances in your home.

electric discharge (ē lek'trik dis'chärj) The loss or release of an electric charge. (D33) A bolt of lightning is an *electric discharge*.

electromagnet (ē lek'trō mag nit) A magnet made when an electric current passes through a wire coiled around an iron core. (D70) A large *electromagnet* can be strong enough to lift heavy metal objects such as cars.

endangered (en dān'jərd) In danger of becoming extinct. (B59) As the destruction of the Amazon rain forest continues, the number of *endangered* species increases.

erosion (ē rō'zhən) The gradual wearing away and removing of rock material by forces such as moving water, wind, and moving ice. (A10, C82) Ocean waves cause *erosion* of the seashore.

evaporation (ē vap ə rā'shən) The process by which liquid water changes to water vapor. (B34) One phase of the water cycle is the *evaporation* of water from lakes, rivers, and oceans.

extinct (ek stiŋkt′) No longer living as a species. (B59) The passenger pigeon is an *extinct* species.

passenger pigeon

fault (fôlt) A break in rock along which rocks have moved. (C89) Forces within Earth's crust produce *faults*.

filament (fil′ə mənt) A long, thin coil of wire that glows when electricity passes through it. (D48) The *filament* in an incandescent light bulb gives off light.

filament

fold (fōld) A bend in a layer of rock. (C81) Forces within Earth can cause a *fold* to form in rock layers.

food chain (fo͞od chān) The path of energy transfer from one living organism to another in an ecosystem. (B27) Energy moves from producers to consumers in a *food chain*.

food web (fo͞od web) The overlapping food chains that link producers, consumers, and decomposers in an ecosystem. (B28) Some consumers in a *food web* eat both plants and animals.

fossil (fäs′əl) The preserved remains or traces of a living thing from the past. (C46) *Fossils* can include imprints of animal skeletons pressed into rock.

fossil fuel (fäs′əl fyo͞o′əl) A fuel that formed from the remains of once-living things and that is nonrenewable. (A47) Natural gas is a *fossil fuel*.

fuse (fyo͞oz) A device in a circuit that contains a metal strip, which melts when the circuit is overheated, thus breaking the circuit. (D52) The *fuse* blew because too many appliances were connected to the same electric circuit.

generator (jen'ər āt ər) A device that changes energy of motion into electrical energy. (D58) The huge *generator* uses water power to produce electricity.

glacier (glā'shər) A huge mass of slow-moving ice that forms over land; glaciers form in areas where the amount of snow that falls is greater than the amount of snow that melts. (A22) As it moves, a *glacier* changes the surface beneath it.

grassland (gras'land) A biome containing many grasses but few trees and having low to moderate rainfall. (B48) Short grasses grow in dry *grasslands*.

hardness (härd'nis) A measure of how easily a mineral can be scratched. (C13) The *hardness* of diamond is greater than that of any other mineral.

hazardous waste (haz'ər dəs wāst) A waste material that dirties the environment and that can kill living things or cause disease. (A65) Some chemicals used to kill insects become *hazardous wastes*.

headland (hed'land) A piece of land that extends out into the water and usually slows down the flow of water that passes it. (A14) The lighthouse stood on a *headland* overlooking the bay.

herbivore (hʉr'bə vôr) A consumer that eats only plants or other producers. (B16) Zebras are *herbivores*.

hypothesis (hī päth'ə sis) An idea about or explanation of how or why something happens. (S6) The *hypothesis* about the expanding universe has been supported by evidence gathered by astronomers.

igneous rock (ig'nē əs räk) A type of rock that forms from melted rock that cools and hardens. (C40) Obsidian is an *igneous rock* that forms when lava cools quickly.

incineration (in sin ər ā'shən) Burning to ashes. (A60) You can get rid of trash by *incineration*.

index fossil (in'deks fäs'əl) A fossil used to determine the relative age of rock. (C76) The remains of a living thing that lived only at a certain time in the past makes a good *index fossil*.

insulator (in'sə lāt ər) A material through which electricity does not move easily. (D42) Wearing rubber gloves when working with electricity can prevent an electric shock because rubber is a good *insulator*.

lake (lāk) A freshwater ecosystem characterized by still water. (B51) *Lakes* support fish, birds, algae, and other forms of life.

landfill (land'fil) An area where trash is buried and covered over with dirt. (A59) In some places, towns decide to build recreation areas, such as parks, on the sites of old *landfills*.

lava (lä'və) Melted rock material that reaches Earth's surface before it cools and hardens. (C41) A volcano carries *lava* to Earth's surface.

lines of force (līnz uv fôrs) The lines that form a pattern showing the size and shape of a magnetic force field. (D19) Iron filings sprinkled over a magnet form *lines of force* that show the strength and the direction of the magnet's force.

litter (lit'ər) Trash that is discarded on the ground or in water rather than being disposed of properly. (A66) The children cleaned up the park by removing all the *litter* they could find.

lodestone (lōd'stōn) A naturally magnetic mineral found at or near Earth's surface. (D22) A piece of *lodestone* will attract iron.

luster (lus'tər) The way that the surface of a mineral looks when it reflects light. (C13) Silver and gold have a shiny, metallic *luster*.

magma (mag'mə) Melted rock material that forms deep within Earth. (C40) Some igneous rocks, such as granite, form from *magma*.

magnet (mag'nit) An object that has the property of attracting certain materials, mainly iron and steel. (D11) The girl used a horseshoe *magnet* to pick up paper clips and staples.

magnetic field (mag net'ik fēld) The space around a magnet within which the force of the magnet can act. (D20) The magnet attracted all the pins within its *magnetic field*.

magnetism (mag'nə tiz əm) A magnet's property of attracting certain materials, mainly iron and steel. (D11) *Magnetism* keeps kitchen magnets attached to a refrigerator door.

mantle (man'təl) A thick layer of rock between the crust and the core of Earth. (C69) The upper part of the *mantle* is solid rock, but below that is a section of rock that can flow.

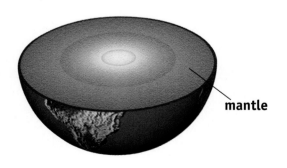

mantle

metamorphic rock (met ə-môr'fik räk) A type of rock that forms from existing rocks because of changes caused by heat, pressure, or chemicals. (C47) Slate is a *metamorphic rock* that forms from the sedimentary rock shale.

mineral (min'ər əl) A solid, found in nature, that has a definite chemical makeup. (A41, C12) Salt, coal, diamond, and gold are some examples of *minerals*.

model (mäd''l) Something used or made to represent an object or an idea. (C68) Layers of clay can be used as a *model* of layers of rock.

mutualism (myo͞o'cho͞o əl iz-əm) A close relationship between two or more organisms in which all organisms benefit. (B20) Bees carrying pollen from flower to flower as they obtain nectar is an example of *mutualism*.

natural resource (nach'ər əl rē'sôrs) Any useful material from Earth, such as water, oil, and minerals. (A31, C31) One reason that trees are an important *natural resource* is that their wood is used to build houses and to make paper.

niche (nich) The role that each species plays in a community. (B9) Bees have an important *niche* in pollinating flowers as they gather nectar to make honey.

nitrogen cycle (nī'trə jən sī'kəl) The cycle through which nitrogen changes into compounds that can be used by living things and then returns to the atmosphere. (B40) The *nitrogen cycle* is important to all life forms because cells need nitrogen to produce protein.

nonrenewable resource (nän-ri nōō'ə bəl rē'sôrs) A natural resource that can't be replaced once it's removed. (A42, C31) Minerals are classified as a *nonrenewable resource* because there's a limited amount of them.

north pole (nôrth pōl) One of the ends of a magnet where the magnetic force is strongest; it points to the north when the magnet moves freely. (D13) *North poles* of magnets repel each other.

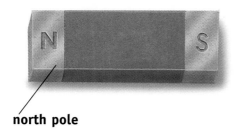
north pole

omnivore (äm'ni vôr) A consumer that eats both plants and animals. (B16) Because they eat both meats and vegetables, many humans are *omnivores*.

open ocean (ō'pən ō'shən) The large saltwater ecosystem containing floating and free-swimming organisms. (B53) Waters of the *open ocean* cover much of Earth's surface.

ore (ôr) A mineral or rock that contains enough of a metal to make mining that metal profitable. (A41, C27) Gold, aluminum, copper, and tin come from *ores*.

packaging (pak'ij iŋ) The wrapping and containers in which items are transported or offered for sale. (A75) *Packaging* protects products from damage but adds to their cost.

parallel circuit (par'ə lel sʉr'kit) An electric circuit having more than one path along which electric current can travel. (D51) Because home circuits are *parallel circuits*, you can switch off one light and others will stay lit.

parasitism (par'ə sīt iz əm) A relationship between two organisms in which one organism lives on or in the other, feeds upon it, and usually harms it. (B19) The way in which fleas and ticks live on dogs and other animals is an example of *parasitism*.

photosynthesis (fōt ō sin'thə sis) The process by which producers, such as plants, make their own food by using energy from the Sun. (B33) *Photosynthesis* takes place primarily in the leaves of plants.

pollutant (pə loot' 'nt) A substance that causes pollution. (A65) The exhaust gases from cars add *pollutants* to the air.

pollution (pə loo'shən) The dirtying of the environment with waste materials or other unwanted substances. (A65) Water *pollution* can kill living things.

population (päp yoo lā'shən) A group of the same kind of organisms that live in an area. (B8) There is a *population* of frogs in that marsh.

producer (prō doos'ər) An organism that makes its own food through photosynthesis. (B16) Plants are the most familiar examples of *producers*.

protein (prō'tēn) Organic compounds that form the structure of living things and that control the processes that take place in living things. (B39) *Proteins* provide the body with materials that help cells grow and repair themselves.

quarry (kwôr'ē) A mine that is usually near or at Earth's surface and from which rock is removed. (C52) Granite, sandstone, limestone, slate, and marble are some of the kinds of rocks that come from a *quarry*.

R

recycle (rē sī′kəl) To process and reuse materials. (A72) Discarded newspapers are *recycled* to make new paper.

relative age (rel′ə tiv āj) The age of an object as compared to that of other objects. (C76) The order of layers of rock shows the *relative ages* of the layers.

renewable resource (ri nōō′ə-bəl rē′sôrs) A resource that can be replaced. (A42, E31) Water is a *renewable resource* because rain increases the supply of water.

river (riv′ər) A freshwater ecosystem characterized by running water. (B50) Salmon are able to swim against the current in a *river*.

river system (riv′ər sis′təm) A river and all the waterways, such as brooks, streams, and rivers, that drain into it. (A11) The Mississippi River and the many waterways feeding into it make up the largest *river system* in the country.

rock (räk) A solid material that is made up of one or more minerals and that may be used for its properties. (A41, C40) Granite is a hard *rock* used in construction.

rock cycle (räk sī′kəl) The continuous series of changes that rocks undergo. (C60) In the *rock cycle*, changes are brought about by factors such as weathering, melting, cooling, or pressure.

S

sand dune (sand dōōn) A mound, hill, or ridge of sand formed by the wind. (A21) *Sand dunes* are common in the desert.

sand dune

sediment (sed′ə mənt) Sand, soil, and rock carried by water, wind, or ice. (A12, C43) The rushing water of the river deposited *sediment* along the riverbanks.

sedimentary rock (sed ə-men′tər ē räk) A type of rock that forms when sediments harden. (C43) Most *sedimentary rocks* form in layers.

series circuit (sir′ēz sʉr′kit) An electric circuit in which the parts are connected in a single path. (D50) Electric current can follow only one path in a *series circuit*.

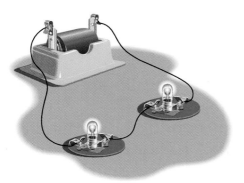

shoreline (shôr′līn) The ecosystem where land and ocean meet. (B52) Tides affect organisms that live along the *shoreline*.

smelting (smelt′iŋ) The process of removing metal from ore. (C28) Workers obtain iron by *smelting* iron ore in a blast furnace.

soil (soil) Loose material that covers much of Earth's land surface and is made up of three layers—topsoil, subsoil, and partly weathered rock. (A30) Plants, grow in soil and insects and worms live in it.

solar cell (sō′lər sel) A device that changes sunlight into electrical energy. (D64) *Solar cells* used in power plants can produce electricity without polluting the air.

solar energy (sō′lər en′ər jē) The clean and relatively low-cost energy from the Sun. (A50, D64) *Solar energy* is used to heat water in some homes.

south pole (south pōl) One of the ends of a magnet where the magnetic force is strongest; it points to the south when the magnet is allowed to move freely. (D13) The *south pole* of one magnet attracts the north pole of another magnet.

static electricity (stat′ik ē lektris′i tē) Electric charges that have built up on the surface of an object. (D31) Walking across a carpet on a cold, dry day can produce *static electricity*.

streak (strēk) The colored powder made by rubbing a mineral against a ceramic surface. (C15) Although pyrite is yellow, it produces a black *streak*.

switch (swich) A device that completes or breaks the path a current can follow in an electric circuit. (D41) In order to turn on the light, you must press the *switch* to complete the circuit.

syncline (sin′klīn) A downward fold of rock layers. (C82) Forces in Earth pushing on rock formed a *syncline*

syncline

taiga (tī′gə) A biome that contains many coniferous trees and in which rainfall is moderate. (B49) In North America the *taiga* is south of the tundra.

theory (thē′ə rē) A hypothesis that is supported by a lot of evidence and is widely accepted by scientists. (S9) The big-bang *theory* offers an explanation for the origin of the universe.

tropical rain forest (träp′i kəl rān fôr′ist) A biome distinguished by lush vegetation, abundant rainfall, and plentiful sunlight. (B48) The *tropical rain forest* supports the greatest variety of life of any biome.

tundra (tun′drə) A biome characterized by cold temperatures and low precipitation. (B49) The *tundra* blooms in summer.

variable (ver′ē ə bəl) The one difference in the setups of a controlled experiment; provides a comparison for testing a hypothesis. (S7) The *variable* in an experiment with plants was the amount of water given each plant.

voltage (vōl′tij) The force of an electric current, measured in volts. (D63) Electric currents of high *voltage* are carried by long-distance power lines.

water cycle (wôt′ər sī′kəl) A
continuous process in which water
moves between the atmosphere
and Earth's surface, including the
use of water by living things. (B34)
The *water cycle* is powered by
energy from the Sun.

weathering (we*th*′ər iŋ) The
physical and chemical processes
by which rock is broken down into
smaller pieces. (A10, C62) Cracks
in rock produced by freezing rainwater or the growth of plant roots
are examples of *weathering*.

wetland (wet′land) Any one of
three ecosystems—marsh, swamp,
or bog—where land and fresh
water meet. (B51) *Wetlands* help
purify water.

INDEX

* Activity

* Activity

CREDITS

ILLUSTRATORS
Cover Genine Smith.

Think Like a Scientist 14: Laurie Hamilton. *border* Genine Smith.

Unit A 11, 13: Susan Johnston Carlson. 13–15: Paul Mirocha. 22–24: Jim Turgeon. 23, 25: Skip Baker. 30–31: Brad Gaber. 32–33: Jim Salvati. 38–39: Dave Joly. 39: Eldon Doty. 40: Brad Gaber. 43: Terry Ravenelli. 44: Terry Boles. 46: Rodica Prato. 47: Martucci Studio. 51: Brad Gaber. 56: Jim Trusilo. 58–59: Robert Roper. 61: Ray Vella. 63: Michael Ingle. 64: Greg Harris. 65: Robert Roper. 68: Greg Harris. 69–71: Bob Ostrom. 71: Eldon Doty. 72–74: Scott MacNeil. 76: Ken Bowser. 77: Randy Chewning.

Unit B 8–9: Robert Hynes. 10–11: Jim Salvati. 15: Wendy Smith-Griswold. 17: Marcos Montiero. 18: Lori Anzalone. 26: David Barber. 27: *border* Terry Boles, *t.* Andy Lendway. 28: Terry Boles. 29: Andy Lendway. 32–35: Don Stewart. 36: Jim Starr. 39–40: Don Stewart. 41: Andy Lendway. 46–49: Rodica Prato. 50–53: Paul Mirocha. 54: Joe LeMonnier. 57: Carlos Ochagavia. 63: Patrick Gnan.

Unit C 12–16: Lingta King. 20: *t.* Eric Larsen, *b.* Wendy Smith-Griswold. 28: Jeanette Adams. 30–31: Bill Morse. 40: Brad Gaber. 47: Robert Pasternack. 55: Scot Ritchie. 58–59: Brad Gaber. 60: Michael Sloan. 68–69: Chuck Carter. 70: Scot Ritchie. 71: Chuck Carter. 74: Eldon Doty. 75: Carlyn Iverson. 76: *t.* Susan Melrath, *b.* Carlyn Iverson. 83: *t.* Robert Pasternack, *b.* Joe LeMonnier. 84: Verlin Miller. 85: Jim Starr. 89: Robert Pasternack. 91: Joe LeMonnier. 93: Chuck Carter.

Unit D 13: Patrick Gnan. 15: Dan McGowan. 22: Brad Gaber. 30–31: Robert Roper. 35: *t.* Jim Effier, *m.* Andrew Shiff. 40: David Winter. 41: Hans & Cassady, Inc. 42–43: Dale Gustafson. 48: Patrick Gnan. 50–51: Hans & Cassady, Inc. 52: Robert Roper. 53: Hans & Cassady, Inc. 60–61: Robert Roper. 62–63: Geoffrey McCormick. 68–69: Wayne Vincent. 70, 72: Robert Roper. 74–76: Michael Sloan.

Science and Math Toolbox *logos* Nancy Tobin. 14–15: Andrew Shiff. *borders* Olivia McElroy.

Glossary 17: Ellen Going Jacobs. 18, 20: Dale Gustafson. 21: *b.l.* Dale Gustafson, *m.r.* Carlyn Iverson. 22: Lori Anzalone. 24: Dale Glasgow & Assoc. 25: Patrick Gnan. 27: Dan McGowan. 28: Hans & Cassidy Inc.

PHOTOGRAPHS

All photographs by Houghton Mifflin Company (HMCo.) unless otherwise noted.

Cover *t.* Superstock; *m.l.* Bill Brooks/Masterfile; *m.r.* Tim Flach/Tony Stone Images; *b.l.* Barbara Leslie/FPG International; *b.r.* Greg Ryan & Sally Beyer/Tony Stone Images.

Table of Contents iv: *l.* Harold Sund/The Image Bank; *r.* Cromosohm/Sohm/The Stock Market. vii: *t.* J.C. Carton/Bruce Coleman Inc.

Think Like A Scientist 2: *t. bkgd.* PhotoDisc, Inc. 3: *t.* PhotoDisc, Inc. 4–5: Chip Henderson Photography.

Unit A 1–3: Kim Heacox/Tony Stone Images. 4: Mark Hopkins. 4–5: Miriam Romais. 10: *l.* E.R. Degginger/Color-Pic, Inc.; *m.* C.C. Lockwood/DRK Photo; *r.* Cameron Davidson/Comstock. 12: *l.* Tom Stack & Associates; *r.* Manfred Gottschalk/Tom Stack & Associates. 13: Scott Blackman/Tom Stack & Associates. 14: *l.* E.R. Degginger/Color-Pic, Inc.; *r.* NASA/Corbis. 15: Bob Daemmrich Photography. 20–21: *bkgd.* Larry Ulrich/DRK Photo; *inset* Breck P. Kent Photography. 21: Breck P. Kent Photography. 22: *l.* E.R. Degginger/Color-Pic, Inc.; *r.* Breck P. Kent Photography. 22–23: © Porterfield/Chickering/Photo Researchers, Inc. 24: Spencer Swanger/Tom Stack & Associates. 26–27: *bkgd.* Richard Hamilton Smith/Corbis; *inset* Thanh H. Dao/USDA-ARS-CPRL. 32: *t.* Harold Sund/The Image Bank; *b.* J.C. Carton/Bruce Coleman Inc. 33: *t.* Kevin Schafer/Tom Stack & Associates; *b.* John Callahan/Tony Stone Images. 34: Grant Huntington for HMCo. 36–37: Grant Huntington for HMCo. 41: Grant Huntington for HMCo. 43: *t.l.* Edward Bower/The Image Bank; *t.r.* Lester Lefkowitz/Tony Stone Images; *b.l.* Lester Lefkowitz/Tony

Extra Practice

On the following pages are questions about each of the Investigations in your book. Use these questions to help you review some of the terms and ideas that you studied. Each review section gives you the page numbers in the book where you can check your answers. Write your answers on a separate sheet of paper.

Contents

Investigation 1 pages A6–A15

Write the term that best completes each sentence.

| erosion | sediment | weathering |

1. The process by which broken-down rock material is carried by moving water, wind, or ice is called ___.

2. The process by which rock is broken into smaller pieces is called ___.

3. Material that is carried by moving water is called ___.

Complete the following exercises.

4. Describe how a river valley becomes deeper and wider.

5. Why are shorelines the places most affected by erosion and weathering?

6. If you lived near a shoreline, how would you protect your home from the effects of erosion and weathering?

Investigation 2 pages A16–A24

Use the terms below to solve each riddle.

| glacier | moraine | sand dune |

7. I am a hill formed when wind deposits a pile of sand.

8. I am a huge mass of slow-moving ice.

9. I am rock material carried by a glacier.

Complete the following exercises.

10. How can wind erosion be prevented?

11. What are two ways in which glaciers shape the land?

12. What are some land features formed by the action of glaciers?

Investigation 1 pages A28–A33

Write the term that best completes each sentence.

conservation	natural resources	topsoil

1. Trees, coal, air, and water are examples of ___.
2. Another term for the wise use of natural resources is ___.
3. A mixture of weathered rock and humus is called ___.

Complete the following exercises.

4. Describe the properties of topsoil, subsoil, and weathered rock.
5. What is the greatest cause of soil loss?
6. Why is it important to conserve soil?

Investigation 2 pages A34–A43

Write the term that best completes each sentence.

minerals	ores	metals

7. Rocks are made up of natural solid substances called ___.
8. Rocks that can be mined for the minerals they contain are called ___.
9. Valuable substances from ores, such as copper and gold, are ___.

Complete the following exercises.

10. Identify two or more minerals.
11. How does a renewable resource differ from a nonrenewable resource?
12. Describe how a pure metal is mined.

Unit A Extra Practice

Investigation 3 pages A44–A50

Write the term that best completes each sentence.

peat	solar energy	fossil fuel

13. Energy from the Sun is called ___.

14. Natural gas, which is made from the remains of once-living things, is a ___.

15. A fuel that comes from the remains of ancient swamp plants is called ___.

Complete the following exercises.

16. Explain how the energy in fossil fuels can be traced back to the Sun.

17. What are some energy sources other than fossil fuels?

18. What are some of the advantages of using solar energy instead of fossil fuels?

Investigation 1 pages A54–A61

Use the terms below to solve each riddle.

ash	incinerator	landfill

1. I am a large hole that is filled, over time, with trash.

2. I am a place where trash is burned.

3. I am the material that results when trash is burned.

Complete the following exercises.

4. How are landfills better for the environment than trash dumps?

5. Why doesn't the trash in a landfill decay quickly?

6. Many cities and towns have laws against burning trash. Do you agree or disagree with such laws? Why?

Investigation 2 pages A62–A67

Write the term that best completes each sentence.

hazardous waste	litter	petroleum

7. Trash that is discarded on the ground or in water is called ___.

8. A pollutant that can harm the environment even in small amounts is called ___.

9. Plastic is made from a nonrenewable resource called ___.

Complete the following exercises.

10. What are some ways that litter in the oceans is harmful?

11. What problems can result from the improper disposal of motor oil, paint, pesticides, and other hazardous wastes?

12. Give examples of how littering can reduce natural resources.

Investigation 3 pages A68–A76

Write the term in each pair that correctly completes each sentence.

13. The processing and reusing of items is called (recycling, packaging).

14. Choosing products that are not overpackaged can help (increase, decrease) the amount of trash in landfills.

15. Pulp is a stage in the process of recycling (paper, plastic).

Complete the following exercises.

16. What is the meaning of the number code on the bottom of some plastic items?

17. What are some advantages and disadvantages of packaging?

18. What are some common objects you use that can be recycled?

Unit B Extra Practice

Investigation 1 pages B6–B11

Write the term that best completes each sentence.

ecosystem	niche	population

1. The interaction of organisms with one another and their physical environment makes up a/an ___.

2. All the organisms of the same kind that live together make up a/an ___.

3. The role that each species plays in a community is its ___.

Complete the following exercises.

4. Identify some ways that people can cause changes in an ecosystem.

5. Identify some natural ways that changes occur in an ecosystem.

6. Give an example of an animal's adaptation to its environment. Tell whether the adaptation is a structure or a behavior.

Investigation 2 pages B12–B20

Write the term in each pair that correctly completes each sentence.

7. A consumer that eats both plants and animals is (a herbivore, an omnivore).

8. A consumer that eats only meat is (an omnivore, a carnivore).

9. A consumer that eats only plants is a (herbivore, carnivore).

Complete the following exercises.

10. What are the three kinds of symbiosis?

11. How do decomposers help the environment?

12. Can an animal be both predator and prey? Explain your answer.

Investigation 1 pages B24–B29

Use the terms below to solve each riddle.

food chain	food web	first-order consumer

1. I show an organism's role in overlapping food chains.
2. I am an organism that eats producers.
3. I am the path of energy transfer from one organism to another.

Complete the following exercises.

4. Why do all food chains include decomposers?
5. How can an organism have more than one role in a food web?
6. Why is a food chain sometimes referred to as an energy chain? What is the original source of the energy? Explain.

Investigation 2 pages B30–B40

Write the term in each pair that correctly completes each sentence.

7. The process by which oxygen is used to break down carbon compounds and release energy is (cell respiration, photosynthesis).
8. Water vapor is released from leaves in a process called (precipitation, transpiration).
9. Compounds that are the building blocks of living things are (bacteria, proteins).

Complete the following exercises.

10. Describe what happens in the carbon dioxide–oxygen cycle.
11. If evaporation stopped occurring, what would happen to the water cycle? Explain your answer.
12. Describe what happens in the nitrogen cycle.

Investigation 1   pages B44–B53

Write the term that best completes each sentence.

| deciduous forest | tundra | tropical rain forest |

1. Heavy rainfall and a warm climate in which animals and plants thrive are characteristics of a ___.

2. A thin layer of snow and ice covers the ground most of the year in a ___.

3. Winters are cold, summers are warm and wet, and maple, oak, and birch trees grow in a ___.

Complete the following exercises.

4. What is a biome? What are some abiotic factors of a biome?

5. Identify and describe two kinds of freshwater ecosystems.

6. Why is it not correct to speak of the oceans as though they were one big ecosystem?

Investigation 2   pages B54–B60

Write the term that best completes each sentence.

| biodiversity | endangered | extinct |

7. If no members of a species are alive, that species is ___.

8. The term used for the great variety of species that exists on Earth is ___.

9. If a species is threatened with extinction, that species is ___.

Complete the following exercises.

10. How does latitude affect the biodiversity of an ecosystem?

11. How does the destruction of a habitat threaten biodiversity?

12. What can be done to prevent the extinction or endangerment of a species?

Investigation 1 pages C6–C21

Write the term that best completes each sentence.

hardness	luster	streak

1. The color of the powder that crumbles from a scratched mineral is called ___.

2. A measure of how easily a mineral can be scratched is called ___.

3. The way a mineral reflects light from its surface is called ___.

Complete the following exercises.

4. What determines the color of a mineral? Why is color not a reliable property for identifying minerals?

5. Which properties of pyrite are like those of gold? Which are different from those of gold?

6. What mineral property do terms such as *dull, pearly, glassy,* and *brilliant* refer to? What does Mohs' scale allow you to estimate?

Investigation 2 pages C22–C32

Use the terms below to solve each riddle.

natural resource	ore	smelting

7. I am a useful material or energy source found in nature.

8. I am a mineral from which a metal can be removed.

9. I am the process of removing metal from ore.

Complete the following exercises.

10. What is the most widespread source of iron? How does adding carbon to iron change iron?

11. Identify three uses of quartz.

12. How do renewable and nonrenewable resources differ? Give an example of each kind of resource.

Investigation 1 pages C36–C49

Write the term in each pair that correctly completes each sentence.

1. Igneous rock is formed from (magma, sediments).

2. The binding of existing rocks, minerals, and organic materials is called (cementation, metamorphism).

3. Fossils are likely to be found in (sedimentary, igneous) rocks.

Complete the following exercises.

4. How does the way basalt forms determine the size of its mineral grains?

5. Explain why magma tends to rise to the surface of Earth.

6. In general, how do metamorphic rocks form?

Investigation 2 pages C50–C55

Use the terms below to solve each riddle.

adobe	crushed stone	quarry

7. I am an open pit in Earth from which certain types of rock are removed.

8. I am bits and pieces of rock used in concrete.

9. I am a sun-dried building material.

Complete the following exercises.

10. Briefly describe how bricks are made.

11. How are bricks and rocks alike, and how do they differ?

12. What are dimension stones, and how are they used?

Investigation 3 pages C56–C62

Write the term that best completes each sentence.

compacting	rock cycle	weathering

13. The series of changes that Earth's rock materials undergo as they change from one kind of rock to another is called the ___.

14. The breaking up of rocks into rock bits, or sediments, is called ___.

15. The squeezing together of sediments is called ___.

Complete the following exercises.

16. What are fossil fuels? Name three types of fossil fuels.

17. What factors cause rocks to change?

18. How does crystallizing occur in igneous rock?

Investigation 1 pages C66–C71

Write the term that best completes each sentence.

crust	mantle	core

1. Earth's thickest layer is the ___.

2. The layer of Earth that has both a solid inner layer and a molten outer layer is the ___.

3. Earth's thinnest layer is the ___.

Complete the following exercises.

4. Which layer of Earth has the greatest temperature and pressure?

5. What is Earth's crust made of?

6. How are earthquake waves used to learn about properties of Earth's layers?

Unit C Extra Practice

Investigation 2 pages C72–C77

Use the terms below to solve each riddle.

| absolute age | index fossil | relative age |

7. I am the remains of a species that lived for a short time but could be found in large numbers over much of Earth.

8. I refer to how old a rock is compared to other rocks.

9. I refer to how old a rock really is.

Complete the following exercises.

10. What is the hollow part of a fossil called? What is the material that fills in the hollow called?

11. What can scientists learn from fossils?

12. Do index fossils give absolute age or relative age? Explain.

Investigation 3 pages C78–C85

Write the term in each pair that correctly completes each sentence.

13. An upward fold of rock layer is called (an anticline, a syncline).

14. The Appalachian Mountains are (folded mountains, dome mountains).

15. Wind, gravity, moving water, and ice can all cause the (erosion, folding) of rock.

Complete the following exercises.

16. How do forces cause a layer of rock to fold?

17. Give examples of two rocks that wear away easily and two rocks that don't wear away easily.

18. How were the Black Hills formed?

Investigation 4 pages C86–C92

Write the term in each pair that correctly completes each sentence.

19. In an earthquake, the place below Earth's surface where movement first occurs along a fault is the (epicenter, focus).

20. The point on Earth's surface directly above the focus of an earthquake is the (epicenter, fault).

21. A break in rock along which movement has occurred is called a (plate, fault).

Complete the following exercises.

22. How was the Grand Canyon formed?

23. What is an earthquake? What is the most common cause of earthquakes?

24. What is a strike-slip fault? How does it differ from a normal fault?

Unit D Extra Practice

Investigation 1 pages D6–D15

Write the term in each pair that correctly completes each sentence.

1. A magnet's property of attracting certain materials is called (gravitation, magnetism).

2. If you put the north pole of one magnet near the south pole of another magnet, the magnets will (attract, repel) each other.

3. The pole of a freely moving magnet that will point south is the (south pole, north pole).

Complete the following exercises.

4. How could a magnet help you determine if an object is made of of iron or not?

5. In what ways is a maglev train different from other trains?

6. How could you use a magnet with marked poles to find the north pole on a magnet with unmarked poles?

Investigation 2 pages D16–D24

Write the term that best completes each sentence.

magnetic field	lodestone	compass

7. In order to be attracted by a magnet, an object must be within the magnet's ___.

8. The naturally magnetic rock discovered more than 2,000 years ago is called ___.

9. A device containing a magnetized needle that shows direction is called a ___.

Complete the following exercises.

10. How could you show a friend a magnet's force field?

11. Name two properties of all magnets.

12. If you wanted to pick up a pile of paper clips, which part of a bar magnet would you use? Explain your answer.

Investigation 1 pages D28–D35

Write the term that best completes each sentence.

| electric charges | electric discharge | static electricity |

1. The movement of negative charges can cause the buildup of electric charges on objects, or ___.

2. Tiny particles of matter can carry units of electricity called ___.

3. Lightning is an example of a/an ___.

Complete the following exercises.

4. How can an object become charged with static electricity?

5. What properties of positive and negative electric charges are similar to the properties of a magnet's poles?

6. Name two ways to stay safe during a lightning storm.

Investigation 2 pages D36–D43

Write the term in each pair that correctly completes each sentence.

7. A path along which electric charges can flow is called an (electric circuit, electric current).

8. A material, such as plastic or wood, that doesn't let electricity move easily through it is called (a conductor, an insulator).

9. A device that opens and closes an electric circuit is a (dry cell, switch).

Complete the following exercises.

10. Describe the parts of a simple electric circuit.

11. Why won't a bulb light in an open, or incomplete, circuit?

12. How could you set up a simple electric circuit in which you could easily control whether electric current flowed or didn't flow?

Unit D Extra Practice

Investigation 3 pages D44–D52

Use the terms below to solve each riddle.

circuit breaker	parallel circuit	series circuit

13. I have only a single path for electric current to follow.

14. I have more than one path for electric current to follow.

15. I open a circuit by turning myself off.

Complete the following exercises.

16. In what ways are fluorescent bulbs better for the environment than incandescent bulbs?

17. What purpose do fuses and circuit breakers serve?

18. If you were going to build a house, would you use series circuits or parallel circuits? Why?

Investigation 1 pages D56–D65

Write the term that best completes each sentence.

generator	solar cell	electric cell

1. A device that changes light into electrical energy is called a/an ___.

2. A device that changes energy of motion into electrical energy is called a/an ___.

3. A device that changes chemical energy into electrical energy is called a/an ___.

Complete the following exercises.

4. How are magnets used to generate electricity?

5. What are transformers used for?

6. What are some advantages of using solar energy to produce electricity?

Digging His Own Grave

Cordova reached down and took Rosa by the arm and jerked her to her feet. "You follow me, Slocum, and she dies a slow death."

"Leave her here, then," Slocum shouted as he strained at his binds.

"She'll be buzzard bait if you even show up on my trail, Slocum!" Cordova shouted from the doorway, pulling her along with him.

"I'll hunt you down if you harm one hair on her head!"

"Go to hell!" Cordova shouted over the roar. The open door flapped in the wild wind; they were gone. The other two bandits raced for the exit holding on to their straw hats and disappeared out of sight. Horses whined and Slocum thought he heard them ride out in the storm. *Son of a bitch.* He rose on his knees, his muscles bulging against the ropes. His breath raged through his nose—Cordova would pay for this.

DON'T MISS THESE
ALL-ACTION WESTERN SERIES
FROM THE BERKLEY PUBLISHING GROUP

THE GUNSMITH by J. R. Roberts
Clint Adams was a legend among lawmen, outlaws, and ladies.
They called him . . . the Gunsmith.

LONGARM by Tabor Evans
The popular long-running series about Deputy U.S. Marshal
Long—his life, his loves, his fight for justice.

SLOCUM by Jake Logan
Today's longest-running action Western. John Slocum rides
a deadly trail of hot blood and cold steel.

BUSHWHACKERS by B. J. Lanagan
An action-packed series by the creators of Longarm! The
rousing adventures of the most brutal gang of cutthroats ever
assembled—Quantrill's Raiders.

DIAMONDBACK by Guy Brewer
Dex Yancey is Diamondback, a Southern gentleman turned
con man when his brother cheats him out of the family fortune. Ladies love him. Gamblers hate him. But nobody pulls
one over on Dex . . . .

WILDGUN by Jack Hanson
The blazing adventures of mountain man Will Barlow—from
the creators of Longarm!

TEXAS TRACKER by Tom Calhoun
Meet J. T. Law: the most relentless—and dangerous—man-
hunter in all Texas. Where sheriffs and posses fail, he's the
best man to bring in the most vicious outlaws—for a price.

JAKE LOGAN

SLOCUM
AND THE TEQUILA ROSE

JOVE BOOKS, NEW YORK

SLOCUM AND THE TEQUILA ROSE

A Jove Book / published by arrangement with
the author

PRINTING HISTORY
Jove edition / December 2003

ISBN: 0-515-13640-9

A JOVE BOOK®
Jove Books are published by The Berkley Publishing Group, a division of Penguin Group (USA) Inc., 375 Hudson Street, New York, New York 10014. JOVE and the "J" design are trademarks belonging to Penguin Group (USA) Inc.

PRINTED IN THE UNITED STATES OF AMERICA

10 9 8 7 6 5 4 3 2 1

Prologue

She knelt at the altar and prayed with all her might to the Virgin Mary. Urgent words spilled from her lips for his deliverance until the sharp crack of the rifles outside the chapel caused her to stop and squeeze her wet eyes shut. Her heart ached with the knowledge that her husband no longer breathed. Never again would he kiss her or make fiery love to her. Not even the Holy Mother nor God Himself could stop the murder of her Estevan by Colonel Disantos's firing squad.

She rose and genuflected before turning to leave. As she started down the aisle, one of the great front doors of the church opened and the bright sunlight shone on the padre's dusty black habit as he hurried inside.

"Isabel, my child," he said and tried to block her exit.

She fought her way past him. Closing her ears to his pleading—*about God's way*. No more would she place her faith in his God. From this time forth, she would place her trust only in a gun until someone said the last rites over that butcher Disantos.

"Wait, my child. Mercy is—you can't—"

She turned at the doorway, jerked the shawl from her head. "You have had your chance, padre. Now it will be my way."

"My child, my child . . . !" he called after her.

Isabel never slackened her steps in the cool air, not yet

heated up by the fiery ball still coming up over the mountains. Filled with a newfound fury, she strode across the hard packed square. She unhitched the flea-bitten gray horse at the rack and stepped in the stirrups as the animal tried to circle around on her. Pulling up her dress to straddle the saddle, she reined him about sharply, then she drove her heels in his side. He bolted away.

"My horse! Oh, my God, she's stealing my horse!" someone shouted behind her, but she already had him in a gallop, giving him his bits and headed for the village gates. Outside on the greasewood flats, she slapped him hard with the reins from side to side and he flew away. Wind in her face, she headed him for the hills, not certain over her future, but knowing what she must do next.

Two days later, she feverishly sewed on the blouse in the jackal of her cousin, Donna Vargas. Beads of sweat ran in rivers from under her armpits and down her face. The salt stung her eyes. At last, she held up the garment to examine her handiwork. This time she would have it completed as she wanted it to be.

In a flash, she pulled the simple peasant blouse over her head and struggled into the new one. Starting down at her waist, she drew up the lacing, pulling the front tight and snug under her firm breasts, then encasing them so her cleavage bulged up. Glancing down, she drew in her breath to make them rise. Even when she exhaled, they remained very visible, supported by the new garment's design.

"My God," Donna said, coming inside and staring at her. "You look like a cheap *puta* in that thing."

"To a man, would I look desirable?" she asked, unblushing at the older woman's words.

"You would look that way without such a-a-a thing to wear. It is shameless."

"Good. Did you get the leather?"

"Yes, but I don't know why." Donna handed her the tanned skin wrapped in a roll. "It's deerskin, like you asked for." She put her hand to her forehead as if taking her own temperature. "And a stolen horse grazes outside my house. I must be crazy helping you."

"No, you are my cousin and my best one," Isabel said with a smile, and hugged her from the side, herding her to the table in the center of the room. "I need you to cut a skirt out of this for me."

"A leather skirt? Why?" Donna stared in disbelief at her.

"Because I need a divided one to ride away on that stolen horse you speak about."

"Mother of God, why are you doing all this?"

"Some day you will understand," Isabel promised her.

"Never. You have just lost your poor husband and now you have lost your mind. Where did you get that stupid horse? Does he belong to that donkey Remale? I think I saw him riding one that looked like that."

"Never mind who he belonged to. I am borrowing him."

"For how long?" Donna asked, helping spread out the deerskin.

"Until I can steal a better one."

"A better one—steal a better one." Donna threw her head back to look at the stick-and-waddle ceiling for celestial help.

Three hours later, Isabel walked back and forth across the room. The divided buckskin skirt slapped her legs with the fringe swirling around her calves with each stride. If only she had a tall looking glass to see what her new outfit really looked like. But there was none, so she had to be satisfied with her own conceptions of the new outfit.

"What do you think?" she asked.

Donna shook her head. "There was once a half Apache-Irish whore up in Tombstone who called herself Tequila Rose. She wore such an outfit and she would screw any man she could convince to pay her and she took on some without money for it, too."

"Is she still there?" Isabel asked.

"No, she was killed in a runaway buckboard wreck."

"Good," Isabel said, and threw her chest out amused by the uplift of her blouse. "That will be my new name, Tequila Rosa."

"You could become a *puta* that easy?" Donna squinted in troubled disbelief at her.

"Who am I? Not a virgin anymore. So who would want me for a bride? Some old man who had already plowed up his first wife until she died of childbearing or hard work. No, my cousin, I intend to work my way through the ranks until I can stick my *pistola* up the ass of that *bastardo* Disantos and blow off the top of his head."

"Oh, my dear God!" Donna crossed herself and fell to her knees, pleading, "Please, Isabel, reconsider—there is nothing out there but angry men to rape and then discard you."

"We shall see," she said, and from the bag she drew out the holster with the belt wrapped around it and the pistol. When she threaded the tongue through the buckle and drew the belt tight at her narrow waist, she made a mental note where it needed a new hole to fit her and took it off.

"A gun! Mother of saints! What do you know about a pistol?"

"When I get it where it fits, I will show you." She plunged the hole punch through the leather, working until the buckle's tongue would go through the opening.

"Fire a pistol . . ." Donna, looking wild-eyed, swept the thick hair streaked in premature gray back from her face. "You can't kill anyone."

"Stop worrying so." Soon she had the holster back on and shoved the Colt back in it. Testing how to draw the revolver, she whipped it out, feeling the heft of the .44. Good thing, she decided, that the barrel was no longer or she couldn't unholster it.

She checked the individual chambers by rolling the cylinder around. Satisfied that five were loaded, she caught her cousin by the arm and drove her outside in the backyard.

"Toss a bottle in the air," she said.

"Loco, loco," Donna mumbled, bending over to pick up a brown one. Underhanded, she tossed it skyward.

The Colt in her hand, Isabel cocked back the hammer, took a quick aim, dropped the muzzle to follow it, and fired. The percussion hurt her ears. Her target shattered in hundreds of shards of brown snow. Black smoke in her face drew water to her eyes, but she holstered the revolver with a swagger.

"Now you tell me I can't shoot."

"But how . . . ?" Donna snuffed the sobbing up her nose.

"Estevan showed me how."

"You can't do this," the crying Donna pleaded.

Hmm, she'd have to show her silly cousin. The Colt in her hand, she shot at a rusty tin can making it jump by fanning back the hammer. The next bullet hit home, the third one sent the can skipping, and the last put it flying over a bunch of greasewood.

"But you never have been to bed with any other man but your husband."

"What's so hard about lying on your back?" She looked at the distant mountains for strength to convince her distraught cousin that she was serious about this gun business. When she finally stuck that muzzle into Disantos's butt and pulled the trigger, then she would know some smug satisfaction.

"What now?" Donna called out in despair.

"I have to clean this pistol," she said, turning back in the doorway. "Shooting fouls them."

"My God, how can I convince you not to do this crazy, foolish thing?" Donna asked, trailing her back inside.

Seated at the table with the Colt already disassembled, Isabel looked into the haggard face of her cousin, who had finally managed to join her by standing beside the table. Red-eyed from crying, Donna dropped on the chair opposite her.

"I've got to get some boiling water," Isabel said, and went to the stove for the cast-iron kettle.

"Oh!" Donna wailed in despair and buried her face in her arms on the table to sob some more. "You are crazy—mad."

Isabel worked on her weapon despite her cousin's pleas and vocal outbursts. The pistol scoured with hot water, dried, oiled, and reloaded, she spun the cylinder around so the hammer fell on the empty one. She reholstered it, then, looking down, she pushed her shoulders forward to make her breasts threaten to pop out of the blouse. Amused at the results, she wished at that moment for some man to try out the power of her new getup.

"I want to thank you," she said softly, to her wet-eyed cousin.

"You're leaving?" Donna asked, in disbelief.

"Oh, yes, but not as your cousin Isabel. From this day forth, I will be Tequila Rosa."

"You better take that old sombrero then." Donna rose wearily and went to the wall, took down the four-peak Chihuahua hat, and handed it to her.

She nodded in thanks, knowing this was Donna's first man's favorite headgear. Carlos had been killed in a knife fight years before, but she kept it there, even when she married Martin, who was shot to death in a Fronterous whorehouse over another woman.

When the hat was in place, Isabel gathered her shoulder-length hair behind her neck. Then something stabbed her. The long hair must go. She took off the sombrero forward, so the chin string came with it.

"Cut my hair," she said.

"No."

"Don't be such a crybaby. Cut my hair." She began to remove her clothing for the shearing. No way she wanted the cut hair on them.

"No."

"Then I'll do it myself." She picked up the scissors to start.

"Oh, stop. I'll do it." Donna rose and took them. "How short?"

"To here." She showed her the place on the back of her neck where she wanted it trimmed to.

Head shaking, her cousin began to cut away the long wavy locks. They fell on the floor in black clumps. When she could feel the air on her neck, she knew Donna was following her instructions.

"Now I need to bathe," she said to her cousin. Taking a coarse towel, she went out to the well and Donna followed.

With buckets of icy water drawn from the well, her cousin rinsed the cut hair from her back and let her lather herself and scalp with the yucca soap, then Donna rinsed it away, too. With Isabel shivering from the cold bath, despite the hot sun, Donna began rubbing her vigorously with the coarse cotton towel.

"It will be a waste of such a beautiful body. Where do you plan to go next?" her cousin asked, under her breath, as she toiled to dry her in the warming sunshine.

"I don't know. Just think how much fun I will have." Isabel shivered with goose bumps on the back of her arms.

Donna looked hard at her and shook her head. "I can see no pleasure in your days ahead. But you can come back here when you need some rest. I can soothe that stupid donkey Ramale who owns that sorry gray horse."

"So you would stoop to that for me?" She drew her head back as if shocked at her cousin's offer.

Donna wrinkled her nose at her. "I did not say I was an angel."

She laughed out loud. "Ah, so my cousin has her own secrets."

"But I am not a loco bronco like you will be."

Isabel kissed her on the cheek, then ran ginger-footed for the house. Dressed, she slipped the sheath for the knife on the holster's belt, then buckled it on her waist. She gave a flip to her short hair with both hands, already near dry. With care, she put on the sombrero over her head, letting it fall on her shoulders and the string catch at her throat.

Donna stood in the doorway and appraised her. Shaking her head in disapproval, she closed her eyes and whistled. "Don't sell it too cheap," she said in surrender. "And come by to see me when you can."

"Rosa will be back," she said and smiled. No time for more words, she turned on her heels and ran outside to catch the gray. A check of the girth and she swung her new skirt over the saddle. Seated, she nodded in satisfaction at the comfort to sit astride wearing the new divided leather dress.

"Wait." Donna ran from the house with her carpetbag. "You may need some of these things."

She tied the grip on the saddle, thanked her cousin, then set the horse for the foothills. A hot wind in her face, she felt new blood rushing through her veins. Salute to her new life as Tequila Rosa and death to that butcher Disantos.

1

The wind out of the southwest bore billowing high clouds of dust toward him. A brown curtain already cut off Slocum's view of the San Rapheal range. His hard-breathing, chestnut stallion danced around under him, still full of vim from his charge to reach the top of the pass for a view of the Tule River Basin. From his vantage point, Slocum could make out the entire drainage of the Rio Tule that would soon to be swallowed by a severe, blinding dust storm. Not good news for a man with a pack train of arms and a tight schedule in which to deliver them.

When he turned back, he could see the line of pack mules pushing their way up the winding stair trail from the deep canyon. As if he didn't have enough to worry about. What would be worse? A blackout by a dust storm, or a *federales* patrol waiting for him somewhere ahead? Either one would be a bust.

He needed to reach the village of Valdez before the full force of the storm struck. There he could rest the mules, buy some corn for them, and hope the storm blew itself out in a day or so.

"*Vamoose*, hombres!" he shouted to his three packers. "*Andalé! Muy pronto!*"

A white bearded face from under a sombrero looked up from the trail. Ernest nodded that he had heard his words.

The canyon erupted in wild shouting and the sounds of the mule hooves began to click faster on the stone ledge. Braying and squeals echoed as the train came alive. In the lead, Gilberto came on the fly aboard the palomino mare. Behind her came the lead mule with three boxes of rifles on his back and the others behind him similarly fitted. Bonded with the yellow mare, the dozen tall mules would follow her to the end of the earth and back.

"We've got to get like hell to Valdez before that storm hits. Put the bell on your mare so they can find her if we get separated in the dust," he shouted at his lead man, who looked at the approaching storm and grimly nodded. Gilberto drew out a copper bell from his saddlebag and leaned forward to strap it on the mare. The ringing drew a smile on both their faces. Gilberto booted her on and went over the crest, taking the trail for the base.

Ernest pulled off when he joined Slocum on the crown. One look at the gathering brown curtain and he agreed. "Be a bad one," the white-bearded, older man said.

"We've got to make Valdez before it hits," Slocum said, catching his hat with one hand as the impatient stud turned under him. "We can rest there. Whoa, Boy."

"*Si, mi amigo.* You sure won't be able to see your hand in front of your face when she hits," Ernest said warily. He booted his dun in the line again and went over the far side, slapping mules' butts to keep them moving.

Slocum's stud horse spun around on his heels twice before he could settle him down again. The fast-passing parade of mules had Big Boy upset; he was missing all the fun. Then Tally came in sight, bringing up the rear and driving the slackers.

"Dust storm's coming." Slocum pointed to the southwest and the short cowboy nodded as he reached to jerk down his gray Stetson.

"Looks like a bugger, too." He acted impressed by the sight of the brown gloom in the distance moving like a wall toward them.

"They get bad in this country," Slocum agreed and they

both fell in behind the train. "Got to run for a place called Valdez, that's down this basin. We can get there, we'll have it made."

"You never said this trip would be easy," the cowboy said loud enough that Slocum heard him over the whistle of the growing wind.

"This could be a tough one. Stay close, listen for the bell, if you can hear it," Slocum said and then bailed off the mountain on his stud. He rode in close and with his reins cracked a straying mule on the butt. The jackass tucked tail and joined the others.

Big Boy, his stallion, would have nothing to do but get back in the lead. Slocum let him have his lead and slide off the mountainside on short cuts. His hind feet tucked underneath him, Big Boy had the balance and moves of a cat. Gathered up, he would leap into stride going down the steepest parts and crossed the huge rocks like they were marbles until, at last, he hit the desert floor and raced to be at the head of the line. Slocum reined him in and nodded to Gilberto.

"How far are we from Valdez?" he shouted to the man.

"Couple of hours."

"At this rate?" he asked, riding beside him in a hard trot.

"If we're lucky." Gilberto pulled a white scarf over his mouth and nose to filter the stinging dust already picking up on the wind.

"If it gets worse than this, we better rope ourselves together.

"*Si, señor.*"

What could be worse? They lacked five days of being to San Micheal. With this storm, there was no way for him to make his meeting with the gun buyers on the appointed day. If they gave up on him—oh, well, there would be others. Maybe not as generous, was all. However, guns and ammo were a better commodity in Mexico than gold.

His face, even covered by a neckerchief, was still stung by the larger flecks. Dust boiled up in his eyes and dimmed his world with each passing hour. Past dim silhouettes of giant cacti that grew in bunches, his outfit pushed southward on the dim track. Heads down, they rode at a trot when they could make their horses and mules face the wind and keep up the gait. Reins and quirts cracked butts to enforce the order. Spur rowels drove the hesitation from their mounts. Mules brayed and horses whined in a fearsome chorus churned by the growing storm's song in their ears that grew bolder by the minute.

Daylight at midday went into a brown night and the forces threatened more than the chin straps holding on their hats. Men's bodies were threatened to be wrenched from their saddles. On foot, Gilberto led the yellow mare. Slocum caught glimpses of him forging ahead as he drove the mules in tighter. Gilberto's hat on his shoulder and his hair turned reddish brunette instead of black. Moving in close, Slocum cussed a mule and lashed him with a quirt. In a leap, the laggard went to the others, braying in protest.

Slocum dropped back to Tally who was herding the last three. Driving them abreast, but still in the saddle, he waved at him. A good cowboy never walked. Slocum smiled under his kerchief at the man's determination to maintain his status. His own eyes were reduced to slits to cut down the attack by the needles and pins striking his face.

Three of the toughest packers that money could hire and they'd earn every dime he paid them for this venture. Out of his saddle and on foot, he ducked beside Big Boy for a moment's respite from the storm's battering forces. Holding the head still, he hurried to the front, running beside the stallion. Their forward march would be slower from there on.

Wind howled like a tornado in his ears. He undid his *raeta* and put the loop over Gilberto's saddle horn, then uncoiled the rest and found Ernest in the churning dust that wrapped around them like they were a raft floating down a violent, white-water river.

"I'll take the end to Tally," Slocum said, making his way to the back. His team roped together, he headed for the lead—but even the stud had trouble to fork his way against the strength of the wind.

"Can we find a ravine?" he shouted at Ernest.

The man shook his head. "We must go on!"

Slocum turned his hat's crown to the force, but doubted how long he could stagger against this growing force. Each step was a challenge and Big Boy, like the others, wanted to turn and put the wind to his tail. Hoping they weren't going in circles, he forced the stud to head into it.

Then he saw something like a fence and blinked. He pushed over to Gilberto and the man nodded excitedly.

"We are at the backside of the corral."

"None too soon," he said and smiled. They'd made it. Whew.

In a few minutes, horses and mules were in the shelter of the shedlike stables. Off came the kerchiefs and scarfs; men tried to rub the tons of grit from their eyes. They stood about in grateful relief to catch their breath. Each man rinsed out his mouth and spat out the mud when the stable boy came around with water in a pail and a gourd dipper for them to drink from.

Slocum still felt the grit on the tops of his molars and, leaning over, tried to dig the sediment from his ears with his little finger. The roar of the storm's forces tore at anything loose outside the small enclosure that sheltered them. Even the walled-in pens were roiling with dust. He felt grateful they were on the lee side.

"Any *federales* here?" he asked the youth, when he came to him with the water.

"No, *señor*. They have not been here in months."

His men nodded in approval among themselves at the information. Then they began unloading their mules. The boxes and pack saddles were stacked by the wall. Then the horses were unsaddled and the animals were rubbed down with knots of hay. While they worked on the animals, the boy forked hay in the mangers. When a mule or horse was through being rubbed down, they turned it out to roll and shake himself in the security of the corral.

While his men prepared nose bags of grain for each one, Slocum left them. He pulled up his kerchief and ducked his head going under the low lintel and outside into the whistling force; he fought the door shut. Headed across the street, he walked half-backward for the cantina to arrange for the crew's supper. Grateful, at last, he reached the building's protection from the wind. The wooden double door at the entrance only rattled when he tried the latch.

"Coming. Coming," someone shouted and soon a man in a white shirt unlatched it and allowed him entry.

"About to blow them off so I had to lock them," he apologized and tried to brush the dirt from his hair as he went behind the bar.

"I understand. I need some food for my crew. Four of us." He looked over the three men playing cards under the flickering yellow lamps. None of them looked like a threat, so he turned back to the bartender.

"Thirty minutes, she can have it ready to serve here," the man said.

"That's fine. I'll have them here by then. Give me a bottle."

"Mescal?"

"Fine," he said, with a sigh, knowing good liquor in this place would be an exception.

The bottle under his arm and paid for, Slocum looked toward the door. The bartender nodded and headed there to let him out. The door unlocked, Slocum pulled up his kerchief and went into the storm. Swirling and wrapping around him, he managed to get back inside the adobe stable building.

"Brought something to drink—" He stopped and looked hard at the new arrival, who swept away a blanket exposing her shapely form. When she turned, her dark eyes met his. Under the high crown hat of a vaquero stood a young woman in a divided buckskin skirt and a blouse laced up the front that about overflowed with her cleavage.

He removed his hat. "*Buenas tardes, señorita.*"

She smiled, pleased, and nodded. "Good to be here."

"Yes, it is. My name's Slocum."

"Tequila Rosa, but you can call me Rosa."

"Well, Rosa, you must have been lucky to find this place."

She agreed with a nod. "You sharing that bottle?"

"I'd love to, right, men?"

They had circled her and quickly agreed, taking off their hats and introducing themselves to her like some kind of knights of the desert. She took the bottle in her gloved hand, turned it up and then, when she finished, wiped her mouth on the back of the glove. "Good enough, *gracias*."

He took back the mescal, not certain that she had even drank any of it. But, who cared? She was easy to look at and obviously she had eyes for him, especially after Ernest had called him, *la patron*. Fine with him; in a land where handsome women were scarce as soaking rains, Tequila Rosa was an inviting rainbow in this stormy desert.

The men took away her horse. They offered to rub it down, and, ignoring her soft protests, they put it in a tiestall, leaving her to stand and talk to Slocum. She came over and leaned her back against a post, standing before him. With a long stem of hay, she teased her full lips and even white teeth, and looked with interest at the crates.

"You're a freighter?" She pointed them out with the stem.

"Sometimes."

"A man of opportunities."

He nodded. "And you?"

"A *campanero* without one."

"Did you lose your man?"

"Yes, to a firing squad. Do you know Colonel Disantos?"

"Never had the pleasure, but I understand he is a fierce man." He offered her the bottle, but when she shook her head, he said, "I must give this bottle to my men. They've worked hard today to get here. Excuse me."

She nodded and made a face like she understood. He took another deep draft from the neck, swallowed hard, considering her, and walked to where they were busy working over her thin horse.

"She says she's a *companero*?" Tally asked, under his breath.

"Yes," he said softly. "Said that Disantos shot her man."

"Oh, that *bastardo* butcher, he's shot many good men,"

Gilberto said and Earnest nodded in agreement.

"She could be a *federale* spy," Slocum said, teasing them more than anything else. He looked back so he could see her intriguing form. She acted uninterested in their business.

"She could question me," Tally said and chuckled.

"You have no secrets." Ernest laughed, then took a hard drink from the neck and made a hushing sound.

Slocum walked back to where she remained with her back to the post and she nodded. "They are very kind to care for my horse."

"Kind men to a pretty woman. We will go across the street and have our supper soon. I am sure there will be food for one more if you would join us."

"I can fix my meal—"

"Don't disappoint them. They would be very honored to eat with you."

She looked away at his words. Obviously he had embarrassed her—strange, for a *companero* to blush. Most of them had been through enough rough life to have a coating of brass all over them. Was she a spy? Hell, he couldn't keep his eyes off her tits long enough to decide.

"You will eat with us?"

She bobbed her head.

"You won't regret it. Come on, guys, Rosa is going to eat supper with us."

They began clapping the dust off their clothing and the small confined area was soon clouded by their effort.

"Aw, hell, boys," he said. "She ain't that fussy."

He felt her take his arm and guide him toward the stable's side door. A last glance back, he saw the mules and horses were eating corn out of their nose bags in the pen.

Outside, he sheltered her under his arm as they went sideways into the wind, holding on to their hats and finally reached the cantina door. He rattled it. Both of them kept close to the building as the others fought the strength of the wind to catch up with them.

"Come in, amigos," the bartender said, over the screaming

whine and held the door with both hands to allow them to enter.

"Need another plate," Slocum said, when the man fastened it back.

"No problem. Ah, *señora*, good to have you."

She swept off her blanket and Slocum tossed it on the end of the bar. They went to the large table set with plates and silverware. Even the gamblers glanced over at Rosa. With raised eyebrows, they turned back to their game. Amused at them, Slocum could imagine their conversation.

He showed her to a chair and slid it under her. She nodded and followed the men's actions when they shook out the cloth napkins in their laps.

"Where are you headed, ma'am?" Tally asked.

She made a small face at Slocum that she did not understand the cowboy. He translated it into Spanish and she nodded with a reply.

"She said, she's going where the wind takes her," Slocum translated.

"Me, too," Tally said and the men laughed.

When she frowned at Slocum, he told her what the cowboy said.

She nodded, but Slocum noticed that the matter made her blush again. Kind of nice to be in the company of such a good-looking young woman who was that unspoiled, or at least acted that way.

"Where are you going?" she asked.

"Flores Grande," Slocum lied to her. For the time being, their true destination did not need to be open for discussion with anyone. He only hoped she did not catch the frown Ernest gave him over his words.

"I have never been there. Is it nice?" she asked.

"No, it's a sewer hole in the desert."

She nodded and two busty older women began bringing steaming platters of browned meat, bowls of frijoles, and stacks of tortillas. The bartender went around the table pouring red wine in their mugs.

"Your name is . . . ?" Slocum asked the man.

"Peako."

"Peako, this is a fine meal," Slocum said and nodded in approval to the two older women. He could see Tally was flirting with the one wearing silver hoop earrings. No language problem there. The short cowboy was obviously making arrangements with her for an after-supper tryst.

"When you go south, *señor*," Rosa asked under her breath, handing him a vessel of frijoles, "could I ride with you a ways?"

He nodded, taking the bowl from her. What was her business? Something about her did not spell simple *companero*. But why would an innocent girl, as she appeared to be, be on the loose like this? There was something more to her than showed, or something she wasn't telling him. And he couldn't take his eyes off those breasts. He could hear the wind howling at the eves. Damn, the storm was raging some more. Delayed like this, they might miss their delivery, and all he was worried about was her tits.

2

Under ordinary circumstances, he would have left one of the men to guard the rifles while they ate. But he doubted anyone would try anything in the midst of this fierce sandstorm. Still, when the five of them burst in the side door of the stables to escape the wind, he was relieved to see the cargo was still stacked like they had left it. Those crates represented too much of his money to have them stolen.

Tally motioned him aside. "If you won't be needing me until later, I may cut out for a while."

"Fine, be careful. We don't need a word out about our cargo or destination."

"Hey, I savvy that much." Tally looked around to be certain Rosa was not too close. "That waitress Mona ain't half bad-looking either."

"No, and she can laugh, I heard her."

"I heard her, too." A smile, a nod, and the cowboy went off.

Slocum searched around for Rosa. She was seated on a bench by herself brushing her short hair. Farther back, squatted on their boot heels, the other two men smoked corn husk cigarettes and talked in low voices.

"Do you live in Mexico?" she asked, busy with her hair when he joined her.

"When I don't live somewhere else," he said and came

over to place one boot on the bench. He studied the churning brown sky going overhead outside their shed.

"What is it like up there in the States?" She put the brush in her lap and looked up at him.

"Different." He shook his head at his own reply. "There is no war going on for one thing."

"I mean, what do people eat and how do they dress?"

"They eat bread, instead of tortillas. Potatoes, instead of beans. Live in houses with wood floors."

"Don't they get slivers in their feet?"

"No, but very far up there, it snows in the winter."

"In the mountains?"

"Oh, yes, and on the plains, too." He sat down beside her and leaned his elbows on his knees.

"Where will you sleep tonight?" she asked softly.

He turned and looked mildly into her brown eyes. "With you?"

She nodded.

He stretched his arms over his head and considered his fate. The notion of having her ripe body made his full stomach churn. The storm outside might be a tough lick to his ambitions and fortune, but a night in bed with the luscious Rosa could be the best turn of luck he'd had in a month of Sundays. He listened to the wind tearing at the walls and roof of the building.

The side door popped open and Slocum bolted to his feet. Too late, the men had guns in their hands aimed at them.

"Hands up or die," the big man ordered, and three more filed inside to back him.

"Who the hell are you?" Slocum demanded with his hands raised.

"Cordova is my name, *Señor* Slocum," the big man with the mustache said, holstering his revolver as his men disarmed them. "And who is she?" he asked with a big smile and a glint of lechery in his eyes.

"Rosa."

"Ah, Rosa, you sure are a fine sight for a man who has no woman." Then he laughed aloud as his men herded Ernest and Gilberto in closer. Tally had already left for his appointment with the laughing waitress, Slocum recalled; he would be no help, he'd be too busy on his own mission to bed the buxom woman with the large, silver hoop earrings.

"What do you want?" Slocum asked.

"The rifles and ammunition, and your mules and horses, of course."

"How did you know about them?" Slocum asked.

"Ah, *señor*, that is my business to know." He walked over and put his crooked forefinger underneath Rosa's chin and forced her to look up at him. "My, my, he has such good taste."

"You have what you came after. Why don't you clear out?"

"In that storm?" The man laughed aloud. "We were lucky to get here."

Cordova's men encircled the four of them, and nodded at their boss's words. The outlaws looked as tough as they came. Shorter than their boss, they wore the cotton clothes of peons, but Slocum had no doubt they were hard cases and would cut his throat without a moment's hesitation. Another reason why he wanted them out of there was for the girl's safety.

"Tie them up," Cordova ordered.

One of the bandits grasped Slocum's raised hand from behind and shoved it down, slipping a loop over his wrist. Soon both his hands were bound behind his back. He had never heard of this Cordova before, though he tried to run the name through his mind. None of Cordova's men was familiar to him either. Strange, too, he thought he knew about all the main players working in the Revolution west of the Sierra Madras. Nonetheless, his lack of tight security had him and his men in a bad spot—if they lived through this night, they'd be lucky.

"Open a box of them guns, Pocko," Cordova said to one of the men after they seated Slocum and his men on the ground. "You, my pretty lady, stay on that bench and don't try anything."

She obeyed, but the paleness on her face told Slocum she feared this man with the full mustache and the deerskin pants. By his clothing, he figured that Cordova considered himself some sort of a dandy. His white silk shirt stained in dust, unbuttoned at the throat, and a gold chain around his neck that glinted even in the dim light of the stables.

Pocko used his thick knife to pry up the boards, and in minutes drew out a new Winchester .44/40. He carried it over to show his boss. Cordova, with the rifle in his hand, came over and smiled at Slocum.

"So, you have these fine rifles for *mi* amigo, Don Diego, no?"

"No, they're for sale. You buying?"

"Buying?" Cordova threw his head back and laughed. His men snickered at his words.

"Buying? You stupid gringo, I have the guns and you have only your ass to sit upon." He turned to his men and they laughed even harder. "This man is loco, no?"

"Yes," came the chorus.

"But if Don Diego does not get his rifles, how much is your life worth in Sonora?" Slocum asked, wondering if the man even knew his pip-squeak gun broker.

"How will he know that I have got them? You are going to tell him?"

Slocum shook his head. "I won't need to tell him. Every peon between here and hell will see you with those boxes and they will tell him."

"Then Don Diego will have to catch me," Cordova said.

"He's very resourceful."

"So are you, *amigo*. You never thought anyone could track you here. Did you?"

"That storm is bad out there."

"Ha! When I saw it coming I rode here, knowing you had no choice but to come here or get buried alive."

"Guess you had good information I was coming this way and what I carried?"

"Ah, *señor*, I even know the day you are to deliver them. But now you can't make it." Cordova smiled, but his dark eyes never matched his mouth's grin. "Load these on those mules—*andalé*, hombres." He used the rifle to indicate the crates.

The three men hurried to obey him. Slocum seated on his butt watched the chaos when they went inside the pen to capture a mule. The jackasses were uncooperative with the bandits and kicked the outlaw, Pocko, so hard against the fence that he laid on the ground, not moving. The other two had a reata on one's neck and the mule flew backward, blowing rollers out his nose. Dragging them around the pen, they were soon stripped of their rope by the wild ones plunging around the pen and over the top of them. Wide-eyed, they both got on their feet and ran for the safety of the corral fence despite Cordova's swearing at them.

"Get those damn mules!" he shouted.

Both men were holding the top rail with both hands. They shook their heads in total fear of the wild braying jackasses boiling around in the pen. Then a mule came by and bit one of them on the leg. Screaming, the man fell head first off the fence into the pen.

"Stupid!" Cordova looked around. "Get those mules!"

"No, no, *señor*, they are *tonto bronco!*"

"I'll crazy ass you two!" Cordova waved his pistol at the pair. But he saw that even under the threat of his Colt, they were not going to get back in the pen with them. His man Pocko still laid unmoving on the ground under the hooves of the upset mules and horses charging around in the pen.

Cordova reached down and took Rosa by the arm and jerked her to her feet. "You follow me, Slocum, and she dies a slow death."

"Leave her here, then," Slocum shouted as he strained at his binds.

"She'll be buzzard bait if you even show up on my trail, Slocum!" Cordova shouted from the doorway, pulling her along with him.

"I'll hunt you down if you harm one hair on her head!"

"Go to hell!" Cordova shouted over the roar. The open door flapped in the wild wind; they were gone. The other two bandits raced for the exit holding on to their straw hats and disappeared out of sight. Horses whined and Slocum thought he heard them ride out in the storm. *Son of a bitch.* He rose on his knees, his muscles bulging against the ropes. His breath raged through his nose—Cordova would pay for this.

"I'm loose," Gilberto said and rushed over to undo his ties. "What will we do now?"

"Get Ernest undone and one of you go get Tally out of bed across the street." He scooped up his six-gun and climbed the fence. "If there's anything left of that bastard in there, he can tell us all about Cordova."

"What about the girl?"

Slocum nodded that, yes, he was thinking about her. "When I learn enough from that hombre," he said climbing over the corral, "I'll go and get her back."

He ducked the spooked mules charging by him and soon was where Pocko laid facedown. Bent over, he disarmed the man of his pistol and knife, then dragged him by the collar to the gate, stopping for the upset animals to file by him and speaking softly to soothe them.

Ernest went across the street for Tally and Gilberto opened the gate for him.

"Is he alive?"

"Yeah, he's moaning some. Let's make him stand and tie him to that post to ask him questions. Better yet, I figure if we pull his arms over his head he'll tell us everything he knows."

Gilberto frowned. "Why is that?"

"That mule that kicked him broke his ribs, and one thing you can't stand with broken ribs is to have your arms above your head. Right, Pocko?"

"Fuck you—"

"Well, we can do that later." Slocum dropped his hold on the bandit's arm and threw a reata over the rafter. Fishing the tail down, he put the loop on the bandit's wrist and nodded at his partner. "You do the same thing. Then we'll haul him up so he can talk to us."

Gilberto rushed over to take his rope off the saddle. Soon it, too, was strung overhead. The door burst open, slammed back by the wind and both men had their guns out and cocked.

"Ease off, only us," Tally said, and shut it. "Ernest said things went to hell in here while I was gone and that they took the girl." The cowboy was busy tucking in his shirt tail and putting the cuffs of the waist overalls down over his boot tops.

"We've got this one bastard they left us, who's going to tell us lots," said Slocum. Ready on his side, he nodded to his partner and they pulled the screaming Pocko off his knees.

"You ready to talk?" Slocum asked, close to his face. The outlaw cried out that he would. They lowered him so he was on his knees again with his arms clutched to his side. Beads of perspiration ran down his face.

"Who's Cordova?" Slocum asked.

"Hordez Cordova—lives at Juarez—wants to be a *generale*."

"Does he have any money?"

"Some, I guess."

"He have an army?"

Bent over, the man shook his head.

"Where will he go after this happened?"

"I don't know. . . ."

With his boot toe, Slocum nudged the outlaw in the side. "You better know."

"Maybe Juarez." Pocko never looked up, holding his arms tight to his body.

"Where is his hideout on this side of the Madras?"

"I don't know."

Slocum leaned over to be certain the man heard what he planned for him if he didn't give the right answer. "Pull him up. In about fifteen minutes, his memory will be improved." Slocum straightened.

"Wait! He's probably going to the village at San Benito."

Slocum looked at Ernest for the directions. His man nodded. "It is south of here, maybe eighty miles."

"Does he have an army there?" Slocum repeated his earlier question, took a handful of the man's hair, jerked his head back, and made him look him in the eye.

"Only a few men."

"Like you?" He put pressure on his fistful of scalp by raising him up.

"No, more stupid peons like them."

He let go of his grip and the man sprawled on the ground. He searched the three faces of his men. Time for him to make a decision. He wiped his mouth with his hand feeling the stiff stubble of three days on the trail.

"Tie him up and put him in the feed room. He doesn't need to know our plans." Tally and Gilberto hauled him away moaning that they were killing him.

"What now, *patron*?"

"I'm going to try to get the girl back. You three need to take the guns south and wait for me north of San Michaels Mission. I'll check out this San Benito, where Cordova is supposed to be headquartered, and find her."

"We can take them to San Michaels," the older man agreed.

"Make no mistake, if this Cordova knows about these arms, then others also know about them. So you better sleep with both eyes open."

"He's put away," Tally said when the other two rejoined him.

They went over his plans again, agreeing that the word must be out about the rifles. Gilberto's cousin's place near their destination would be where they would meet again. They would stay with him until Slocum arrived or, if forced to move to save the rifles, they would leave him word where they went.

Slocum agreed.

"You can't leave in this storm," Tally said. "Hell, you'll only get lost and never find her."

"I will draw you a map to this San Benito," Ernest offered.

"Good. Then I'll sleep a little while, let this wind die down some, and then I'll ride out. There's a big moon somewhere above this crap blowing around."

"You be careful, *patron*," Ernest said, making a map with a pencil on the back of a sheet of feed prices.

Slocum nodded as the man pointed out various landmarks.

"Who's in charge down there?" he asked.

"One time the rebels, the next time the *federales*. It is on the main road."

"Why do you figure that this hombre chose there for his headquarters?"

"They said he came from Chihuahua. Maybe he didn't know any better."

"No, he's no fool. He hired some dumb soldiers this time, but Cordova's not a fool."

"You think he plans to come back and will try to take the rifles again?" Gilberto asked.

"I know he intends to try. But first, he must hire some tougher mule skinners."

"Where will he get them?"

"I don't know. Burro drivers are used to docile little creatures. Them Missouri long ears are not for the likes of those men that came with him." Slocum chuckled and they did, too.

"They never saw us saddle them with a chain twitch on their lips to make them hold still," Tally said.

"They ain't seen nothing till they tried and failed here tonight." Slocum laughed again about their wreck, but his concerns were on Rosa and her safety.

"We can get them there," Ernest promised, and they shook out their blankets in the darkening shed.

Slocum knew he wouldn't sleep for long, but it might be days before he had another chance. His eyes closed quickly and he began to dream. Cannon fire rolled across the land, he was back behind the rail fences sniping at Yankees. He'd shot two officers that day, both leading a charge. The warm fall sun felt good on his clothes, the musty-smelling oak leaves piled in the fence corner where he could poke his rifle through and take another Blue Coat that ventured in his line of fire.

3

He sat up and listened. The wind had finally settled down. In the darkness of the shed, he wondered how long before he awoke that the storm had laid. Best for him to get Big Boy saddled and ride. Moonlight streamed in the window. Good. Enough light so that he wouldn't stumble over the top of Cordova without first seeing him.

In the moonlight, he lead Big Boy from the pen while he saddled him. Ernest came and squatted close by.

"Wind been down long?" he asked, feeding the girth leathers through the ring.

"No, it awoke you and me both."

"I figure he went south to his headquarters, if he could find his way."

"Why'd he pull out like that without the weapons? You figured why he did that?"

"Yeah," Slocum said, pulling the latigo tight and tying it. "He wanted us to bring the weapons to him since his men couldn't handle our animals. If he'd turned our mules lose, he might never recover the rifles—this way he knows we're coming with them."

"Not so dumb, is he?" Ernest shifted his weight to his heels as he made tracks in the dirt with a stick. Then he rose and went for Slocum's blankets. He began to roll them up.

"No, he's not, and that concerns me, Ernest. I'm going to

try to find him and get Rosa back. But you boys keep your
eyes and ears open. And bring her gray horse along. She
may need it."

"We will. *Vaya con Dios, la patron.*"

"Same to you, amigo." Slocum took his blanket roll from
the man and tied it on behind the cantle. In a second, he was
on board the saddle and ready to ride out. His man went to
open the large door for him to go through.

"Keep your guard up," Slocum reminded him and started
up the moon-lighted street. He had a date with destiny and
Cordova, who was somewhere out there with her. Rosa's
personal safety ate a hole in the lining of his stomach.

Mid-morning, he reached a small village on the bank of
the Rio Tule. The river water was still dingy from the day
before's storm, but already women were on the banks, kneeling with their washing. He rode up and checked the Boy.
Some of the women looked up at him and frowned.

"I am looking for a man and a woman who might have
rode through here." he said, loud enough that they could hear
him over the river's rush.

A few nodded they had heard him, others never looked up
from their washing. Some of the women were on their knees,
busy dousing clothing in the river. They wore no tops and
their breasts ranged from flat and flabby to hard, pointed
ones.

At last, a gray-haired woman rose, she whipped a strand
of errant hair back from her face, and squinted to look up at
him. "Was she wearing a sombrero?"

"*Si.* You saw her?" Slocum whirled around to face her.

"Yes, very early. She and three men rode by here at dawn.
Going south."

"*Gracias.*" He leaned over and handed her a dollar.

His gift drew a pleased grin on her face. Two others rushed
over to see what he paid her. They *ohh*ed and *ahh*ed about
her money and some more women came to learn about her
reward as Slocum turned his horse to leave.

"I saw her, too. Where is my money?" one called out after
him.

How much time did he have to rescue Rosa from the clutches of Cordova? The notion that they were four hours ahead of him bothered him even more. He set the stallion into a long trot headed southward with a wave at the rest of the women. Behind his back, the women laughed and some shouted after him about things they would do to him for such a sum. He laughed at their bold bragging, but had other things more pressing on his mind.

The hot desert air smelled of creosote and the strong aroma filled his nose. Here and there roadrunners darted about looking for a meal of reptile, or other bird eggs. A cottontail rabbit hopped away for new shelter in a pile of dead brush, and a big jack kicked up his heels, only to stop and look back, to see if he was being pursued.

Overhead, the sun grew hotter. The stallion bobbed his head, trotting hard with plenty of reserves.

He topped a small rise and saw for an instant the glint of sunlight off metal. Not even taking time to think, out of instinct, he dove off the stallion and hit hard on his arm behind a clump of greasewood. The crack of a rifle shot carried across his head.

He rubbed the sore spot below his shoulder where he lit on it. Where was the shooter? On the next rise, he guessed. He searched for Boy; the stud had spooked sideways when he dove off of him and probably saved himself as well. Taught to ground tie, Slocum knew he wouldn't go far dragging the reins. But he needed the long gun out of the saddle to ever face off with this assassin.

Another shot went zinging off over his head and he kept low. Cordova must have left one of his men behind to kill him and if he failed to, at least give him more time to escape. Damn, where had Boy gone? He began crawfishing backward to get to the draw behind him. That should give him enough cover—another shot ricocheted off the ground a few feet away.

Head low and not knowing if he faced one or two adversaries, he eased off the ridge and into the wash. He felt certain whoever was out there had been left with orders to take him out, to give Cordova more time to escape.

In the draw, he felt for the Colt and made certain it was deep in the holster. Then he ran with his head down hoping to circle or get to another vantage point from which the shooter would never expect him. Another shot's report ripped across the land. Good. They still thought he was back there. He rounded the bend and there stood the stud, pawing the ground and wrinkling his nose at a saddled mare tied to a paloverde tree. Must be the shooter's mount.

"We ain't got time for that," he said to the worked-up stallion. He gathered the reins, swung in the saddle, and booted the stud away from the temptation of the mare. Then he began to consider his next move. If he stayed and fought this bandit, he could waste lots of time. Even get shot up. But if he took the man's mount and rode away, then that one would be left there on foot and never catch up.

He spurred the stud to get his attention and jerked him hard enough with the spade bit to settle Boy, then he rode in and took the reins of the bandit's mare to lead her away. Boy made a throatal threat at his new companion, but Slocum spoke sharply and then he pushed both horses down the draw in a hard lope. *Sorry, we can do this gunfight another day when I have more time, hombre.*

How far ahead were Cordova and Rosa? He stood in the stirrups and looked back, trying to see the shooter as he circled south again. He knew his scam would disappoint the man. Only thing he hadn't seen was the man's face back there so he could identify him. He spurred Boy to go even faster. That meant Cordova only had one man with him. Evened things better for him.

He reined Boy up on the high ground after sundown. The squalor of Casa Tulia spread out on the flat beneath him. Yellow lights dotted the location of jackals and businesses. This would be the most likely place for Cordova to stop, thinking his men had cut off any pursuit. But still, the outlaw's guard would be up. How could he ride in . . . ? No, he would need a change of clothing to be less obvious and go in on foot. He glanced over at the hard-breathing bay mare he had led all afternoon. She might be enough collateral to get him such an outfit.

He pushed the stallion off the hillside. Cautiously, he headed for a house with a corral on the outskirts. A place to stable Boy and perhaps exchange the bay for his costume.

"Ah, *señor*, it is a fine mare," the man said, holding up the lantern to examine the animal. "But I have no money to buy such an animal."

"Wait, you have a sombrero, a poncho, and a place to keep my horse while I do some things in the village?"

"But why my clothing?"

Slocum clapped him on the shoulder. "I want no one to know my business here. In your clothing I won't look like a gringo, no?"

"What business do you have here?"

"You know a good whorehouse?"

"Ah, *si, señor*," the man said, with a big grin, and then looked around as if someone might have heard him. "Montoya's is the one you want. They got the prettiest *putas* there." He lowered his voice and took off his sombrero. "No old fat ones with loose pussies, huh?" Handing over the hat, his teeth shined behind the grin in the growing darkness.

"Right. Montoya's? How can I find it?"

"You go up on the hill. Look for the Chinese lanterns and listen for the music. They got good music, too. Sometimes I like to do it to good music, huh? You like to do it with the music?"

"Oh, yes," Slocum said, putting on the man's hat. "You are too kind, *señor* . . . ?"

"Gomez." He stripped off the poncho and handed it over to him. "If my cousin's mare is in heat, can I breed her to your big horse tonight, too?" Gomez laughed and pointed at the pen. "That horse he is making me a colt now."

Slocum nodded, looking as Boy grunted and shoved his huge dick into the hunkered-down bay mare.

"Be sure to have him right back here. I may not be long with my business."

"Aw, take all night, *señor*. Those girls, they don't have much business on a weeknight, and you can use them again and again for a little more money than they would charge for ten minutes, huh?"

"You have the stallion back here in two hours." He couldn't risk not having his stud to ride out of there, if he recovered her.

"Oh, I won't need him unless—"

Dressed in his new outfit, Slocum nodded that he had heard the man and left for the village.

"On top of the hill!" Gomez shouted after him in the night.

Slocum made his way, ignoring the curs that barked at him. He moved toward the lights, where he assumed he would find the business district. Regretting he had never seen Cordova's horse in Valdez, because if they were hitched somewhere outside, he expected it to be much more than the bay mare he'd brought there.

He worked his way past the lower-class cantinas. A drunk came out of the second one and about collided with him. He stepped back for the unsteady man who went on. A quick look inside the smoky interior, he saw nothing that looked like Cordova and continued up the street.

The music from the large cantina floated on the night's air. A fiddle and a trumpet played the song. He could hear the sounds of women's shrill voices, crying out and laughing. Noises that only whores made when having fun and pestering customers to dance, to feel them, to buy them watered-down drinks, or outright challenging men to fuck them.

Then at the hitch rail, a fine barb horse dropped his head and snorted wearily. Slocum moved closer. He slipped in between it and another mount. In the darkness, the only light was that which filtered out the dirty small windows or came past the bat-wing doors.

He slid the familiar rifle out of the scabbard and levered out the cartridges, stuffing them in his pocket. It was a fine hand-tooled saddle. He slid his knife cautiously between the girth and the still-sweaty horse's skin, then drew it back with the edge slicing into the girth strings enough to weaken them.

He turned and began to unload the new rifle on the second horse.

Stopped halfway, he watched a customer push his way outside and mumble to himself as he stood before the swinging doors. Slocum acted as if he was busy pissing between the two horses and the man soon went on. He completed his task and then weakened the other girth with his knife, too.

Where was she? If he came in the front way, they'd go for their guns and she might get hurt. Better to come in from the rear, try to locate them, and then spring his trap.

In back, he half-stumbled over a bottle and caught his balance in time. Broken glass crunched under his boot soles, no place for a barefoot Mexican. On the back steps, he saw the glow of a cigarette.

"Ho," she said in a husky voice. "What do you need?"

"A favor," he said, seeing the *puta* who sat there.

"Ha," she said, and waved her cigarette. "They cost money, amigo. No free ones here."

He took a place on the stairs beside her. Her cheap perfume about gagged him. "I have money."

"Good. What do you want to do?"

"I want you to tell me where the woman who is wearing a sombrero and a leather skirt is sitting inside the cantina."

"Huh?"

"Hush. I have two pesos for that information."

As if impressed by his generosity, she lowered her voice. "For that much you can have my body all night."

"My sister . . . ," he said softly.

"Oh," she said. "They are halfway up in a booth on the right."

He dug in his pants and paid her. "Is the big man with her facing toward the front door?"

"Yes," she said, dropping the coins down the front of her blouse with a clink. "You going to kill him?"

"No, I only want my sister. Who's with him?"

"Another *pistolero*." She wrinkled her nose and tugged on her low neckline.

"Could you get him out of there and in your room?"

"He might hurt me if he knew—"

"How will he know I paid you three more pesos to take him back there and fuck him?"

"I don't know, but you must be rich to pay this much." She ground out the cigarette as if anxious to earn her pay.

"My sister . . ."

"I heard you say that. Get your sister out of there and beat her ass good for running off with that rich bastard, huh?"

He nodded, so she would see him and put three more pesos in her palm.

"*Gracias.* When I get this *pistolero* to my door, I will shout like I just found it. 'My, what a big dick you have, hombre. Like an elephant, no?' "

"Good, I'll take care of the rest. I don't want her hurt."

She clapped him on the shoulder and stood up. "I wish I had a brother like you. Be ready, he might only last a few minutes in bed with me." Then she rose wearily and laughed at her own joke.

He watched her disappear in the back doorway and he rose to his feet. From his vantage point, he could look down the corridor and watched her pull on the reluctant bandit. When he popped up, he ducked back out of sight. Soon the man and she came out of a main part together and headed down the hallway.

She did good work for her money He heard her chiding him and bringing him along. His back pressed to the wall, Slocum listened.

"Oh, *chingaso*, hombre, you never said you had a dick big as an elephant's! Come in here."

"Yeah," the bandit shouted, and Slocum waited thirty seconds more for the closing of the door. He started in the building, his head down keeping close to booths. Under his poncho, he drew his Colt and carried it close to his leg. When he reached the booth that he felt certain was Cordova's, he raised the pistol, came around, and struck him on the top of the head with the butt. Cordova sprawled facedown on the tabletop. With a fistful of his collar, he jerked the limp man's body out and struck him again, hard, over the head.

"Come on," he said to the wide-eyed Rosa.

Quick as a cat, she slid over and joined him. He turned to the stunned customers who had hushed since the whole thing began. "No one make a move. This is my sister and this bastard kidnapped her. I should have killed him, but you can for me."

He tossed a gold twenty-dollar piece on the bar. "That should buy you drinks. Keep him here for ten minutes." A cheer went up as he herded her behind him, keeping an eye on them. Then with a head toss toward the front doors, he ran after her. Outside in the night, she asked breathlessly, "Which way?"

"Get on your horse, not his."

She indicated she had heard him, ducked under the hitch rack, and backed a long-headed one out into the street. He looked back over the cantina's doors to check. No one made a move in their direction and the music had started again. Good. He came around where she sat her horse and nodded in approval to her. He holstered his gun, grabbed the saddle horn,. and swung up behind her in one fluid motion. This might work.

"Let's get the hell out of here," he said in her ear, guiding her to the right.

4

"I couldn't believe it was you," Rosa said as Slocum tightened the girth on his saddle.

"Got lucky." He could see Gomez coming from the house.

"That you, *señor?*"

"*Si*, you can have your clothing back, I won't need it any longer," he said, putting the man's sombrero on the corral post and whipped off the poncho. His own clothing restored, he smiled when Gomez realized that a woman sat on the horse.

"Oh, *señora—*"

"She's with me," Slocum said and hitched up his gun belt to mount his anxious stallion.

"Did she come from Montoya's?"

"No," Slocum said, amused. "She came from the cantina."

"You work fast." The man blinked, inspecting his clothing on the corral post. "You brought my things back, too. What about the bay mare?"

"You may have her and her colt." They didn't need her anyway since she had Cordova's bay to ride and he wanted nothing to slow them down.

"Oh, *gracias*, amigo. You are very generous. You, too, fine lady."

Slocum cast a look toward the hill. Time for him and her to get the hell out of Casa Tulia. He waved at Gomez in the starlight and he guided the way northward. Maybe he could catch his pack train. Had Cordova learned his lesson? Only time would tell about him, he decided, as he looked over at her riding stirrup-to-stirrup—same good-looking cleavage. Whew.

In dawn's first light, he spotted the trace of dust on the horizon. A dozen mules and three horses made enough, he could see it from a distance of several miles as a smokelike vapor. The old man was keeping them to the east of his tracks, so they didn't collide with Cordova again.

"That's the pack train," he said, pointing to the east.

"They've made good time," she said and smiled.

"Yes, we better catch them. They might have more surprises."

"I'm ready," she said, patting the brown horse on the neck. He was breathing hard, but despite his slender stature, he showed lots of bottom, keeping up with the stud all night.

"They will have your gray horse with them," he said.

"Oh, yes, my horse." Then she laughed as if amused by the whole matter.

"Something wrong?"

She shook her head. "Someday I will tell the story about that horse and my cousin Donna. It may not be that funny, except it struck me as that."

"If I hadn't cut Cordova's cinch we could have taken his fancy barb."

"Oh, I thought you were afraid it would be recognized. You cut his cinch?" She looked in disbelief at him.

A smile split his sun-cracked lips. "Well, not all the way, but I guarantee it will break if you strain it, and soon."

"So, not only will he have a sore head, but a sore butt. What is wrong with your shoulder? You keep moving it."

"It'll be fine. That *pistolero* he left to kill me caused me to hurt myself dodging his bullets."

"Is he dead?"

"Cordova may think so; he's walking to Tulia. I didn't have time for him, so I took his horse and left him to walk."

She threw her head back and laughed until at last she bent

over to recover. "You have fun with these killers."

"Only if they let me. Let's go meet the fellas again." He booted Boy off in a long trot and she came beside him.

"In another place, would you have killed Cordova, instead of battering him over the head?" she asked.

"Depends. He never killed us. I'm hoping he's learned his lesson." Then he shook his head. "But I fear his obsession to become a *generale* may kill him."

"I see. When you get to this place you are going and sell these guns, then what will you do?" she asked.

"Oh, get in some other mischief."

"Like what?"

"Well, if I had a pretty woman to go along, I might go hide up in the Sierra Madras for a while."

She was looking ahead so he couldn't read the expression on her face. He wondered what her future plans were. But she was avoiding any commitment as far as he could tell.

"Guess that wasn't a good enough offer?" he asked, coaxing her for a reply.

"Good enough, but I have some unfinished business I must do." He saw the hardness and determination in her gaze, looking straight ahead. It told him she had uncompleted things still to be resolved in her life. No telling how long ago since her husband had been executed either; he must still be on her mind.

"Fine, it was just an offer."

She smiled at him. "I think that would be fun."

"I know: business before pleasure." He rose in the stirrups to take some pressure off the seat of his pants. If he was right in his calculations, in an hour, they'd be back with the pack mules and his men.

How far would she go with them? Was she a spy or simply someone with her own vendetta?

"Do you have a gun I might borrow?" she asked, as they began to gallop their horses across a smooth greasewood flat.

"Have a thirty caliber boot gun that's big enough for you."

"Good. I hope someone saved my Colt. It belonged to my dead husband."

"If they don't have it, I'll fix you up with one when we make camp."

"That would be great."

He nodded, certain that one of his men had recovered her weapon. The creak of leather, the hard-breathing horses they rode, the drum of their hooves, wind in his face, he wondered about the *companero* in the seat beside him. Not many women he ever rode shoulder-to-shoulder with like this one. And his terrible fascination with her breasts—maybe she had another blouse to wear.

They caught up with the mules and riders in mid-afternoon, out of sight in a dry wash. Up on top of the high point, Gilberto was using his brass telescope to survey the way ahead. Ernest and Tally were giving the animals a nose bag with corn in it.

"What happened?" Tally asked, with his best smile for her. He ran over to assist her.

Her Spanish had him scratching his head.

Ernest nodded in approval at her and translated for the cowboy, "Oh, Slocum, dressed as a Mexican, slipped into a cantina and cold-conked Cordova on the head. The rest of the time they've been riding."

"Made pretty fast time catching up, I'd say." Tally shook his head and finished fitting their horses with nose bags.

Slocum handed her some jerky and she nodded taking it.

"You better sleep for a while, you look tired." he said.

"I could have fallen out of the saddle going down there with Cordova, but now . . ." She shrugged.

"Sleep an hour, we can spare that much."

"What about you? You've been up two nights and a day."

"I'll get some rest," he promised her.

Slocum waved Gilberto off his point. He came down the crumbling bank of the dry wash on his heels.

"You need to scout ahead of us from now on. She can ride the yellow mare at the head of the train. Maybe that way we can get through without meeting any more bandits. How many days will it take us to get there?" he asked Ernest, who was the best man on mileage in this country.

"Two, two and a half days."

"I'll take it." He drew some more saliva in his mouth for the peppery jerky he was chewing on. "I'm getting some sleep. Keep on guard."

He saw her wink at him from her pallet on the ground as he unfurled his blankets. Then she rolled over and buried her face in the ground cloth to shut out the sun. No shade handy, he'd have to do the same thing.

No more than his eyelids closed and the thunder of cannons roared in his ears. Where was he? His rifle in his right hand, he carried two Yankee Colt pistols in his waistband. Some dead captain's armory, they were only .30 caliber, but the matched set bore mother of pearl handles. On the barrels, the fine engraving read: ESPECIALLY FOR YOU, JONATHAN T. BEDFORD CAPTAIN, THIRD COMPANY, ILLINOIS 4TH CAVALRY.

He packed them for nine months. In hand-to-hand combat with the enemy, they served him well and the accuracy of the small bore amazed him. Deep in the Tennessee wilderness, he recalled a card game where he lost them with four ladies in his hand. His suspicion about the winner's talent at shuffling deals wasn't exposed for two months.

When the gambler received a mortal wound not ten yards away, his mate shouted, "Why, you oughter see this. The sumbitch's got cards up both sleeves."

Slocum recalled ducking through hot fire to reach the man's side. The gambler's face was already gray and the blood coming from his chest wound was crimson red, and ran like a river. He laid down his rifle and shook him to try to wake him before he died. Somehow he wanted to tell the cheating bastard what he thought of him. Of course, the pistols were long gone.

For a few minutes, there was only he and the dying corporal from North Carolina. The battle was no longer in Slocum's ears. He knew he was screaming and cursing at the top of his lungs at this rotten dog who had duped him out of the only worthwhile things he had possessed in three years of war.

Finally, he used his aching fingers that gripped the gambler's coat edges to lay him back down. He bent over and picked up the bloodstained face cards and shoved them in his back pocket.

"You all right, Sergeant Slocum?" someone asked.

He blinked his eyes at the officer beside him and nodded. "Just fine, sir."

"Good," the man said, looking relieved. "I thought you'd lost it. I don't want to fight this war without you, Slocum."

"I'll try not to let it happen again, sir."

"No, we all need to scream once in a while, and get it out of our systems." The captain turned his head to listen to the bugler message. "You better get our men rounded up, we're pulling back to a better position."

"Nice thing to call retreating, sir." He moved out to get the others on their way. They'd been doing lots of that in the past months—this go-to-a-better-position crap.

He sat up in the darkness and blinked his eyes. "Why did you let me sleep so long?"

"Lady's orders," Tally said, stirring the fire.

He nodded and threw back the blanket. Someone must have put it over him. Close to sundown, from the red light flooding his vision. He looked up into her brown eyes and saw the steaming cup of coffee she presented to him. Squatted before him, he wondered how much she had slept.

"Spirits fill your dreams?" she asked.

"Sometimes when I'm real tired."

"I know what you mean."

He took the cup and blew the steam off the top. "Looks hot. Why did you let me sleep so long?"

She nodded. "That coffee is hot, and you needed the rest."

"We could have been closer." He looked down and studied the dancing campfire light on the rich brown skin of her bustline. Was she trying to slow him down? How could he be certain? He supposed he would know all that when he watched the cards fall out of her sleeves.

"We'll make it there," he said to settle any concern, and searched the other faces around the campfire. They nodded to him, and sipped on her fresh coffee.

It was the loud crack of a rifle, and dust sprayed all over him and in his eyes. He heard the order: "Don't move. Get your hands up."

The handle of the cup dropped from his hand and clanged on the ground as he and the others raised their hands.

"Cordova's man," she hissed and he nodded.

"You don't want to die, keep them up," the bandit threatened, and moved down the hillside with the rifle leveled at them.

It must be the ambusher that he had left on foot the day before, Slocum decided. He, no doubt, had spotted their dust and worked across country to head them off. If he hadn't slept so long they would have left him. His fault for not taking him out when he had the chance. He could regret lots of things in his life at times like this.

"Get their guns, *puta*. Ah, Cordova will be glad to see you. He will be ready to stick his big hard-on in you." The man laughed aloud. "And you, gringo, you thought when you took my horse you would never see me again, huh?"

"Right," he said as she lifted his Colt and then quickly stuck it in the waistband of her skirt.

Her somber face telegraphed something to Slocum, but he was uncertain what she planned to do. In a swish of her fringe hem, she went to relieve the others of their arms.

"Be careful," Slocum hissed after her. "He's bad."

"Cordova will be happy when I bring him the mules, guns, and her tight ass, won't he?" The man shoved the sombrero on the back of his head with the muzzle of his rifle and nodded to himself in a smug fashion.

"What—?" The *pistolero* gasped, frowned, and two shots took him in the chest. The force of the bullets sprawled him on his back and his rifle went off harmlessly in the air.

Slocum whirled to see which one of his men had shot the bandit. The smoking pistol in her right hand told him everything; she rushed over and hugged him, mumbling, "I had to. I had to."

His gaze on the star-lighted, silhouette of the faraway mother mountains; he laid his cheek on top of her head. "You saved our lives, Rosa. Yes, you had to."

5

They wasted no time breaking camp. Mules were caught. The chain on a short stick called a "twitch" was applied to the animals' upper lip and twisted tight. This forced the mules to stand and not kick while the cross-buck saddle was strapped. While being restrained, the jackasses blew boogers out of their noses, hee-hawed in complaint while the packers dodged their flying heels until the last one was securely loaded.

Slocum shook his head in dismay as their efforts reached completion. If mules weren't so damn tough and sure-footed, he would never mess with them. But the hard-headed things were a lot like himself: They didn't like to be harnessed up.

Rosa came on the run, leading her gray horse, and when she joined him she swung in the saddle. "Which way?"

"South," he said and she nodded. They left camp in a long trot. The dead bandit was left on the ground for vulture bait, with their protesting jasshonkies braying at the rising sun. This day and one more hard ride should put them at the San Michael Mission, and he hoped to meet his buyers. Be good to be rid of their cargo; maybe then he'd have some private time with her. He glanced over at her low-cut blouse as she rode beside him—my God, but they looked like sugar and cream. Thoughts of them drew the saliva in his mouth.

He was still busy considering her two shots; she fired with

such accuracy. Both rounds struck the outlaw in the chest. Either one would have killed him, unless the powder had been bad and then the force of the lead bullet diminished. Whew, that was some shooting. One thing for certain, she was no stranger with a pistol.

"Who taught you how to shoot?" Riding beside her as their horses churned up the alkali dust, he glanced over to see her response.

"He did."

"You must have had lots of practice."

She softly smiled and nodded. "My ears still ring from all of it."

"I'll bet. We should be able to find water and food ahead at a hacienda. I must warn you that Señor Sanchez is an old lover of women. He will be impressed by your good looks and charm."

She nodded and winked at him. "I will do my best to entertain him."

He checked the stallion with a tug on the reins. Boy's trot was about to turn into a racing pace. "You don't have to do too much for the old man," he said to her.

She laughed into the hot wind that whipped their faces. A free sound that made him nod with confidence—any sorrow over the shooting of the bandit had been short-lived. The bandit deserved none of her frets anyway. The outlaw lived by the gun and died by it. Then, as they trotted on across the greasewood flats, she posed a confident smile for Slocum. He considered how she could have melted an iceberg. And he was still fascinated with her cleavage. Damn, he wanted to knead them in his hands and taste the honey.

They arrived at the Sanchez hacienda long after dark. Lamps lighted the area near the gate to the house where they reined up.

"Ah, Slocum, *mi* amigo," Señor Sanchez said, in his melodious baritone voice. He came from under the archway with a cane to aid his hurried gait. "You have come to brighten my day. And you have a bride, too, this time?"

"Tequila Rosa, meet Señor Sanchez," he said, and dismounted heavily, his legs stiff from the long hours in the saddle. "You know my men?"

"Ah, yes, Glberto, Tally, and my old *compadre* Ernest." He hugged the shorter, older man and they both exchanged pleasantries.

"Put the horses and mules in the corral. My men will help you unload and come to the house quickly. We have wine, and Juanita has just cooked a fat goat." Then the snowy-haired man bowed for Rosa. "Welcome to the Sanchez Hacienda, my dear, lovely girl."

She bound off the horse and a young boy rushed in and took her reins as if on cue.

"Good lad," Sanchez said, and gave her the crook of his arm. "You have been in the company of barbarians, my dear. Come, let a real gentleman lead you into the house where I have the amenities for you to freshen yourself, of course."

Slocum nodded in approval and the two went off. He wished to speak to Sanchez's *segundo*, Louis. The man stood back in the shadows with his arms folded over his barrel chest, close to the six-foot wall that enclosed the house and sprawling garden of flowers that Slocum could smell on the night wind.

"Hey, *amigo*," Slocum said and walked over to him.

"Ah, you trade some more?"

"It is only a job, and a dangerous one at that. Yesterday, a killer jumped us. Today, another tried to take our things and mules."

The man crossed himself and shook his head.

"Don't cry for them. They only got what they deserved."

"I know, but the days are over when we could grow crops and raise cattle in this land and live in peace. Raiders come all the time, demanding money and food. If we don't play tribute, then we must kill them. The graveyards will soon be overfull."

"Fools, who expect something for nothing. You ever heard of this Cordova who wants to become a general?"

"No, but there is a pirate who calls himself Fernando Hertz."

Slocum blinked at the man. "Who's he?"

"A bad hombre. You can't miss him, he has a patch over his left eye. They say someone gouged it out for him with his thumb in a bar fight."

"I'll watch out for him. This Cordova came with three men and jumped us in a dust storm in Valdez. The mules spooked his men or we'd have lost everything."

"Your mules spooked them?"

"They were burro drivers. He kidnapped my *companero* and I had to get her back yesterday. Then, one of his men that I had set afoot tried to take us this morning. It has been a very frustrating trip so far."

"Sounds like it. Watch out for this Hertz, too, he's a backshooter."

"*Gracias*, I will. Now, I better get to the house before Sanchez seduces her."

The *segundo* laughed at his words and moved for the pens, no doubt to help supervise the unpacking. Slocum took off his hat and swept his hair back. The thoughts of good food, a hot bath later, and a bed relaxed his stiff back muscles.

The table was set and he smiled at the ample Juanita, his housekeeper, as she ordered her young girls about the long table setting out food. The centerpiece was a freshly cooked young goat on a huge platter. When Juanita discovered his presence, she came over with a goblet of wine for him.

"Ah, hombre, they have not shot or maimed you yet?"

"Their bullets are made of soft clay and their horses too short-legged."

"Well, I see you have a lovely one riding with you this time."

He winked at her and in a soft voice spoke to her. "Yes, but she is a child beside your beauty and wonderful ways."

She pursed her full lips together and the mischief twinkled in her brown eyes. "Ah, you will return again, alone, and I will be here."

"*Gracias*," he said.

Acting satisfied, she went off in a swish of her skirt, directing her helpers with arm-waving orders. He looked up in time to see Rosa enter the room. Her face fresh and her short hair brushed into a sheen. She wore some borrowed clothing, a peasant blouse, and full red skirt.

"They're pounding my skirt with corn meal and laundering my blouse," she said, nodding to the girl who handed her a glass of wine.

"You look very lovely," he said, then sipped some wine.

"How rich is this hombre?"

"He has thousands of hectares. It was originally a land grant from the king. He has so many employees, the government in Mexico City leaves him alone."

"I understand."

"But you are impressed?"

"Yes, I have only heard of such riches." She smiled and indicated they were to have company. His men, looking cleaner, came into the hall, and from the other doorway, his cane tapping the floor, the patron joined them.

"Food grows cold," he said, and waved his hand for them to be seated.

"Ah, *mia* Rosa, you must join me." He bowed and she looked to Slocum for help. He made a short bob of his head in approval.

"*Gracias*," she said and curtsied for him. Sanchez showed her the crook of his arm.

"You are a princess and you must sit by my side," the old man said and led her to his end of the table. "You, Slocum, you must command the other end. Your men are all right. Take your places. Oh, my bad manners. I will seat the lovely Rosa, then you may be seated."

After Sanchez scooted the chair under her, Slocum took his place and shared a look of approval over the setup with Tally. The servant girls brought around the plates of yams, rice in steaming pots, frijoles, black beans, tortillas, and the platter of *cabrito*.

A rich flavor of mesquite smoke and the tenderness of the meat melted in Slocum's mouth. He savored the richness of the goat, telling himself how this feast made up for all their past meals of jerky. Soon musicians began to play. Two guitar players and a trumpeter accompanied the tall young man who sang the folk songs of his people. Stories of a wild horse that escaped his would-be capturers, the loves of men and sweethearts who died. The horn's blast filled the two-story room to the peeled-log rafters high above them.

In the flickering soft light of the multi-candled chandelier as he filled his hunger, Slocum watched Sanchez with his white goatee bobbing as he talked to Rosa. Too far away, and hindered by the music to hear his words, he knew the man was young again, hoping to seduce this fresh flower in a shrivelled-up land. The lust of a man for a beautiful woman never left his mind. He recalled once seeing an ancient great-grandfather lying within hours of his last breath, raise the worn blanket and try to coax some teenage servant girl onto the cot with him.

Soon the patron and Rosa danced to the soft tune of the band. His bad leg jerked, but head high and her hand in the air, he still circled her around with plenty of grace. Then when the song ended, he went to the wall and took down a sombrero and tossed it at her feet. With a tambourine in her hand that a servant girl brought her, she shed her sandals and listened to the band's new song. Then, beating the drum face over her head, she began to dance around the sombrero.

Her twists and turns to the fast beat drew the attention of even the servants who soon filled the archways around the room to observe her. Slocum and his men were on their feet to see the show. His guts roiled at her lithe steps and, despite the others, he realized that this dance was for him. Goose bumps broke out on the back of his arms. He thought about hugging them as she whirled and spun around the high-crowned hat. Then it was over and she bowed to the applause that grew louder until she blinked at the enthusiastic shouting and compliments.

Then Sanchez came to her rescue and led her back to her seat. He raised his goblet and nodded to the others at the table. "I toast the lovely Rosa, who dances with the fury of a woman untethered."

The others hoisted their glasses high and gave approval to his salute.

"And to our generous host, Don Sanchez!" Slocum shouted and they joined him.

"*Gracias*," Sanchez said, then turned to his servants. "Take these fine guests to their rooms, and you, my dear, I shall return you to *mia* amigo," he said to her and showed her his arm.

"Slocum, I know you cannot enjoy my hospitality long, so I shall excuse you from our usual lengthy conversation about what happens in this land." He took Rosa's hand and kissed it, then he bowed. "For an old man's pleasure-filled evening, I thank you, my love."

She nodded and smiled at him.

"Another time, I promise, I will have hours to spend talking."

"I shall look forward to that visit." Looking more bent in the shoulders, Sanchez raised his gaze to meet Slocum and then he nodded in approval. "May God be with you, my son."

"You, too, amigo." He watched the suddenly fragile-looking man turn, his cane tapping on the tile floor, heading for the side archway.

"How old is he?" she asked softly.

"Who knows? Perhaps ninety."

"You think so old?" she asked, hugging his arm.

"Maybe older."

"Who are his heirs?"

"The workers."

She looked up at him and frowned as he escorted her through the back arches. "I'll explain," he promised her and turned to Ernest who stood at the side of the room. "When the rooster crows, let us be ready to ride."

"*Si*." And his man was gone.

Slocum turned back to her. "His sons have all died. He has no heirs."

"What from?"

"Some just from old age. Oh, I recall him telling me how one was lost at sea going to Spain. Another was shot in a duel over a woman, and bandits garotted another one."

"All this and no heirs?" She shook her head in disbelief as they went down the dimly lighted hallway.

He paused and opened a familiar doorway. The high bed against the wall gleamed with snowy white sheets. Two copper bathtubs of steaming water sat in the center and she issued a soft, "Oh," at the sight of them.

"Guess we still smell bad," Slocum said and began to toe off his boots. She rushed over and read the note on the bed.

"Says for you to toss your clothes and boots into the hallway. They will be cleaned and repaired by morning."

"Or replaced," he said, unbuckling his gun belt.

"Really?" she asked, testing the bathwater with her finger.

"Don Sanchez is a generous man. I'm sure you could stay here and dance for him."

She whirled around and furrowed her thin black brows at him. "I have things—"

"Things to do?" he asked, taking off his shirt and dropping it on the floor.

"Yes."

"How about a bath? I will look the other way."

Then showing some newfound tough resolve, she raised her chin. "No need. You have seen plenty of naked women before."

"If you wish, I can get you a private room."

She laughed to dismiss his offer and bent over to strip off the blouse. The garment on both arms over her head, she wagged her hips, moved her shoulders together, and made her pear-shaped breasts swing invitingly at him. "And miss all the fun. No thanks," she said and began untying the strings at her waist.

"You're poison," he said and unbuttoned his pants. Aware that she was naked and stood close enough to him that her musk filled his nose. When he looked up, she took his face in her slender hands and her lips pressed to his. His pants fell to his ankles and he pulled her into his arms. The room's cool night air swept over his skin as they sought each other's mouth with a blinding hunger.

At last, his head filled with a heady swarm; he tried to clear it. "We better use this water before it gets cold."

She twisted away, her finger came out from under his chin. "I guess we should." Then she gave a deep sigh and stepped into her tub. Cupping both of her breasts, she looked back at him. "You won't get much sleep tonight either."

Ready to settle in his own water, he smiled. "Trust me, neither will you."

"Great," she said, seated up to her neck and flicked water at him.

Their bodies at last clean and dry, they piled into the feather bed with their mouths afire for each other. They hand-searched each other until the explosion of passion consumed them. Then, Slocum waded through the fluffy feather bed and Rosa scooted down, spreading her legs apart for his entry.

Her head thrown back, mouth open, she cried aloud at his entry. Her back curved with her hips raised to him, she hunched with the wild abandonment of one consumed by a madness. Her fingernails dug into the skin on his back. With a newfound fury, he pounded her, savoring the waves of passion that contracted around his painfully hard erection. His eyes closed and, both arms stiff holding his weight off of her, he waged war on her. Then she pulled him down so he was on top of her stomach and her rock-hard nipples became buried in his chest.

He reached back and gripped both cheeks of her ass in his fingers and used this advantage to probe her even deeper. Her *ahh*s, he soon discovered, were not from his weight on her, but from the pleasure of his force.

Then she thrust herself hard against him and cried out. He felt the force rise from his testicles and his gun exploded. She fainted under him and he struggled to push himself up.

"Mother of God . . . ," she mumbled. "Never in my life . . . have I felt such a thing."

With a wink at her, he bent over to kiss her left nipple. She clutched him to it and began to cry.

He paused. "Have I hurt you?"

"No, but I am sad that I am so weak. I can't do it again."

He laid a finger beside her nose and tweaked it. "My plan. So we get some sleep."

Dreamily, she stretched her arms over her head and twisted to the right and left. "You are a devil. But I'll sleep good."

6

In the dust churned up by the mules, the hacienda helpers and Slocum's men repacked them. He stood aside with the patron and they talked in soft voices.

"The rebels say they will make Mexico a country stronger than yours," the don said.

"Promises and some lies, I fear."

"Ah, I once wished to go to your country to visit the big cities, but the war up there forbid me going then, and now I guess I've gotten too old to try."

"They are pretty in pictures. But they are like the rest of the world: Their alleys are full of smelly garbage, rats, bandits, and cutthroats. Their streets have pickpockets, cheating games, woman of the night who would rob you for your gold teeth, bankers who loan money at high interest, and police on the take."

"Ha, I could find that here. Now I am glad I never went there, amigo."

They shook hands and parted with a promise that they must meet again. Slocum glanced over and saw Rosa coming from the house in her freshened clothing. Her eyes looked still half asleep as she stood on her toes and kissed their host on the cheek.

"Ha!" he shouted. "Go on, Slocum, Rosa has agreed to stay here with me."

He nodded and undid the reins. Ready to mount, he stuck his boot toe in the stirrup. "She's got bad habits. You would hate her."

"Ah, amigo, maybe you have lied to me about the cities, too."

Slocum touched his hat and nodded for the men to start out with the train. "Guess you'll never know since you gave her that fine gray pony to ride away on."

She stopped and frowned at him as the boy came forward leading a prancing, dish-faced mare. Her snowy mane rippled as she danced about. She carried the blood of the barb, from the desert's of Africa where they ran swift and forever. The pure blood of a few such stock still ran in the protected herds on great haciendas like this one.

She bit her lower lip as if undecided, then she bolted in the saddle and swept off her sombrero. "To *mi* amigo, Don Sanchez, I shall always be indebted."

"*Via condias, mi amigos*," he shouted at them and they thundered out of the yard.

Soon stirrup-to-stirrup, she rode her pony beside him at the head of the train. Still looking entranced by the generous gift, she shook her head and glanced over at him. "Why do all this for me? I only danced for him."

"He saw something in you."

She tried to shake off his answer. "Oh, all men do things for a reason. Even you, Slocum."

"Don Sanchez has unlimited wealth. He has no heir, but the people who support him. Whatever he saw in you, he wanted rewarded."

"You know my purpose. Would you give me such a gift knowing that if you were him?"

"I don't have the wisdom of the don."

She twisted half around in the saddle to look through their trailing dust at the fading hacienda. When she turned back, she nodded. "Oh, yes, you have the wisdom all right, and the shaft of a great stallion as well."

Then her melodious laughter rang like silver bells. Somehow he wanted to capture and hold the last few hours forever.

Too good to be true. By nightfall, they would be at the mission. Would his buyers still be there? Only time would tell, but also this hombre, Cordova, might be there waiting, and the bandito Hertz whom he had been warned about.

With what might develop so threatening, perhaps he should send her away. These and other concerns that the future held niggled him all morning riding south. Through the greasewood flats, they hurried. Each man with a repeater across his lap in the saddle, searching for the first sign of pursuit, driving his mules through the roiling dust for their destination.

Slocum and she loped off to the side to a high point, dismounted, and used his telescope to scan for signs of others' dust. Nothing, and that bothered him, because it meant they had an ambush set up somewhere ahead. He nodded to her when he was ready to ride on and she remounted.

"What next?"

"Speak to Ernest. He knows the land better," he said, and pushed his horse for the train, catching up with them. She easily rode beside him on the gray.

Slocum reined in beside the older man. "How can we ride in and not be seen?"

"Come down the dry arroyo from the east."

"Show us the way."

Ernest agreed with a nod and Slocum hurried for the front of the train. He pulled Boy to a trot and settled in with her beside him.

"You can't ride into the mission," he said.

"Why not? I can shoot and fight like a man." Her angry face scowled with impatience at him.

"These men will be desperate."

"Then let them be desperate enough to die."

"Ah, I can see you don't listen."

"I will go with you."

He sighed and nodded. "It might get you hurt, and I'd kick myself all the way back to Arizona."

She wrinkled her nose to dismiss his concern. "There are many more *companeros*."

Upset by his inability to change her mind, he shook his head and squinted at the foothills on their left. "No, you're special, Rosa. Don Sanchez knew it, and I do, too."

He stood in the stirrups and surveyed the desert through the heat waves. Why did he feel he was riding into the Valley of Death? A bad thing, to go against his gut feelings—they usually were right. Somehow, he needed to turn things in his favor. As they raced southward, a million ideas churned through his mind, of how to make contact with his broker, Diego, and not let the rifles fall into the hands of his enemies or the *federales*. If they knew of his shipment—and they had many eyes and ears—they would be there, too.

All the notions only added to his concern. The wells of the mission were ahead. He raised a hand and halted them. Nothing looked out of the ordinary around the hovels and dying cottonwoods, but he wanted to be certain.

"I'll ride in and check. You all stay out here and wait until all is clear." At the click of a cylinder, he swung his head around to see her inspecting her Colt.

"That goes for you, too," he said.

"I'll circle in from the west," she said, and holstered the pistol before he could stop her and bolted away on her gray.

Too late. He scowled after her and the charging barb mare. Anger gripped him as he sent his horse into a hard lope for the wells. As he rode, he drew his Winchester out of his scabbard, last seeing her disappear into an arroyo and still put out with her stubborn boldness.

At the outskirts of the small community, he drew his horse down to a walk. Breathing hard and bobbing his head, the animal danced past the first jackal and Slocum saw no one, save a few thin chickens dusting themselves in the road that flushed for the shade at his approach. No dogs barked and he dried his palms on his pants, then regripped the stock of the Winchester in his right hand.

"Hands up!" came the command. And a rifle-armed man in white peon clothing and a sombrero stood up on the roof and pointed a Mauser rifle at him. Then another did the same on the left. His heart sunk.

"Drop that rifle!"

Then a pistol shot shattered the air and he twisted to bring his rifle muzzle up, when the bandit on the right pitched headfirst off the roof. Slocum's shot went wild, but the outlaw on his left screamed and disappeared. The drum of Rosa's gray's hooves were loud when she swung the mare around the adobe into his sight.

"More of them in the back." She tossed her head behind her and kept on toward the second casa. Her pistol spoke again and a man cried out. He sent Boy to the right around the hovel and reloaded the rifle on his way. He discovered a half dozen more bandits trying to get on their horses in the dry wash.

"Hold it!" he shouted and their resistance began to melt. He stood in the stirrups and pointed the rifle at them menacingly. "Who wants to die first?"

"Not us."

One man gave a lurch and was in the saddle, grabbing for his reins. Slocum's iron centered on his back; he squeezed the trigger. When the Winchester cracked, the bandit fell off the far side of the spooked horse and laid still on his back in the sand.

"Anyone else? Drop your arms and be careful."

The bandits began to obey; he glanced aside for a second. He saw the gray as she drove the wounded outlaw ahead of her horse. His bloody arm told the story; she directed him to join the rest.

"What else?" she asked.

"Get the train up here," he said and dismounted.

"Yes, sir, *mi capitan*." She saluted him with her pistol and holstered it before she tore out for the pack train.

Damn her, she was a tough enough soldier. He moved his prisoners aside from their horses and guns, then he made them sit on the ground.

"Who sent you?" he demanded.

No answer. Fuming mad, he surveyed them for the weakest-looking of the six. Seeing one hardly more than a

teen, he walked over and shoved the muzzle of the rifle in
his face.

"You will be the first one I shoot." He cocked the hammer
back to emphasize his point. "I will shoot you because you
are the youngest. Unless someone tells me what I want to
know."

"Hertz! Hertz," the boy babbled, wide-eyed.

"Where in the hell is Hertz now?" Slocum pushed the
muzzle back in the boy's face.

"Selling your rifles to the buyers."

"Good. I'd say he's damn sure conceded, ain't he?"

The flush-faced youth swallowed and nodded.

His men and mules began arriving. Ernest rode over to
help him. "Who are these *bastardos*?" the older man asked.

"They work for Hertz."

Ernest nodded. "We going to shoot them?"

"I ain't decided. We may just gather their arms and horses,
then let them walk out of here."

Rosa rejoined them after riding around the village. "Did
you ask them where the *federales* are at?"

He shook his head and she dismounted. Hands on her hips,
she began to walk back and forth before them.

"Where is that butcher Disantos?" A scowl at them, she
continued her pacing. "Tell me if you treasure your *heuvos*."

"We don't know, *señorita*."

"Someone has information." She swept up a large knife
from the pile of their arms and tested the edge on her thumb,
then nodded in approval.

"Who wishes to be the first steer?" Her hard gaze was on
the cowering bandits who avoided looking at her. "You and
you," she said, and pointed at two men. "You take him by
the arms and hold him down for me."

In disbelief, her two chosen ones looked shaken and didn't
move.

"Get his pants down or I'll do you first."

"Disantos's coming to . . . to stop the gun sale," the intended victim said, in a high-pitched voice. "That is why
Hertz needed to sell the guns today."

Slocum nodded in approval and winked at Ernest. "Guess she got more out of them than I did."

"But you didn't have that damn knife." Ernest chuckled and both men laughed.

Holding it by the tip, she threw the knife at the pile and it went halfway to the hilt in the hard soil. Then she walked over and gathered her horse.

Slocum crossed over and stopped beside her stirrup. "You leaving?"

She nodded, looking far away at something.

"Could I ask where for?"

"Your secrets are safe with me."

"I never doubted that. I'm more concerned about your plans. They make me believe that you're on a suicide mission."

She started to rein the gray mare around. "That's my business."

"Rosa, this *federale* you speak of. He'll get his in the end."

Her head held high, she checked the mare. "He will, when I stick my gun barrel up his ass."

"Wait—" But his words fell on deaf ears, for she spurred the mare from camp and left in a cloud of dust.

"She's mad at us?" Ernest asked.

"No, she has greater and deeper concerns."

"Who does she intend to stick in the ass with her pistol?" he asked.

"Colonel Disantos. You know him?"

"Yes. A butcher. But he is like a fox, very smart."

"But even foxes get horny," Slocum said. As tough as she appeared, the *federale* officer would match her. It all mattered on how much he craved a good-looking woman in his bed, and whether or not she could slip inside his confidence enough to reach the place where she could administer her promise. Slocum had more to worry about than her revenge; the gun sales and getting out of there quick enough to avoid the *federales* worried him more than her efforts to give the man a gunpowder enema.

7

San Michaels Mission sat among some palms in the valley dotted with small irrigated fields. Slocum left his men and animals in a dry wash to wait for his return from scouting the place. He could make out the smattering of small hovels surrounding the whitewashed church. A vast open space was used as the pony parking lot before the churchyard gates, and ringing this area were some adobe stores and cantinas. Slocum dismounted at the saloon. Six hipshot horses stood flicking their tails at flies at the rack. He tied the reins to the bar. With his thumb, he undid the rawhide thong that held his Colt in the holster for safety's sake. Nothing looked out of place, so he headed for the open doorway.

He entered the sour-smelling cantina and let his eyes adjust to the darkness, then he eased his way toward the bar, seeing several men at a side table.

"Do I know you?" A short man in a business suit stood up and spoke in a heavily accented English. He adjusted the monocle in his right eye. "I know you, don't I?"

Slocum gave him a hard once-over, then mildly shook his head. "My first time here."

"No! No, I know you. You are John Goddy."

Slocum shook his head to dismiss the man's accusation. "My name's Earl. Earl Dobbs."

"I know you," the man insisted.

"Must be a look-alike." He turned to the bartender and ordered mescal.

The mustached bartender nodded, obviously amused by the German's insistence and set a glass on the bar to half fill.

"Who's he?" Slocum asked with a head toss.

"I never saw him before today. Them others are locals," the bartender said and motioned to the glass. "Two bits American."

"Cheaper in pesos?"

"Same price."

"Good," Slocum said, and paid the barkeep, seeing the hatless man with the eyepiece was coming toward him.

"I do say you resemble Herr Goddy," the man insisted, joining him at the bar and ordering a beer.

Five foot eight, perhaps, and wearing a road-dusty black coat, his white shirt was open at the throat and the string tie loose around his collar. He looked like a misplaced tourist.

"Earl Dobbs," Slocum said, repeating his phony name. "And whatever brought you to this end of hell?"

"I was on my way to the Pacific coast when I was robbed and beaten. My name is Otto Thuringer."

"Take all your money, Otto?"

"Most of it. I was hoping to find a way north to the States, and there I could get more funds from the fatherland to continue my travels."

"I'm not going that way," Slocum said, tasting his mescal. Nothing great, but it cut the trail dust from his throat.

They both looked up at the sound of a fast-approaching horse being whoaed close to the door, then a small man under a sombrero came bursting in. "*Vamoose,* hombres, *los federales* are coming!"

"What does that mean?" Thuringer asked, looking around as if confused.

"The way them guys are heading out, I'd say they don't aim to be here when the soldiers arrive." The four men that had sat at the table with his newfound friend were rushing for the doors.

"What have they done?"

"Don't have to do much to not want to see the *federales* around here."

"Oh, my, where shall I go then?" His head swiveled around as if searching for some hideout.

"Any way that will take you in the opposite direction of them."

"Oh my, what will I ride?" He looked distressed at Slocum and the bartender.

"Catch a burro," the man said, busy polishing glasses behind the bar.

"What if it belongs to someone?"

"Burros belong to whoever rides them."

"You have a horse?" Thuringer asked Slocum

"Yes."

"Then you don't need a burro."

"No," Slocum said.

"Oh, my," the man said, readjusting his monocle as he ran out the front doors.

Slocum turned back to the bar about to ask the barkeep if he knew anything about this bandit Hertz, when he heard a horse galloping away. Had that bastard . . . ? Hand on his Colt, Slocum rushed to the front doorway in time to see the man's black coattails flapping as he raced away on his stallion. Too far away to shoot at him with a pistol, Slocum turned back and saw the bartender in the doorway.

"There is a woman down the dry wash that will hide you. Her name is Lou." The barkeeper pointed the way.

"That way?" Slocum asked, seeing no sign of the dust yet from the soldiers, but convinced they must be close.

"Down the wash a ways and on the right."

"*Gracias*," he said and squinting against the glare, started for the dry creek bed.

He needed a horse worst of all, but even a base to hide in until dark might save him answering serious questions to Colonel Disantos. The dry sand crumbled under his boots and he soon decided that to walk on the exposed caliche would leave fewer tracks. The sheer brown bank was over twelve feet tall and he wondered if he might pass her place without seeing it, but he set out in long strides.

The wall soon grew shorter and he spotted a small jackal and ramada in some greenery. He climbed out of the wash, over the stick fence, and crossed the rows of new corn plants. Someone wearing a wide-brimmed hat stood up under the shade to observe him. She was what he considered ample-bodied, dressed in a red skirt and white peasant blouse.

He paused and nodded to her, still unable to see her face for the hat. "Good day. The bartender said I might stay here until dark."

"For my money," she said, circling around him like an inspector, "you can stay longer than that." Then she laughed deep and throaty. "My name is Louise, they call me Lou."

"Slocum is mine."

"Welcome." She took him by the waist, shoved a large boob into his side, and headed him for the shade. "I was needing some distraction this afternoon anyway."

"Good," he said, looking down at the top of her huge hat. "What's your business?"

"Someone stole my horse about the time that they said the *federales* were on their way to the mission."

She flung off the sombrero and from under it appeared a handsome brown face with large eyes and a full mouth. Her look was full of expectation, and he fulfilled it by bending over, kissing her, and drawing her full, firm breasts against his chest. Her intention was for him to stay bent over for a while, and to savor his mouth on hers; she locked her hands behind his neck. He cupped the large halves of her butt in his hands to feel some more of her. When at last they parted for breath, she smiled.

"Now that's what I call a kiss. You eat lately?" she asked.

"This morning."

"Good, you aren't starved." She looked around with her hands on her wide hips.

"What is it?"

"We better go inside. Ain't too hot in there. Besides, the bed's a better place than that hammock to do it in, huh?"

He nodded, looking to the north, but still saw no telltale

sign of the troop movement. A company of *federales* riders would make lots of dust on any of the roads leading to the mission. Where were they?

"You coming?" she asked from the back doorway.

"Of course," he said, observing her undoing the strings at her waist that held her skirt.

"Those *federales* won't get there until sundown," she said nonchalantly over her shoulder.

Hoping she was right, he followed her inside, undoing his gun belt buckle and swept it off to hang it over the chair. After a good take of her thick short legs, he toed off his boots. Looked like he was in for an interesting afternoon, after all his concern walking down there about how he could hardly wait for dark.

"You have no man?" he asked her, unbuttoning his shirt as she fussed over remaking the bed.

"You," she said and grinned, lifting the blouse up for full exposure of her melon-sized breasts. The garment stretched on her arms above her head, she shook her ample hips provocatively at him and grinned.

He nodded in approval.

"I like a man who knows what he wants." Her wanton laughter sounded free.

His pants on the chair, he began to undo his one-piece underwear. She quickly moved in front of him to take over the job. While she worked on his buttons, he weighted the right boob in his palm, then the left one. She shoved the underwear off his shoulders and then traced her nipple over the lower part of his muscle-corded belly as she pushed it off his hips. His one leg finally out, she bent over for him to raise the other foot. Despite the afternoon's heat, a cool breeze came through the jackal and swept his bare skin.

She dropped to her knees and took his dick in one hand. "Looked so good I thought I better taste it first."

Her next move caught his breath when she kissed the nose of it. His fingers combed through her thick hair until he cupped the back of her head. He closed his eyes to the pleasure as her tongue ran around the head and sent lightening up his spine. Then her lips closed on the shaft and the snake-like hot tongue began to ply the underside of his dick.

He thought for a minute, when her fingertips touched the bottom of his sack, he'd explode. The actions of her ring of fire grew faster and faster until he pulled her upward. More than anything he urgently wanted her in the bed and underneath him to finish this business. Blind with a need to bury his painfully full erection in her, he at last managed to lift her up and herd her to the inviting mattress and covers. There, with her lying on her back, looking mildly drunk on their passion, he crawled between her uplifted knees and shoved his shaft into her.

A cry of pleasure escaped her lips. She threw her head back so he could see her throat and the muscles of her jaw tightened. Spastic muscles inside her began to clutch his aching dick as he fought to reach the bottom of her well.

At last, the head of his probe struck something deep inside her. In his arms, he gathered her legs sticking up on both sides of him and began to punch home his dick faster and faster into her. Then he drove it all the way in for the final plunge. Fire shot out the end of his swollen tool and he strained to be in her as far as he could be, savoring the tightness of her swollen cunt and all the relaxing drain that spread through him.

Sweat ran down his cheeks as he let go of her legs and straightened his back. She reached up with a cloth and dried his face for him. He gave her a smile when she also wiped dry his slick manhood. Then when he moved off of her, she used the rag to stanch the flow from between her legs. At last, sprawled on the bed beside her, he idly teased one of her firm nipples with the ball of his thumb.

"So, where will you go next, gringo?"

"Who said I was leaving you?"

"Ha, your dick has a short memory."

"I'm looking for a man called Diego."

"You have business with this Diego?"

"No, he had business with me. But he wasn't there for our appointment. Instead, some bandito named Hertz sent some of his *pistoleros* to rob me. I expected Diego to meet me here at the mission."

"You think he would be there with the *federales* coming?" She cocked an eyebrow in disbelief at him.

"Yes, because they only knew about that a short while ago."

"Word was all over that there was to be a big gun deal made here?" She cocked her head to the side for his reply.

"Diego must have put out the word then." Slocum considered why the man would do such a thing to him and how he owed him a kick in the butt.

She nodded, then reached down and ran her palm over his muscle-corded belly. "You must be the seller."

"I could be if someone else hasn't stolen them."

"Why would a gun buyer give such information away?"

"Same thing I have been asking myself for the last thirty minutes. Maybe to buy them cheaper from the thieves." He scooted closer to her as her short fingers closed around his shaft and she began to pull gently on it.

"Ah, *si*, I would never have thought of that."

"Neither did I until a few minutes ago," he said and raised her chin on the side of his hand to kiss her. Her lips melting under his, her hard tongue searching his mouth. He closed his eyes to savor the pleasure. This round with her, he would take more time. When his hand ran over the mound of her belly and into the pubic hair, she rolled over onto her back and spread her legs. His index finger soon found the roset and with him rubbing it with his fingertips, it soon turned into a stiff bud.

"Oh," she cried out, "I hope you never find those buyers."

After sundown, the day's heat had begun to expire. He stood shirtless in the night, leaning against the pole of the ramada. Over her flickering pit fire, she roasted a goat haunch. The flame's reflection danced on her face's smooth complexion as she squatted before her cooking. In his fingers was a corn shuck cigarette, whose nicotine had already settled him some. Their afternoon of lovemaking left him feeling somewhat depleted, but also well satisfied. Time for him to think about securing a horse and going to find his men.

He hoped nothing had disturbed the pack train and packers. Where was his broker, Diego? If this whole thing was planned by Diego to get him to take the risk of bringing those guns down there, so they could be stolen once that he got there and then delivered to Diego at half the price, there would be hell to pay.

"Tell me, Lou. Where can I find Diego?"

"Who knows?" She turned up her light-colored palms in question.

"Then where is this Hertz and his bandits?

"They say they are in the hills. Somewhere above the falls." She never looked up at him from her cooking.

"Waterfalls?"

"Silver Falls."

Then he remembered them. "I've heard of them, but it has been years."

"No one likes to go up there. Those bandits are up there and the *bronco* Apaches, too."

"Some of Geronimo's leftovers, huh? The ones who did not go in?"

"Yes." She glanced back at him and nodded. "All the time, they steal young women from the ranches for their squaws and from the foolish woodcutters who go up there."

"Who could show me their place?"

"The Apaches'?" She gave him a disapproving head shake at the notion.

"No, the bandits'."

With a long butcher knife, she cut off a hunk of the goat roast and handed it to him. Hot enough that he tossed it from hand to hand to cool. At last, he took a bite and gave his approval. The meat's fragrant flavor flooded his mouth with saliva. With a twang of the smoke flavor and the spices, the goodness of the meat impressed him.

Raising up with some effort, hands on her hips, she turned to look at him. "I know the way to Hertz's camp."

"But you have a big garden and livestock."

"I have relatives that, for a fee, would come stay here and see about everything."

"I'm interested. I can pay for that," he said, ready for another bite of her barbecue.

"When can we go?"

"I must find my men first. Then I would come back here and we could go. What will you tell them—I mean, about your needing to leave here?"

"Oh, that I have a man who wants to marry me and is taking me to see his parents."

He looked down and could see under her shawl that her shoulders were shaking with her quiet laughter. "Yes, Lou, I think you would tell them something like that."

Deep in his thoughts, he looked away in the night. Somewhere out in the darkness full of insects' chirping, there was a horse. He needed one.

"How will I find something to ride out there?"

"After we eat, we can go and buy a horse from Manuel." She waved toward the southwest.

"A good horse?"

"He can carry you."

"What will you tell this Manuel."

"That you need his horse."

"I'll pay him."

"I know that."

"Will he talk to the *federales*?"

She frowned at him in disapproval. "I'll cut his *heuvos* off if he does."

He drew a deep breath up his nose. The rich aroma of her cooking and the fire filled his nostrils. Her plan for securing him a mount sounded simple enough. His greatest concern for the moment was the safety of the men and the guns.

After her meal filled his belly, they set out in the starlight for Manuel's. On the way, she told him about the many men who were anxious to have their hands on his guns.

"You know this Hordez Cordova?" he asked as they approached the outline of a jackal.

"He's a tough hombre. What did he want from you?"

"He came to Valdez to try to steal them, but his men could not handle the mules."

"Was he angry when you stopped him?" Then she held up her finger to silence his reply when they drew closer to Manuel's place. "Manuel! Manuel! Louise out here, I need to talk with you."

"Louise? What is wrong?"

"I need to buy your horse," she said to a shirtless man buttoning his pants as he came out in the starlight.

"My horse?"

"Yes, how much *dinero*?"

"Oh, *mucho*."

She held her hand to restrain Slocum. "It is for a special friend of mine. We need your old saddle, too."

"Twenty pesos, then."

She turned with her hand out. Slocum put the money in her palm.

"Here," she said, paying him with a jingle of the coins and reached for the rope he held in his hand.

"Who is with you? Do I know him?"

"No, and you better not see him either."

"I savvy. I will go back inside then." The man headed for the dark doorway.

"*Gracias*" she said after him and they went to the pen. Bars down, they captured the sleepy buckskin and led him out. Then he tossed the pads and old saddle on his back.

She straightened the girth on her side so he could lace it on his. "When will you return?"

"I hope in a day. I'll bring a horse for you to ride when I come back."

He saw her smile pleased in the darkness. "*Si*, then we can go find this Hertz."

"I'll be ready to go there on my return."

"So will I, hombre. So will I."

He took the reins and kissed her hard. Her proud breasts dug into him and he felt himself grow heady on her hot mouth. At last, he lifted his head and nodded in approval at her. "I should be back in a day."

"Take care of yourself." She clapped him on the arm.

With that, he swung in the saddle and trotted off to the east to circle wide around the mission. Somewhere in the north, his men and the rifles were camped. That no one had found them was his major concern, listening to the coyotes yipping at the quarter moon that he used for his light.

"Who's out there?" a sharp voice asked.

"Slocum."

"Thank God. Tally saw someone riding your stud horse. We were worried he had killed you," Gilberto said, coming out the mesquite with the rifle in his hands.

"No, some damn German named Otto Thuringer stole him from the hitch rack when they hollered the *federales* were coming." Slocum led the hard-breathing buckskin by the reins as he walked with his man to their camp in the wash.

"He's back," Ernest said, waking Tally from his bedroll.

"Well, we figured—" the cowboy said, tossing back his cover.

"No, he stole Boy. I had to go find another horse. No sign of my man, Diego, nor any word about him being there."

"No. But yesterday was when he was supposed to meet you, right?" Ernest asked.

"Yes, but I suspect that we've been double-crossed. I think that Diego has put all these would-be bandits up to robbing us and then planned on buying the guns cheaper from them."

"What now?"

"Well, word must be out about the gun sale and Disantos has heard about it, too, and that's why he's came down here."

"What can we do now?"

"Stash them someplace they can't be found." Slocum's mind was spinning like a top searching for a solution.

"Where would that be?" Ernest asked, scratching his head. **"Why, they will look everywhere we've been, and it would take a helluva deep hole to bury all of them, too."**

"A haystack might cover them." He looked around at his men for their reply.

"Where is there that much hay in Mexico?" Tally asked and the others agreed.

"We have few people that we can trust here," Ernest said.

Slocum agreed. "I am going in the hills to look for this Hertz. Somehow he and Diego, I think, are in cahoots. If I can find Diego, then I'll know if he's serious about someone's buying the guns or has been playing games with us. If he's not serious, then we'll get the hell out of here."

"You've sold him guns before, haven't you?" Tally asked.

Slocum nodded. Three times, and each time things went smoothly. Why did he think that little pipsqueak was into a double cross this time? Because too many outsiders knew about the shipment and there could only be one reason for that—Diego told them. If he did, then he had a reason, and that was to get them stolen, so he could buy them cheaper from the second party.

Uncertain about his own business, Slocum wondered for a moment about the *companero*. No sign of her at the mission. Had she ridden on to meet the colonel? No reason to doubt her loyalty, but she was hell-bent on revenge and that might get her killed. One slip with a bastard like Disantos and her pretty throat would be slit from ear to ear. No time to worry about her, she chose her personal course and he had enough of his own problems.

It would be dawn soon and he needed two stout horses. Manuel's buckskin wasn't hardly more than a two-year-old mustang and not what he considered adequate for his purposes.

"Where can we get two tough horses for me to ride?"

"Two?" Ernest asked.

"I have a guide taking me to look for Diego and Hertz."

"We have an extra horse that we took from Cordova's man," Tally said.

Slocum nodded, recalling the bay. It would do for one. He didn't dare take one of the men's mounts; they would need them. Where was that crazy German horse thief that took his stud? He hoped Boy had thrown him off a bluff. But wishing for things to happen didn't solve his horse-shortage problem. He'd have to ride the bay back there, and lead the scrubby buckskin who was still snorting and coughing a few feet away from him. Maybe the thin mustang could carry Lou to the mountains—he'd have to do until he could get her a better mount. With a head shake, he busied himself unlacing the wet latigoes to switch the saddle to the one that Ernest led up in the dark.

"There is a cemetery at Tres Madras," Ernest said, working on the other side of the horse. "What if we bury the guns there until you find a buyer?"

"Does anyone live up there?" Slocum tried to recall riding through the place. He remembered the mission long abandoned and no priest or activities were taking place there.

"The mission was shut down when the Apaches got so bad that everyone quit the area. Only a few old people farm that valley since the big spring went dry."

"You would need to make them look like graves."

"We can get them all in two graves," Ernest said as the other two packers came in close.

"What do you two think?" Slocum asked the others as he jerked down the stirrup on his side.

"Be safer than trying to defend them here. They might send several *pistoleros* out for them," Tally said.

Slocum scratched the beard stubble on his cheek in deep thought. "After you bury them, then you boys ride back toward Vargas slow like. Anyone stops you, you can say I sold them."

"You won't need us?" Gilberto asked, looking at him with concern.

"No. I can find you if I do need you; otherwise, I'll meet you in Naco in two weeks with your pay."

The men nodded their heads in the starlight. Time to ride if he was going to make it back to Lou's place before dawn. Otherwise, he'd have to wait until nightfall again. He swung in the saddle and reined in the bay.

"Whose graves will they be under?" he asked.

"Joe Brown and Juan Terria."

"Good, I can remember that." Slocum waved to them and set out in a lope leading the buckskin behind.

The ride to Lou's place under the stars went smoothly enough and he reined the hard-breathing bay up in her yard. She rushed out of the jackal under her wide sombrero and tossed a saddle on the buckskin.

"Hear anything?" he asked, holding the mustang up close to make him stand still for her.

"Disantos arrived," she said, busy lacing the latigos.

"You see him?"

"Yes, but he was too occupied with some young *puta* to notice me."

"Tequila Rosa." He pursed his lips and recalled her fine body and their lovemaking.

She frowned at him under the starlight. "You know her?"

"Yes, if it's her."

"Then why is she with that bastard?" She pushed the hat back to frown at him.

"He shot her husband."

"So?"

"Her idea of revenge is sticking the barrel of her Colt up his ass."

"Ah, I hope she does it soon."

"He cause any trouble at the mission?"

She shook her head to dismiss his concern and then she stepped in the stirrup to toss her leg over the horse's butt. Slocum clung to the bridle fearing the mustang might try to buck and wanted to be sure to contain him for her.

"I can ride," she protested.

With a shrug, he let go and went for his own horse. The buckskin acted all right for her. Perhaps he had him worn down enough not to buck. For her sake, he hoped so and they loped to the east. Already a faint hint of purple outlined the far-away Sierra Madras—time for them to get out of sight of the *federales*.

•   •   •

By noon, they were in the foothills and even the wind on his face felt cooler. He liked the fresher air. How much farther must they ride, he asked her, whenever they halted to rest their animals. So far the tough mustang had carried her all right. The bay was no Boy, but tolerable to ride. Better than the shorter-backed buckskin she was on, who rode only a fraction easier than a pack mule.

"How far to their camp?" he asked, when they paused to water in the intermittent potholes he found in a creek bed. A few cottonwoods, their leaves rattled overhead in the midday breeze. With a big yawn, he took off his hat and wiped his sweaty forehead on a dusty sleeve.

"A couple hours ahead. You tired?" she asked.

"I'll make it for a while."

"We can hobble them and take a siesta in the shade," she offered.

"How far do you really think we are from the bandit's camp?"

"If they are at the *rancheria* I think they are at, maybe three hours away."

"Lets hobble them," he said and went to get the restrains from his saddlebags. "I'd rather scout them at night."

"Fine," she said and took the rope hobbles he handed her. The buckskin turned loose, she put a blanket roll on her shoulder and started for the shade.

After a search around, he followed her. She flipped out the red blanket in the shade and, satisfied, she began undoing her skirt.

"We going to siesta or what?" he asked, unbuckling his gun belt.

"Whatever you want to do," she said and shed the garment exposing her bare legs.

The insects chirped and some small wrens fussed about over these invaders to their territory. Naked, she set down the sombrero, still standing with her feet apart, and loosened up the bun to free her long black hair that reached the middle of her back.

He sat down and pulled off his boots. "I'm surprised you have no man."

"What do I need a man for? Then hombres like you would never come along."

"You've had some men?"

"Oh, yes, and they got shot or knifed and then what? I used to cry about them, too."

She sat down on the blanket beside him and stretched her brown legs out before her with her arms back to support her. Her eyes closed, she turned her face skyward. The massive breasts reminded him of how good they felt and tasted. Were his men getting the gun funeral completed? Good enough idea, only there was no telling how well it would work.

"Such a shame we simply aren't on a picnic, and not on this rotten business of looking for that bandit Hertz," she complained.

He rolled over and used his bent arm to support his head. "Aw, maybe we can do that, too."

With a pleased smile for him, she began to brush her long tresses. "Get some sleep. I will watch for anyone. When you awake we can do whatever you want to do."

He reached over and patted her bare leg. "I'll be ready."

"Good, by then I will, too," she said, and laughed.

He closed his gritty eyes and her laughter was the last thing he remembered.

8

"That's their camp," Lou said from beside him as they bellied down on the still-warm rock ledge above the activity. Light from campfires shown red on the faces of the revelers. The mariachi music rang out and the laughter of haughty women sounded only a few feet away from him.

Some girl was dancing around a hat on the ground and taking off her clothing. She removed her blouse and whirled like a top, waving it at the growing crowd around her. With plenty of shouting men to egg her on, she was enjoying shaking her exposed tits at them. Soon she was out of her skirt and the fire's orange flare reflected off her shapely butt, which she wiggled in their faces. She drew a loud roar of approval from her horny audience.

"If I was her I would get naked, too," Lou said. "Her ass is much prettier than her face."

Slocum chuckled out his nose. "I don't see that little rat Diego in the crowd. You see Hertz in the crowd?"

"Did the one who stole your horse have a monocle?" She turned him and pointed in the crowd at a figure in the firelight.

"Yes." Indignant at even the thought of the horse thief, Slocum raised up to look for him.

Slocum adjusted his eyeglass as he spotted Thuringer among the rowdy crowd of men cheering on the stripper.

The German horse rustler leered at the naked girl like he was some kind of an inspector.

"Otto!" Someone pounded him on the back so hard it about sent him into her. "Take that *puta* and make her scream!"

Otto drew his head back and looked aghast at the notion. Slocum smiled. Was the dumb bastard a virgin? He acted like he either didn't know what to do with her or didn't dare.

By then, the German had help getting ready; the bandits were undressing him. Someone unfurled a blanket and soon it was spread on the ground. Despite his protests, the ones undressing him soon had him naked as a pile of snow. His prize for the contest was already lying on her back ready with her raised legs spread apart. They physically put him on top of her. Slocum watched her grin. The *puta* reached down and no doubt inserted him in place.

The roar of the onlookers grew even louder and their instructions for the poor man to stuff it farther into her became more vivid. Women and men both crowded around to view them, so the conjugating pair became obscured from Slocum on the bluff.

"There," Lou said in his ear and directed his attention to a man standing aside in the firelight, observing it all with his arms folded over his chest. "That's Hertz."

Slocum could see Hertz wore fringed leather pants and a snowy white shirt. Tall for a Mexican, he guessed him close to six feet. The outlaw leader wore two six-guns in silver mounted holsters and had black, wavy hair that came to his collar. Slocum decided he could recognize this hombre anywhere.

Obviously finished with her, Thuringer rose to his feet, holding his clothes in a wad, and staggered backward out of the crowd. He walked shakily away, using the bundle to hide his privates, embarrassed by his state of undress.

"My cousin!" Hertz shouted to the man, then put his arm on the kraut's shoulder. "They got you bred, no?"

"Bred? Oh, yes."

"Get dressed, amigo, and we will go celebrate."

Herman stood nodding his head as if uncertain of anything. "They always do that?" he asked Hertz, above the cheers of the men as the gang bang continued.

"Ah, horny men have horny women and who could stop them?"

"Not me."

"Me either." Hertz laughed aloud at the man's obvious plight. "Get dressed."

"I will."

Lou elbowed Slocum. "You think that your man Diego is down there?"

"If he is, then he's their prisoner in a tent. Everyone else in camp, I think, came to try his hand at screwing that woman, or watching someone else do it to her."

"Or try." She shook her head in disapproval. "The last one couldn't get his dick hard enough to go into her."

"Ah, but there's more."

"This one on her now was ready."

"Good. I'm going to scout the camp for Diego while they're so busy with her."

"Be careful." She raised up on her elbow to scowl at him, then shook her head in disapproval. "It will be dangerous down there. Watch out."

"I will. Danged if I don't believe that he may be held against his will if he's here."

In the night, he heard the familiar whistle of his stallion. It drew a smile on his face, when he rose, and he clapped her on the shoulder. "That's my horse."

Darkness served him well. He put on a sombrero he found at the edge of camp. He stashed his own stetson and then used a horse-smelling blanket for a wrap against the cooling night air. He grunted at a drunk who staggered by him, muttering something about the *puta* business. Obviously too drunk to help her, the poor man looked headed for a place to crash. Slocum moved carefully past the area where three women tended the beef quarters on spits cooking over beds of red hot coals. The aroma reminded his empty stomach how long it was since he last ate.

"Not ready," some woman said, to shoo him away as if she thought he was checking on their progress.

He nodded his head and moved into the shadows. Three tents were set up in a row. From where he stopped, he could hear all the cheering at the gang bang that was on the other side of them. Two tents were dark; in the third, he could see someone's silhouette on the illuminated canvas. Perhaps one of Hertz's men. Slocum waited in the darkness while a couple passed by his place.

"She was ugly," the woman insisted.

"Who was looking at her face?" the man said sharply.

"She probably has a pussy as big as a horse collar by now," the woman replied.

"I don't want her anyway."

"Oh, now you say that."

They were gone toward the back of the camp still arguing. Slocum slipped across the path that went through camp and soon was behind the tents, pausing to listen at each one.

He heard nothing and at last stood behind the lighted one. The sounds of a quill pen scratching on paper by someone proficient at writing was, no doubt, the same one who had made the outline. Was it the horse thief Thuringer? If it was him, Slocum considered going inside and clobbering him over the head before he left this place.

"You have that letter ready for the messenger, *Jefe*?" the voice, Slocum recognized as Hertz's, rang out.

"*Si, señor*. I told them to deliver the money for the guns or Don Diego would be buzzard bait in three days."

"Good, that bastard Diego should be worth a couple of hundred dollars, no?"

"Well, if they think we really have the guns, too, they will pay for them even if they don't care about him."

"Our man at the mission said tonight that the *federales* looked like they would camp there forever. And that damn Slocum will never bring those guns there if that fat ass colonel stays there very long."

"Perhaps we can decoy the colonel away."

"Ah, now you are thinking, *Jefe*."

"We will send some men to make a raid on San José and the *federales* will all go there to see about it and leave San Michael's."

"But that would not last long enough for Slocum to come into town with the weapons."

"How would he know that? We will send him a letter to come and it will be signed by Diego to meet him there and to bring the rifles with him."

"Suppose Diego's money people learn that Slocum still has the rifles."

"Then they may not pay that money for his ransom."

Both men laughed.

Slocum stood back from the starlight under the mesquite bush. Where were they holding Diego? He drew the knife from behind his back and went to the first tent. A soft screech and he had an opening in the back to peer inside. Crates of something. Inside the tent, he struck and cupped a match to shine on the wood surface of the top box.

Property of the U.S. Army. Twenty-five grenade rounds, mountain howitzer ammo. He felt around in the dark. No mountain howitzer in the tent, unless it was in the case, too. Damn, what did Hertz aim to do, start a real war? This was contraband, stolen from Fort Huachucua munitions, no doubt. Not for sale by any arms agent he knew on the border. He eased himself out. One more tent to check, then he might have to give up trying to find that banty rooster Diego.

His knife slit the back panel of the second tent and he soon stepped inside. "Diego?" he hissed and the muffled sound led him through the darkness to a cot.

"Shut up," he warned the gun buyer as he removed his gag.

"That you, Slocum?" He gasped for his breath.

"Yes, but we've got to get out of here fast." He cut the ropes on the man's hands and feet, then sat him up on the cot.

"I don't think I can walk. I've been tied up for three days.

Last time they let me loose to pee I had to crawl." Diego was bent over rubbing his legs.

"You better learn how to walk and fast." Slocum shook his head and put his knife away. "It's a hundred yards to the horses. We need to make it there. That's past those women cooking—I smell kerosene."

"Coal oil," Diego said. "They've got a lantern in here."

"They got a can of it in here, too?"

"I think so."

"Good," he said, and began his search in the dark. Soon the two-gallon can was in his hand by the wooden bail, then he found the lantern.

"You feeling anything in your legs yet?" he asked the man.

"No, they're all pins and needles."

"Get on my back."

"Where're we going?"

"To blow up the munitions in the next tent."

"I—I can't run."

"You won't have to."

"But that will blow the roof off the whole place."

"Don't worry, I'll get you out of here. How did he get them grenades anyway?"

"Not for me. I saw them, is all. You ain't going to leave me here?"

"No." He backed up and the smaller man soon clung to his back. Outside, Slocum checked around and then moved, bent over under his load, to the first tent.

"Get down. I have to spread this coal oil over them boxes."

Diego reluctantly eased himself off Slocum's back. Bracing himself off his knees, the gun broker groaned.

"Be quiet or you may never hurt again," Slocum hissed. He was inside in a flash, pouring the pungent coal oil over the crates. The sharp odor ran up his nose; he set down the empty can, and backed out. Huddled around the lantern, he struck a match that caused Diego to suck in his breath. The flame applied to the wick, Slocum used his sombrero to shade the light. Slow like, the wick's flame came on stronger.

"I'll throw this inside," Slocum said softly. "Then you get

up on my back and hold on to me with one hand and fire my Colt as we run. Not all at once. But snap shots to get them out of the way. Ready?"

"I guess. Sure hope you don't fall."

"Go." Slocum parted the canvas and swung the lantern inside. The glass crashed and a loud whoop of the spilled coal oil caught fire. Diego scrambled onto Slocum's back like a squirrel going up a tree. Slocum held the man's legs and began to run for the ramadas. He felt Diego manage to draw his Colt. The hammer cocked, the report about deafened Slocum, but the gunshot put the women running hysterically for cover, screaming like he had wounded them.

"There's fire at the tents!" came the shouts.

"Get down," he said to Diego at the horse line. He looked for his stallion, but not for long. No luck finding him, but he was running out of time. He forced a bit in the mouth of a stout-looking roan and tossed Diego on the horse's back.

"Shoot if you see one of them coming," he said and made a jaw bridle from a rope for another horse that was handy. In a bound, he was on the animal's back and then drove his spooked mount in close enough to slash the picket rope that the others were all tied to.

"Fire that Colt. We need to stampede them," he shouted and began waving his blanket at the upset animals. That and the gun shot sent all the wide-eyed horses in a panic away from camp. Slocum hollered at them as they rushed down the draw after the herd. He heard a few wild shots at his back, but they were already out of pistol range.

"Are them howitzer rounds ever going off?" Diego shouted, riding beside him.

"When they get hot enough. Keep riding, they still may knock us off our horses when they blow."

A screaming round detonated first, then fireworks erupted at their backside. The horses doubled their speed at the next explosion. Slocum glanced back and saw a great fireball in the air. Wouldn't be many survivors if they were close to that hell.

He reined up and saw Lou's outline coming, leading the buckskin off the ridge.

"What in the hell went off back there?" she asked.

"A couple of tons of ammunition."

"I never saw nothing like it. You must be Diego."

"Yes, I am Don Diego."

"He's been tied up so long he can't walk. She's Lou. Can you do something for him?" Slocum asked her.

"Maybe. There's some hot-water springs a couple hours from here. They might do him some good." She shook her head. "Where did you get that hat?"

"Found it."

"Poor trade. How did he get out then if he can't walk?"

"I carried him on my back. We haven't got all night to talk."

"This way," she said and took the lead.

Slocum looked back. It would take Hertz some time to get his outfit back together after this. That is, if he even lived to tell about the explosion. Shame that he hadn't had the time to find his stud horse Boy and recover him, too. But all those horses were scattered in the night by their rouse.

He had Diego, his gun broker, and that needed to be enough for one night. Following Diego and Lou in a long lope, he hoped his boys had the rifles buried. All he needed was for some other bandits to get their hands on them. He looked at the quarter moon rising in the east. Sure had become hard to make a few bucks this time with his gun running. Why, before he got through with all of this, he'd be lucky even to pay for all of his expenses.

9

Sulphur from the hot springs burned the inside of Slocum's nostrils. The various steaming pots dotted the ground and the stark white figure seated on his butt in the middle of one looked like a skeleton. On guard, Slocum gnawed on the tough jerky with a Winchester across his lap.

"You figure that they'll believe that note that Hertz sent my business associates?" Diego asked.

"Won't be anyone there to collect it if they do pay it."

"You think that explosion killed all of them?"

"If not, they won't be able to hear themselves fart for several weeks."

Diego laughed and tried to raise up.

"That hot springs helping you?"

"Yeah, I can walk some." Diego began to dry himself off. Even at a distance, it was obvious that the hot water had reddened the lower half of his body for he looked like a white-and-red top.

Diego dressed and with two canes made his way with difficulty over to Slocum. He dropped down on a large boulder and made a pained face.

"Getting any feeling in your feet yet?" Slocum asked, then gnawed off another saliva-softened bite of his jerky.

"I'm better. Lots better than I was when you found me."

"Good, I'm not playing piggyback anymore."

"Who's this Lou?" Diego tossed his head toward the woman bent over the fire cooking them some food.

"A witch, a doctor. I don't know, but you owe her a lot. She led me up here to find you."

"Why did you come looking for me?"

" 'Cause you weren't where you said you'd be in San Michael's."

"Yeah, but you risked your life to carry me out—"

"Diego, I've risked other parts of my body this trip, too. Quit worrying about it. We need for you to get me my money and I'll deliver the rifles."

"I fear that the one with the money has gone back."

"Where?"

"I can't say. But he'll be coming back shortly when I send him word you're here."

Slocum scowled at his stalling. "Diego, you better pray he does or I'm going to hold your head under in one of these stinking pots till you drown."

Diego's small shoulders shuddered at the threat. "I need to get to a telegraph."

"Sure, and when the *federales* intercept that message, you'll have Disantos down our necks like *that*." Slocum snapped his fingers to make a point with the man.

"Disantos is here?" Diego looked bewildered.

"Yes. He's at San Michael's waiting like a big fat tom cat at a rat hole for us."

"What'll we do?"

"I'm thinking on that."

"Then I need to send word to him, at a camp west of here."

"You able to ride there?"

"I rode up here."

"You can use my saddle. How far away is it?"

"Twenty miles, maybe more."

Slocum nodded. "I'll tell her."

"She going along?" Diego scowled like her presence upset him.

Slocum stopped. "Sure, why?"

"Just asking. You can't be too safe in this country anymore."

"She's a safe one. Don't worry about her. Who're we going to meet?"

"My man."

"What the hell's his name?"

"I can't say."

"You don't want me to leave your ass here, you better spit it out."

"Victorio Romo."

"Never heard of him. Let's see if she's close to having that cooked." He strode over to her. "That food about ready?"

She looked up. "You in a rush?"

"Yes, we're going to go find the moneyman."

"Should I stay here?"

"No. I may need some backup."

"Fine." She shared a pleasant smile with him over his inviting her. "The food will be ready in a few minutes."

"Good, this jerky ain't much."

"You've never stopped long enough for me to cook anything."

He left her at the small fire and walked back to Diego. "Be ready in a short while. Then we can ride."

"Slocum, I had no way—"

"I ever find out you have been behind all this bullshit I've had on this trip, I'll stomp your ass in the hard ground." He glared at the small man. And the little sumbitch better believe he meant it. The distant Madras looked worlds away—he wanted this gun business over.

"I know. I'm sorry."

"No being sorry, I simply want my money and want out of here. I don't have no great love for *federales*. They make me itch."

"Me, too," Diego said, as they both nodded to Lou's summons for them to come and eat.

Slocum took the bowl of food she handed him. Seated cross-legged on the ground, he spooned in the mixture of meat, rice, and peppers. Still in deep thought about the entire situation, he wondered if his men had succeeded in their "funeral plans." No way to know for certain, but he had lots of faith in the three. And Rosa—was she sleeping with the colonel, yet? Damn, he grew mad thinking about her in that mans bed.

After they ate, they rode all afternoon down the mountain and across the desert floor, careful to avoid contact with anyone. Long past sundown they were crossing a wide greasewood flat under the stars.

"How much farther?' he asked Diego.

"Five or six miles." The man shrugged and booted his horse to make him continue.

"You know this place?" Slocum twisted in the saddle to look at her.

"There's a well at the base of that small mountain." She pointed to the southwest where the outline stood out against the night sky.

"That's where they are," Diego said.

"Who will be there?" Slocum asked.

"Romo and some men."

"Of course. He'll have the money?"

"Oh, yes."

"You ever heard of Victorio Romo?" Slocum asked her, and she shook her head.

"Moneymen are always mysterious," Diego said.

"You never used him before?"

"You have to change moneymen from time to time."

"Maybe that is why I've been at war all the way from the border down here."

"What?"

"Too damn many folks knew about this shipment. Somewhere there's a mole in our outfits, I'm not certain who it is either."

"I'm wondering myself," Diego said, looking around in the night.

An hour later, they drew up near the looming hill's silhouette.

"This is where they should be," Diego said.

"No sign of any fire." Slocum looked hard toward the base. The night insects sizzled and evening breeze swept his face. No moon yet, so only the starlight to show him anything.

"Hold up, and you two wait here. I'll go scout it on foot." He dismounted, handed his reins to Lou, and nodded to Diego. "If it's clear to ride in, I'll give you a whistle."

"Funny, they don't have a fire," Diego said.

"Be careful, I don't like it." Lou's husky voice was tinged with a ring of caution and concern.

"I will," and he headed off into the darkness on foot. Using a sandy draw, he hurried with his Colt hammer freed of the thong. His ears were atune to the night sounds and ready to perceive anything out of the ordinary. Then the whiff of a dead fire carried to his nose. An acrid smell of ashes, and he paused, making out the dark shapes of mesquite bushes. Something lay prone on the ground. He drew his Colt, testing the air, straining to hear anything that might give away some-one-in-waiting's presence. Nothing.

In a crouching run, he crossed the open space and knelt beside the first body. Dead. He touched the man's hand: dead, he knew, by the coldness of the skin. This one had gone to his reward. But from the deceased's clothing, he ascertained this was a peon. Checking all around, he moved to the next body, bent over to make as poor a target as possible. Another in white clothing, but a bloodier victim than his first find. This one had had his throat cut from ear to ear. Were there other dead? On his haunches, he searched around, but saw nothing.

He used his hand to test the ashes in the fire ring. Most of the heat was gone. It had been at least noontime since there had been a blaze. Where was Diego's man? The one with the money? Hertz could not have done these murders. The blowup of the night before had no doubt left him still looking for his run-off horses. No one of the others in this carousel of bad characters had masterminded this. Was it done for the gun money? Perhaps Diego would know.

He straightened and whistled for them to come on in. Somewhere off in the desert, a sun dog howled. Though in deep concentration, Slocum heard the mournful call. More to this whole thing than he could even guess. Then several other coyotes joined in the chorus and his two companions arrived.

"Where is Victorio?" Diego asked, looking around in the starlight.

"I found two dead men so far. Doubt either is Romo, but you can go look over there."

"Oh, no!" Diego gave an obvious shudder of revulsion.

"What does Victorio look like?" Lou asked, with an edge of impatience. "Dead men can't hurt you. It's the live ones that can strike back like a sidewinders."

"A big man. Tall as Slocum. Had a mustache and wore a couple of gold rings."

"He ain't over there," Slocum said to inform them. "They're both short and never owned a gold ring in their lives."

"Where is he, then?"

"Diego, your man isn't here. I need my money for those rifles and to get the hell out of here."

"I don't understand why these men are dead and he's gone."

"I do. All these bastards trying to get in on this shipment have more bandits working for them than ants on a honey pot. And I'm not too certain you didn't sic them on me."

"No, I never did that," Diego pleaded.

"I ever hear you did, you better pack your bags and get for China because I'm coming after you."

"I didn't. Now listen, Slocum, I need to find this guy. He has the money for the rifles . . . or he did have it."

"He hasn't gotten it here by noon tomorrow, you are out of the gun deal. Period."

"Don't say that. He wants the rifles and he's got the money."

"Start a fire?" she asked.

Slocum shook his head. "I don't know who they are that did this and they may circle back."

"Give me some matches," Lou said. "I'll try to identify those dead ones for you."

"Thanks," he said, digging for some matches from his vest pocket.

She took them and went to the first man, rolled him over by pulling on his stiff arm. Diego made a sick moan as if pained when she snapped a match on fire with her thumbnail and held it close to the dead man's face.

"Know him?" Slocum asked, looking over her shoulder as she bent closer. Then the light went out and the smell of sulphur filled his nostrils.

"Bustmente is that one over there's name. I think this one's name is Phillip."

"Where are they from?" Slocum asked, straightening.

"They work for him," Diego said.

"This gun buyer, Romo?"

"Yes, but if they are dead, where is he?" The short man searched around in the night.

"You have two options: He's dead and we ain't found him, or they took him away."

"Who took him?"

"Damn it, Diego. If I knew who it was who had him, why in the hell would I be asking you?"

"Oh, damn, Slocum, I don't know anything."

"Where does this Romo live?"

"I ain't certain."

"By damn, I'm sick and tired of your evasive answers. First, I never heard of this Victorio. Second, I think you're lying to me."

"All right, all right. The man who was supposed to be here is Omar Shard."

"You're saying that crooked bastard from Frio Grande is the one paying for the rifles?"

"I—I knew if I told you you'd be mad."

"Mad? That thief would sell his own grandmother into slavery."

"Easy, Slocum. This was an honest deal." Diego held out his hands to ward off any attack. "I promise you I never thought—"

"You never thought by teaming up with him. I trusted you

to make a good deal, but not one with that weasel."

"Even I have heard of that swindler," Lou said and shook her head in disapproval.

"I can find another buyer. I promise. Give me a few days."

Slocum shook his head. "From now on I'll find my own buyers. Cinch up your horse, Lou."

"We're going?"

"Yes. I've done my last business with this lying coyote." He tried to simmer his growing temper. Diego had brokered his last arms deal for him. In the stupid man's desperation to make money, he'd sold himself to the lowest of all—Omar Shard, a name infamous in Mexico for his trickery and bad dealings.

Not only had the man's conniving plans to steal the rifles rather than pay for them put his life in jeopardy, but his men's lives as well. When this was over, he intended to make the trade merchant pay for it, too. For the moment, getting his money for the rifles needed to be his goal.

"Here," she said and handed him his reins.

"Diego, I better not have to lay eyes on you again." He put his boot toe in the stirrup and swung aboard.

"Oh, please, you can't leave me out here." Diego looked around like a desperate man, seeing Lou taking away his horse.

"Hide and watch." Slocum gave a head toss to the east and Lou set out in the lead with Diego's mount in tow.

"Don't leave me! They'll kill me!"

Too damn bad. The cooling night wind swept his face. They short loped their ponies through the starlight. His mind was flooded with the names of possible buyers. Perhaps he should leave the area and start over again. Make the gun sale elsewhere, with this region so filled with two-legged vultures ready to swoop down on him.

"Where can we hide for a day or so and rest our horses?" he asked, riding beside her.

"I know a *ranchera*."

"Good. Can we be there by first light?"

"*Si*."

Slocum glanced over his shoulder. Nothing behind them in the starlight. He should have beaten that stupid Diego to within an inch of his life. That runty ignorant . . . No, he had done the best thing. Leave him to rot out there. Sever all his ties with the little bastard and never do business with him again. How could Diego have been so dumb to do business with such a disrespectable crook? A shudder of revulsion shook his shoulders.

He glanced aside and smiled at the ample-bodied Lou. At least he had good company to share his bad luck with.

10

The rancher that came from the jackal to greet them was her cousin Cy Mendoza. A broad smile on his handsome face, the man looked to be in his forties. Short but muscular-appearing, he struck out his hand to Slocum when Lou introduced them, then he hugged her.

A younger woman, very pregnant, came to the doorway of the jackal and smiled at them.

"My Maria," Mendoza said and Slocum removed his old sombrero and nodded to her.

"We need to rest here for a few days," Lou explained.

"Stay as long you want." His dark eyes held a questioning look for Slocum that he would never ask out loud.

"Some bad business dealings," Slocum said, to explain.

"Ah, bad business is the ways of the times, *mi* amigo."

Slocum shook his head. "Not with people who hold your trust."

"That is bad. Put your horses in the corral. Maria will cook some food and we can visit, surely about more pleasant things."

Slocum agreed with the man. Then Lou insisted that he go with Cy and took their sweaty horses to the pen. Both men walked toward the ramada.

"How's ranching?" Slocum asked.

"The bandits all the time steal my cattle and good horses.

The *federales* take them and leave me worthless paper. No one has money to buy them. To drive the cattle to the border would be like asking to have them stolen."

"These are tough times for everyone," Slocum agreed.

"Maria, this is *Señor* Slocum," he said to his wife, who was on her knees at the cooking fire, reaching past her large swollen belly to make tortillas on a black grill.

Her coy smile warmed him. Slocum nodded to her again as Mendoza spoke to her about his cousin Lou and how they planned to stay with them for a few days.

"Will it be a boy or a girl?" Slocum asked Mendoza, seated on a wooden bench the man offered him.

"Ah, a boy I hope. But I would love a girl as well."

"Your first?"

Mendoza looked off at the saw-toothed mountains. Slowly, he shook his head. "I have had two wives before Maria. They and my children are all buried out there." He pointed to the north.

Slocum could see beyond the prickly pear patch, the sun-weathered crosses. He nodded that he understood the man's losses.

"A man should never have to bury his children. Some I lost to diseases. There are no doctors here. My second wife was killed by bandits."

"You know these men?"

"Bandits." Mendoza shrugged his thin shoulders, looking even smaller seated beside him. "They have no names. They rob, rape, and kill innocent people until they are killed."

"You have any idea who they were?"

Mendoza shook his head and reached in his leather vest pocket. He handed Slocum a silver *concho* hammered by hand from a coin. It was made in the pattern of a cross with two slits in the center to thread leather through.

"They lost this here?" Slocum asked, holding it up to look for any mark. There were no initials or name on the underside. Still, he knew the work had been done by a good silversmith. He handed the piece over to Lou who had joined them.

"Doris's killers left that," Mendoza said, with his gaze on the ground.

She nodded and turned it over in her palm. "I have never seen such a *concho* before." Then she gave it back to Slocum.

"I won't forget it," Slocum said. His mind more on how to sell his arms and survive the sale than who had worn the silver cross. He passed it back to the man.

"Ah, let's eat," Mendoza said, acting brighter and pocketing the piece in his vest.

The morning sun climbed higher. After the mouth-watering meal of beef and frijoles, Slocum and Lou set out for the tank to bathe. She carried a bedroll for them to repose upon while they waited for their clothes to dry. Mendoza wished them well and saddled a horse to ride out and check on his cattle.

The path through the head-high mesquite was well worn. They found a basin of water over half full and covering an acre. Built with a slip, the project represented long hours of work. Well designed, it captured the small wash's surplus. At their approach, some longhorn cows with calves raised their heads. Water dripped from their muzzles while they eyed the invaders suspiciously, then drank their fill and slipped away.

"Have you decided how to sell your guns?" she asked, unfurling the bedroll.

He shook his head. "No, but I'll come up with someone."

Her fingers busy undoing the ribbons that tied her skirt's waist, she sighed. "Hard to find anyone that you can trust."

"I may not try to sell them for now." He toed off his boots and then unbuckled his gun belt, laying it on the bedroll.

She took off the blouse over her head, exposing her full breasts. With a deep inhale up his nose, he turned back to undo his pants. Shedding them and the shirt, he smiled as she stepped over and began to unbutton his underwear.

"Dangerous business," he said.

She looked up and smiled. "I want lots of dangerous business like this."

"That can be arranged. Let's get a layer or two of dirt off first."

"We might smell less like a horse." Her laughter rang out.

Somewhere off in the chaparral, a covey of topknotted doves, considering the water hole, made their *whit-woo* calls. A raven passed overhead, scolding them for their nakedness as they waded into the water. He was soon waist deep and struck out to swim. Long strokes with his arms and he reached the far side. Using his hands and the water to get his too-long hair back, he gazed over to where she worked to lather her light-brown body with soap.

Where was Rosa? Had she found her colonel? So determined, so beautiful—he hoped that her thirst for bloody revenge did not destroy her. He had enough problems of his own to fill a big sack. He swam back.

"You ready for a soaping?" she asked.

"I guess. You giving it?"

"Of course," she said and waded over to him.

Soon she was soaping him with the bar. Lather began to cover his chest, armpits, and shoulders. She worked furiously. Soon her hands found his privates and he sucked in his breath as she worked them over with her soapy fingers. A hold of him, she looked up and smiled confidently. "Ah, at last I have you."

He smiled and kissed her.

Later, out of breath when he finished, she looked shaken. "Whew, I would ride to hell and back with you."

"Ah, Lou. You have been a good ways on that route already."

"When I get this soap off you . . ."

"Yes," he whispered in her ear and nibbled on her neck. "I can hardly wait."

"Me, either." She began throwing handfulls of water on him, then she made a face. Determined, she came in close enough so her nipples were pushed into him and put her hand on top of his head. "Under you go."

Rinsed off, they rushed for the bedroll. She sat down, after she hung their washed clothing, and smiled up at him. "Ready."

He glanced down at his half-erect dick and agreed. On his knees, he waded between her thick legs parted for him. Looking down at the patch of black pubic hair that disappeared in a V, he inserted the head of his shaft into her. Then, using both arms to brace himself over her, he began to haunch it deeper. She gave a great sigh and arched her back toward him. Her hands reached out and pulled him down on top of her.

They both began to bump their hips together. His erection grew harder and the walls of her cunt began to swell. They fought for air as the fury of their lovemaking increased to wilder and wilder. Soon the signs of finality began to appear. The head of his dick ballooned to skintight proportions. Her moans of pleasure grew louder. She raised her butt off the blanket to receive him and the world exploded inside her.

For a minute, the bright sun eclipsed for him and he fell into a deep chasm of surrender. He looked down and her thick eyelashes were closed. When they finally opened, her vision looked swarmed and she shook her head.

"I want to ride all the way to hell and back if it's going to be like this," she said dreamily.

While their clothing dried, he smoked a corn shuck cigarette she rolled for him. His mind so blank, he wondered if he could ever devise a plan to sell the rifles.

"Where will we go next?" she asked, hugging her legs.

"Perhaps I should go back to the border. Every revolutionary and bandit knows I have the rifles and wants them. Up there I can sell them to someone and then be out of harm's way, too."

"If you must go back I would understand." Still she looked upset by his words.

"I can take you home. . . ."

She shook her head. "I can ride back in a half day from here all right. You know where my casa is."

"I know. I won't forget."

"Good. I will expect you to visit me."

He put his arm on her shoulder and hugged her. Be more fun to stay and play with her than what he must do next. All his money, and then some, was invested in those damn rifles. Deep in his thoughts, he studied a buzzard on the wing. Shame he couldn't fly like that bird.

"When you ride north, if you stay near the Verde, you can visit and stay overnight with my sister at Benito. I'll draw you a map to her place."

Amused, he grinned at her. "You have relatives all over the place."

"Big family. And you?"

"One brother. I haven't seen him in years."

"What a shame." She laughed, then pushed to her feet to check on their clothing.

"Dry enough," she announced.

He rose looking off to the saw-edged mountains. Already, he knew he would miss her and her free ways of making love. Damn, no home, no roots, only looking back for the next one that got after him. He put on the shirt she handed him.

Early the next morning, Lou tied the bedroll on behind his saddle. A small red rooster stirred about the corral, topping a willing hen or two and crowing about it.

"I'm glad you don't have to crow about it," she said, swinging on his arm.

"You thinking your cousin and his bride would not have gotten any sleep last night?"

She chuckled. "I sure didn't get much."

"Lou, I have some money. . . ."

"You will need it. I will be fine." Then she laid her index finger by his nose and tapped on the bridge. "You must come see me."

"I promise I will."

"My sister's name is Felicia. But you must ask for Felica O'Dell. That is a secret signal that you were sent by me."

She released him and hunched her shoulders as if they were stiff.

"You going home today?" he asked, ready to get in the saddle.

Sleepy-eyed, she looked up at him and shook her head. "No, I am going to get some rest. Why, I may sleep all day and all night."

They both laughed as he parted, telling her to give his regards and thanks to Mendoza. He set the pony northward. Her map led him the back way, which he appreciated.

"Is this the casa of Felicia O'Dell?" Slocum asked, from the front yard in the starlight.

"Lou sent you," the woman said from the doorway and clutched the shawl tighter around her. A thinner woman than her sister, Lou, she looked to be in her thirties, but in the poor light he could only speculate on the rest.

"She said that I could find you here," he said and dismounted. "I only need to rest a few hours."

"Fine. Put the horse in the pen in back. I have some food that is still warm. Are the *federales* looking for you?"

"Them and others," he said, with grin for her as she joined him to walk to the pen. "I am not interfering—I mean, do you have a husband?"

"No. He's dead."

"Sorry."

"No reason for that. You didn't kill him."

"No, ma'am, it wasn't me." They both laughed.

Seated cross-legged on the rug inside her hut by the flickering light of a single smoky candle, he ate her spicy beans and they filled a void in his empty belly. Then she brought him honey and a flour tortilla for dessert.

"There is a pallet over there," she indicated when he finished.

"Is it yours?" he asked.

The candle's red glow reflected off her straight cheek when she smiled at him. "I can share it."

"Thanks," he said and toed off his boots. "But I must warn you, I may fall asleep before I get there."

"I understand," she said and blew out the light.

In the night, he awoke with a start. His left hand cupped a pear-shaped breast, and curved like a bowl with her bare back against him was his bed partner. Still dark outside, he listened to the sounds. Horses and the creak of saddle leather sounded to him like the cavalry was going past. Dogs were yapping at them. If they intended to camp or stay at this small community for any length of time, his existence would be no secret once the sun came up.

Damn. She snuggled her slender butt into him and he closed his gritty eyes for some relief. Hell, he better wake her up and get on the move.

11

In the first light of dawn, O'Dell came hurrying back. Out of breath with her skirt in her hand, she rounded the house. "Colonel Disantos is with them." She bent over to catch some air. "And he's looking for you."

Slocum threaded the latigo leather through the cinch ring. No time for regrets, but he should have left in the night. To try to clear his mind, he shook his head, then drew the girth up tight. No matter, he had no intentions of falling into the colonel's hands.

"We can take the dry wash. They are all half asleep and have no knowledge you are here."

"Lead the way," he said, with the reins in his hand. "I appreciate—"

She looked back, shook her head to stop him. "No regrets. My sister does not often send such a big man to me."

"Perhaps another time," he said, catching up with her and looking around as they descended into the deep arroyo.

"Yes. You must be careful, hombre."

" 'I will," he said, listening to the sounds in the distance. A stallion's shrill scream carried. Sounded familiar enough. All stallions sounded alike—but Disantos could have his Boy. And what about the *companero*, Rosa? Was she there, too?

"Did the colonel have a woman with him?"

"I don't know. I only asked a few questions of some people I trusted."

On a mission to get him out of there, she hurried down the sand-crusted bed of the wash. He had to step out to keep up. A shame he didn't have more time, he decided, looking at her shapely waist and backside under the skirt. To cut off any sounds his horse might make, he kept close to the animal's head as his boots churned the loose sand. A whiff of their cooking smoke reached his nose; he hoped the *federales* were too busy to bother with one straggler heading out.

Where the side wash opened into a wide, dry river bed, she stopped him.

"Some day, you must come back and finish what you started in your sleep."

He nodded, looking down at her. A quick hard kiss and he better ride. That mission completed, he checked the girth and then swung aboard, licking his lips. She tasted like honey, enough so it drew the saliva in his mouth.

"*Señora* O'Dell, I am grateful." He whirled the horse and set out in a run across the wide flat arroyo for the far side. Somewhere a rooster was crowing and the quail in the greasewood called back and forth. It was morning and time for him to be getting on. The sun had begun to gild the eastern sky with gold.

He found the camp of some woodcutters late in the afternoon. Three older men with long gray beards. Unarmed, they started at his arrival.

"We have no money," the tallest one said.

"No worry, *mi* amigos. I'm only passing through. If I may buy some tortillas?"

"Get off your horse, hombre. No one should buy food. We have no tortillas, but we have plenty of frijoles."

He nodded to the threesome and dismounted. With hobbles from the saddlebags, he let the pony graze on the dry grass and hung the bridle on the horn. Sweeping off the old sombrero, he wiped his gritty forehead on his dust-floured sleeve. Then with a spoon from his kit, he joined them.

"Hot today," he said to the men who were again seated on the ground.

The tall one served him and nodded in agreement.

"We lost our tortilla maker," he said.

"She left with a boy who had a stiff dick," the full-faced one said and then he laughed. His amusement drew a frown of disapproval from the tall one who pulled on his beard.

"They tease me, but they never had to please a *puta* who wanted it all the time," the tall one complained.

"I understand," Slocum said.

"Ah," the full-faced one said and shook his head to dismiss Slocum's concern. "She only wanted it every year."

Even the tall one laughed as he took his place. "See what I must work with?"

"Very unfortunate," Slocum said, then he tasted the beans. They could use more salt, but perhaps the tortilla maker took that with her, too.

"I don't wish to pry, but you look like a man on the run?" the tall one said.

"Yes."

"Do you head for the border?"

"Is there anything I should know?"

The tall one nodded. "They say that the *federales* are patrolling it looking for someone."

With a slow nod, Slocum looked off at the bloody sunset. "You hear of a name?"

"Slowsum, I think was what he said."

"What do they want this one for?"

"The *Commandante* Disantos says he's the one who leads the revolution in Sonora."

"Then he must be a big man with lots of soldiers at his side?"

"I guess so."

He slept for a few hours at a distance from their fire where they snored and laid like mummies wrapped in their threadbare cotton blankets. When the moon rose, he saddled the pony and used the North Star for a compass to ride on.

He reached Conejos on the border in midday. No sign of

any patrols so far, as he studied the buildings from his vantage point, but no sign of army tents nor the cavalry horse herd if they were in the village. To avoid them any way, he rode around the place, stopping at a safe harbor with a man called Theo, who stabled his horse in a corral with his two others.

Unsaddled, the weary animal rolled in the dust for relief. When he rose, he stood with his four feet spread apart and shook vigorously. Slocum nodded to the man.

"I may be gone for a while."

"No worry, your *cabello* will be safe here."

"Are there soldiers in the village?"

"They come and go. But be careful, there are many people you can no longer trust."

He thanked the man and paid him two pesos for the horse's keep. Then with a blanket from his bedroll draped over his stooped shoulders, he headed for the town. Listening and watching everything, he managed to ease his way into the center of the village and at last went through the garbage-stinking alley to the back door of the El Toro Cat House.

"Is *Señora* Malone here?" he asked in a quiet voice.

"No bums in here! Go away! Go way!" the buxom woman cook shouted, waving a large butcher knife at him to speed his dismissal.

"What is it, Donna?" The woman in the doorway behind the cook peered hard at him. "What does he want?"

"Something for free. Maybe food."

Her reddish chestnut hair caught highlights on the many curls. She squinted hard with her hands on her full hips. From where he stood he could imagine Dossie's fleshy body encased in the expensive corset that made her breasts pop out of the low-cut dress.

"Who're you?"

He swept off the sombrero and smiled. "Some call me Slocum."

"Ah, sweet Jesus, I'd never know you." On the verge of running over to hug him, she hesitated. "Man, no wonder she wanted to run you off. You look like hell and smell worse."

He rubbed the whisker bristles over his mouth, then he raised his gaze to meet hers. "I've been there."

"I can believe that. Donna have a bath drawn for him— in my room. Go! Do it now! Whew, shed those clothes right there. I don't want my room to smell like I slept with a hoss."

"Here?" He looked around.

"Yes, right here. Hell, honey, you ain't got anything these gals of mine ain't seen before. Course, the size might make them faint. Give me that gun belt and throw that dirty sombrero out in the alley." She came over and took charge of his undressing.

"Ain't the gawdamn *federales* looking for you, honey?" His holster slung over her shoulder, she took his big knife and scabbard, too.

"They say they are. Colonel Disantos been around here?"

"Some. He rode out a few days ago. He shot two prisoners in the square before he left."

"Who were they?"

"*Pistoleros*, I guess. They never came in here. One was an older man, I think his name was *Ernest*." She shook her curls as if in deep thought. "Gilberto was the other."

"That bastard! Those men worked for me." He stopped unbuttoning his shirt. The news of their deaths felt like a swift kick in the crotch. Damn, oh, damn, they didn't need to be killed. "Did he say why he shot them?"

"Why else does he shoot them? Revolutionaries! The cemeteries are full of them. Hell, if they were all soldiers, they would have whipped his hard ass by now. Get your clothes off." With a swish of her stiff dress, she went to the cupboard and took down a bottle of good whiskey by the neck.

"We can have an Irish wake for them. In my room. Aw, quit acting like some bashful boy, and get your damn, dirty union suit off."

A hot wind came in the back door and swept his bare butt after he shed the long faded-to-yellow underwear. His attire in a pile on the floor, he marched dutifully barefooted after her swinging butt. In the parlor, he looked up to see three of her girls hanging over the top rail to examine his fortune.

"Go back to bed," she said, marching up the stairs holding up her skirt in one hand, the whiskey in the other, and the holster threatening to fall off her bare shoulder every step of the way. "This is my meat. Get your own."

Their giggles forced him to smile, though he felt his face redden.

"When I get him curried down, he won't look half bad," she said and turned to grin privately at him.

"Ain't got much to work on," he said and kept climbing.

"His name is Mr. Benton and he's from St. Louis, if anyone asks. Dick Benton."

"Yeah, we can see that," one of them said, and at that comment the three faces over the railing disappeared.

"Smart mouths. You can't hire good help anymore."

"They looked all right to me," he said with a shrug.

"Gawdamn, a mare burro's ass would probably look good to you."

"Hadn't seen one."

"Good thing," she said and they went down the hall to where two young Latin girls were exiting a door with an empty pail in each hand. They nodded to her and to him, looking a little taken aback by his state of undress. Then snickering, they ran off.

A generous breeze billowed out the lace curtains on the windows. The tin bathtub with its steaming water in the center of the spacious apartment looked inviting. He went over and tested it. She hung his holster on a ladder-back chair close by and set the whiskey on the seat. With a nod for him to get in, she went back to the door and shouted for one of her helpers.

"Get in," she said with impatience ringing in her voice. "I'll be out of this dress in a minute and then I'll use a brush on you."

"You called?" the young girl asked from the doorway.

"Yes. Unhook my dress and hang it up. I have a tough job ahead of me and I don't want soap and water all over it."

"Yes, ma'am." The girl curtsied and went to work on the back of the dress. Soon Dossie's garment was peeled off and she stood with her feet apart in the stark white corset. She looked exactly as he had imagined she would.

"Time to get to work," she said and picked up a long-handled brush. "You hang that dress up nice," she said to the girl.

"Yes, ma'am."

He reached over for the whiskey and bit the cork out of the top. The cork spat away on the floor, he turned the brown bottle up. His thoughts filled with the disappointment that two of his own men were dead at the hands of that butcher Disantos. Maybe a loaded gun shoved up his ass wasn't a tough enough way for that murderous devil to be sent to hell.

Where was that *companero*?

"What did you do this time to piss off the authorities?" she asked, getting on her knees, brandishing the long-handled brush and a bar of soap. Her full cleavage floated on top of the corset in his face with the lacy material only covering half of her nipples.

"Took a few hunting rifles down south."

She nodded that she understood, scrubbing his back with gusto.

"Did you succeed?"

"No, I got double-crossed. The buyer sent bandits to steal them so he could buy them at half price from them."

"No honor among thieves." She shook her head in disapproval.

"You mean bastards on either side can't be trusted?" He rubbed soap on his left arm and lathered it.

"Same thing. More and more of Mexico becomes the place of the untrustworthy."

"Did they bury those men?"

"Yes. The church did, with a full funeral, which means that someone paid for it."

He looked at her hard. Who would do such a thing? Tally, the cowboy? Obviously he was not executed with them, but the Mexican Army hated shooting U.S. citizens. The American counsel always made a big fuss in the federal district over such executions. To keep in good graces with their superiors in Mexico City, they refrained from such sentences for gringos. Instead they shot them in the back of the head at close range out in the desert for trying to escape or their bodies were left out there to become so-called victims of the revolutionaries.

"See if there is a gringo called Tally across the border."

"He one of your men?"

"Yes. You know him?"

She shook her head and continued her efforts. "Raise up; your butt needs to be scrubbed now."

He frowned at her brush. "Go easy with that damn thing."

"I know what to protect," she said and moved behind him.

His bath complete, he stood behind the waving curtains and viewed the busy street below. Vendors and traffic intermingled. Where was Tally anyway? He could see the border guards for both sides loafing around their opposing shacks.

"Your clothing is coming," she said, standing at his back. A fingertip traced down the bare skin. "You have several bullet holes in you, no?"

"Any of them leaking?"

"No, thank goodness. You probably have not eaten since . . . when?"

"Last night, I had frijoles with some woodcutters in the foothills."

She laid the side of her face on his back. Her arms went around him to clasp her hands over his muscle-corded belly. "Oh, hombre, what will you do next?"

"Take you to bed?"

"No! I mean like what will you do after that?"

"Go see what I can salvage. The guns are hidden. I must make a new deal in Mexico and collect my money."

"You don't think the men told the colonel where they were before he shot them?"

"No, I'd about stake my life on it. They never told him anything."

Her perfume began to curl up his nose, she turned him around and pursed her lips for him to kiss. Damn, where was Tally?

12

Close to midnight, Slocum, on the American side, eased his way up the alley to the back door of the Hill, McComb, and Dunavan Warehouse. His new stiff waist overalls made scratchy noises when they rubbed together as he walked. He bellied himself up on the dock and then testing the air for any sounds before he rose to his feet. Easing his way to the yellow, illuminated four-pane window, his hand rested on his gun butt.

A familiar figure worked on the books inside at a desk. Slocum scratched on the glass. Blinking his eyes, Charlie Dunavan looked up from his ledgers and squinted to try to see who it was. Unhooking the wire earpieces of his glasses, he set them down and crossed to the window.

"Who's out there?"

"Slocum."

"Come to the back door, I'll unlock it."

With a sweep of the dark alley and docks, seeing nothing out of the way, he went to the door. Soon the sounds of the door being unbolted and it came open.

"Thought you might be dead," the balding man said.

"Not yet. Disantos got two of my boys, I heard."

"Your man Tally tried to bribe the guards so he could get them out." Dunavan shook his head warily in the light from the office lamp spilling out on the warehouse floor. "Nothing

111

any of us could do. Sorry. Did you get your arms sold?"

"No. Diego was dealing with Omar Shard. Shard's plot was to let us get the arms down there and then have some bandits steal them so they could buy them at a reduced price."

"You still have the arms?"

"I think so. They've been hidden."

"What will you do next?"

"Hire some men to go back and sell them."

"Have a seat," Dunavan offered, indicating the captain's chair before his desk.

"Who sold some bandit grenades for a cannon?"

Dunavan blinked and shook his head. "Your guess. What were they?"

"U.S. Army issue."

"Probably stolen at Fort Huachucua. I can check."

"It isn't important. Where's Tally staying?"

"At the Grand Hotel."

"Get him word to meet me. I better not contact him myself." Slocum took a piece of paper, dipped a quill pen in the ink well, and scribbled, "El Toro Cat House. Ask for Dick Benton." For a few seconds, he blew on it to dry the ink and handed it across the table to Dunavan.

"What can I do? I fear there won't be many men around here willing to run Disantos's gauntlet with you for any price after he shot those men."

"See who you can find for me."

"Where should I send them?"

"They want work and can ride and shoot, they need to meet me here Friday. No guts, I don't want them."

"What if I put the word out in Mexico?"

"I don't care. I want ten men."

"What do you plan to do?"

"Clean up some of the country south of the border."

Dunavan leaned back in his chair and shook his head. "*Federales*, bandits, and the rest. You and ten men are going to clean them all out?"

"And one double-dealing merchant, too."

Dunavan nodded as if he understood. "They have got your back up."

"You don't know how high either."

"I'll get this to Tally in the morning." He waved the note at him. "Where do you want these men to meet you if I find them?"

"I'll have Tally find a safe place. He can let you know."

Dunavan tented his fingertips and did spider push-ups with them as if in deep consideration. "I hope you succeed."

Slocum nodded. "We will. See you, and thanks."

"I ain't done much yet," Dunavan said and followed him to the back door. After letting him out, they said good night and wished each other good luck.

Slocum searched the dark alley, then, like a cat, he slipped away in the darkness. Thirty minutes later, he entered the back door of the cat house, and took the ladder in the pantry up to Dossie's apartment. A new Boss of the Plains Stetson hung on the brass bedpost. A present, no doubt, for him to complete his new outfit. He lifted it off the post and began to examine the fine silk binding. Then he worked the brim to turn it up a little more on the sides. Seated on a straight-back chair, he was so engrossed he started when the door opened.

"You're back," Dossie said with a wide smile, her silk dress rustling. She crossed the room and bent over to kiss him.

"Like the hat?" she asked when she straightened.

"Beautiful."

"Now what will you do?" He went to the window, to study the street below.

"Go back, get my arms, and sell them."

"With whom?" She frowned, concerned-looking.

"Ten tough men. Armed to the teeth."

"Where will you find these men?"

"Here and over there." He tried on the hat and looked at himself in the tall oval looking glass on a stand. It would do.

"I've wasted all my money on all those damn clothes. . . ." She shook her head in disapproval.

He strode over and took her in his arms. A glance down at the lovely cleavage and he smiled at her. "I ain't no damn fancy French poodle you can put in a sweater and keep on a leash."

She threw back her head and laughed. "No, by Gawd, you ain't no poodle. But I aim to get my money's worth out of you before you leave again."

Her hand began to grope his crotch, until she wiggled out of his embrace. Busy fingers tore loose his holster, then shoved the galluses off his shoulders. The loose-fitting, unshrunken pants fell to his knees about the same time she tore open his underwear and snatched his dick in her hand.

"Ah, how long do I have you?" She began to gently pull on his shaft.

"Oh, off and on till Friday."

"Not long enough. How much money do you need?" Her warm breath in his ear, her tongue followed as she stood on her toes to reach him.

"Perhaps seven hundred."

"Liar." She pressed her breasts into his chest. "I'll get you a thousand."

"But what if I can't pay you back . . . ?"

Her grip tightened on his dick. "You better come back with this in one piece and I'll let you pay me back at a dollar for every toss in the bed."

"That'll take years."

"So?"

He swept her up in his arms and dropped her unceremoniously on the bed. His gaze on her, he toed off his new soft boots and finished shedding his pants. Then he stripped off his shirt and underwear. She crawfished up the bed until her curly hair was spilled around her face on the pillows.

"I suppose you plan to do it to me in this damn corset." Her green eyes looked to the ceiling's tin tiles for some form of celestial help. "Why the hell are men so interested in some kind of bondage for their women?"

He bent over and kissed her right tit until the nipple bobbed up and he could suck on it. She threw her head back and moaned. "Do it, crap, I can't stand it any longer."

On the bed, he climbed across her leg and readied himself for the assault. Anxious for this assault, she moved down in the bed, her snowy legs spread apart; he nosed his throbbing dick into her and she screamed like a wildcat caught in a steel trap.

Then she swallowed and clapped a hand over her mouth. "Shit fire, I'll have them all in here. I never locked the gawdamn door either." Then swept up in his efforts, she arched her back for him to go deeper and began to moan. The rough surface of the corset wore on his skin, but by then he was too immersed in his fury to notice anything but the passion in the end of his dick. Then when he knew he was going to come, he reached under her, grabbed both cheeks of her ass and drove himself to the hilt. He strained the explosion out the head of his fiery shaft and felt his back muscles give the final effort.

They collapsed in a pile. Both sucking air and blinded by the force of their efforts, they laid in a crumpled pile with him on top of her.

"Maybe I'll double your pay," she said, running her fingers through the too-long hair on the back of his head.

"Good."

He laid his head down on her cleavage. Lots to do in a short while. But once the word was out he was coming back, the element of surprise would be gone. He needed that worse than anything.

She tried to raise up at a knock on the door. "What?"

"A man downstairs wants to talk to Dick."

"Tell him to go fuck himself—" She scowled over the girl's interruption.

"No, I need to talk to him," he silenced her. "Give me five minutes. Tell him I'll be right down."

"Who's that?" Dossie hissed at him as he disengaged himself from her.

"My man Tally."

"Oh, I couldn't figure anyone but these whores knew you as Dick." They both laughed.

He used the ladder to go downstairs and shocked the cowboy who stood with his butt against the counter when he emerged from the pantry.

"You doing magic now?" Tally frowned in disbelief.

"Some. Good to see you," Slocum said softly, and went across the food-smelling kitchen to close the door to the hallway,

"Dunavan said you were hiring some guns and going back."

"That's my aim. Sorry I wasn't here. Thanks for putting them in the cemetery."

"That's all right. Them two never told Disantos nothing."

"I heard that you tried to bribe the guards. Thanks."

"I did all I could. Son of a bitch. Disantos must have expected trouble; he traded guards every night that last week. Ones that I paid were never left alone. . . ." He dropped his head, took off his hat, and beat his leg with it. "If I'd charged the damn place—"

"Wouldn't done any good. Got you killed. I'm sorry I had some problems in Mexico or I'd've been back here sooner."

"What do we need to do?" Tally looked up at him.

"Shoe the mules, get supplies, a half dozen boxes of dynamite, fuses and caps. Ammo, some new rifles, cartridge firing pistols."

"How many?"

"Ten rifles, forty-forties, pistols in the same caliber. Two-dozen bandoliers and load them. So everyone has enough ammo. Get every man, two pistol holsters to fit over his saddle horn. That, plus the guns that they carry, we should be all right."

"How much food we need?"

"Enough for two weeks."

"What if we can't get, well, say nine men tough enough?"

"Then we go with what we have. See about acquiring some good stout saddle horses, too. Some of them may need better mounts than their own."

"One pack mule to carry oats?"

"Good. Now where can we assemble them?"

"A ranch over by the Mule Shoes. Ward Bellows won't let a word out about us."

"Hard to find?"

"No, take the W Bar Seven sign to the right off the Bisbee Road."

"Get it set up. Get your supplies gathered, I have the money. I'll be checking with Dunavan and sending the ones I hire to you. And I'll tell them that Dick Benson hired them for the password."

"Good, then I'll know any ringer shows up and says that Slocum hired them, right?"

Tally looked around. "Any chance of a man getting a little in here?"

The door pushed open and both men looked up as Dossie came in. "Sorry, did I interrupt?" she asked.

"No, we were through. This is my man, Tally," Slocum said. "And right now, he needs a little female attention."

She frowned and turned her head to the side to consider him. "Bet he's got one big as a stud hoss." Then she threw her arm across his shoulder and began to herd him toward the parlor. "Blonde, brunette, or redhead? Fat, skinny, or so-so?"

"I'll know her when I see her."

"Shit, let me pick one that will do you some good," she confided.

"Okay."

"That-a boy. Hell, looks ain't all there is to a woman. Some of them pretty ones won't get their ass off the mattress. You know what I mean?"

"Exactly. Yes, ma'am." And the door closed behind them.

The last thing that Slocum heard was her loud laughter. He glanced back at the pantry—things were taking shape. Climb back up and read the newspaper; why, he had a couple hours to rest before his "banker" came back to repossess his poor dick. He closed his eyes in mild dread and shook his head.

13

The Indian dropped off a peaked-assed pinto. An unblocked hat square on his head with his greasy braids dancing on his shoulder, Slocum watched him climb the dock steps. Dark eyes, wary-looking about like a wild animal. He wore a bleached-out shirt, denim pants with a tear in the leg, and a large knife sheathed in his gun holster.

Looking up from his whittling, Slocum nodded to the Indian. "Help you?"

The buck folded his hands over his chest and nodded.

"Who sent you?" Slocum looked up at him and considered how much was tough and how much was bluff.

"Said you needed tough man."

"Who?"

"Old German storekeeper at Paradise. Name's Volkner."

Slocum nodded that was one of Dunavan's customers. "You got any family?" He turned back to his whittling with the big knife on the chuck of juniper.

"No. Squaw died."

"Okay. You got a good bow and some arrows?" He looked up to check the man's reaction. It would make a silent way to take out a sentry. In case they needed it.

The nod was affirmative

"Bring it. And tell my man Tally up there you need a good horse."

"What you pay?"

"A hundred in gold if you live for two weeks' worth of riding."

"Where's this Tally at?"

"W Bar Seven up in the Mule Shoes?" He waited for the man's answer that he knew of the ranch.

The Indian nodded. "Go up there now?"

"Yes. What do they call you?"

The name was a gutteral word in Apache.

"I'll call you Indian, I can say that. Wait, you tell him Dick Benson hired you or he'll kill you."

Amused, Indian grinned. "Dick Benson. Me savvy good."

Two more men showed up. One had a wife and five kids, Slocum shook his head and thanked the man. The other, a freckle-faced bear of a Texan—Red Caughman. He kept cupping his hand over his mouth and wiping it the whole time they talked in the shade of the warehouse porch. When they finished, Slocum stopped him.

"Be damn sure that you tell my man Tally out there that Dick Benson hired you."

The man blinked his blue eyes. "Huh?"

"'Cause he'll blow your ass away for being a spy if you forget."

"Aw, hell, I'll remember that."

"Good, it's your ass."

Butterfield came next. Thin as a razorback hog, he wore a black suit and a bowler hat. Slocum figured him for a gambler looking for a new stake to start back over.

No one objected to the sum of money he promised them and he told them to ride out to the ranch and report to Tally. Interviews grew slimmer by Thursday. Three odds and ends hired, Indian, Red, and Butterfield, and none of the others that applied looked or acted tough enough for his needs.

Slocum stood on the dock, the juniper block in his hands whittled down to a small piece of pungent-smelling wood. Two riders under sombreros came up the alley on jaded horses. Mexicans, but he didn't recognize them. Wide sombreros, they reined up at the dock and dismounted.

Something struck him as familiar about them and then with a broad smile on her face, Lou winked at him as she hitched the gun belt on her hip.

"We come for work."

He blinked in disbelief and O'Dell nodded that it was she. "We came to help you."

He shook his head. "I need *pistoleros*."

"We are good ones."

"Lou, I can't hide behind women's skirts."

"Listen, we can outshoot and outride most men; besides she's also coming to help."

"Who?" he asked, looking down the alley for the sight of someone.

"Your *companero*, Tequila Rosa."

He frowned at them.

"You forget the beautiful one so soon? Mother of God, he must have forgotten us in a minute," Lou said to her sister. "If he—"

"Serious?" He felt taken aback by the information.

"We're serious."

"How did you hear about me?"

"Are there any secrets in the border land?"

He ripped away a large shaving from the block and sighed. "No. Tally is out at the ranch off the Bisbee Road."

"He ready for us?"

"I doubt it. Two—no, three women. Lord help him." He tried to clear his thoughts, still shaken by news of Rosa's return. "I'll be ready to ride out there in an hour. When does she come?"

"After dark."

"We'll send someone back for her. Why after dark?"

Lou shrugged. "She said to say when she was coming to meet you."

"I don't think she was happy either," O'Dell said, looking at her sister for confirmation.

"I know why she's not happy, she hasn't had the chance to kill Disantos yet." Slocum shook his head in defeat.

Thoughts of her body made his stomach roil—and he thought he was over her.

"You two better ride up to the ranch and get your arms and things. I plan to leave in the morning."

"See what I told you?" Lou said to her sister.

"What's that?" he asked.

"The word was you would cross the border Sunday."

"Who told them that?"

Both women turned up their palms and looked innocent.

"Sunday's good. They may try to stop us then," he said, pleased that the gossip was misleading about the day of their departure. "Get out there to the W Bar Seven ranch off the Bisbee Road. You'll need better horses. And be sure to tell my man Tally that Dick Benson sent you or he might kill you."

Lou stepped over and kissed him on the mouth. Then she laughed aloud when her sister did the same thing.

"Get the hell out of here!"

"*Si*, Captain Benson," Lou said and they both saluted.

When they rode off, he rushed across the border and gathered his things at the El Toro, kissed Dossie good-bye, and recovered his horse from the man's pen. Before sundown, he rode back across the border like any rich, *Norte Americano* rancher would do. The horse hitched, he found a place to wait in the shadows of the warehouse, which was closed for the night. Timbers creaked in protest as the building settled back down.

"How many do you have?" Dunavan asked, looking at his pocket watch as he locked the walk-through door behind himself.

"There will be eight."

"Not enough is there?"

"Enough, if we get some breaks."

"I think you're foolish going down there against the *federales* and all those bandits with those small numbers."

"I'll know all about that in a week."

"I hope God loves you." And the man started off.

"In ten days, you'll know."

"I expect news reports by the sagebrush telegraph will beat you back here."

Slocum nodded as he heard the sounds of a single horse coming up the alley. He went to the edge of the platform and saw in the half light a rider on a dancing horse. The horse snorted in a rumble out of his throat and Slocum knew why when he saw the animal in the twilight, why she came so late. Lou was returning Big Boy to him.

He vaulted off the deck and hurried to undo the girth on his bay.

"No need," she said in a husky whisper, reining Boy up beside him. "He wears a good saddle." She leaned out to hand him the reins. "He is your grand stud, isn't he?"

"Yes," he said and swung up, feeling the power again between his knees and the fiery spirit of the big horse under him again.

"I'll ride your horse," she said, and unhitched the reins. "Where do we go?"

"To the ranch to get ready."

She nodded that she heard him.

"Oh, yes, and *gracia*." He drew in a deep breath to settle himself. No one had brought him such a present in years. He clapped Boy on the neck, pleased over his return.

"Won't the colonel miss him?" he asked.

"Who cares," she said and they left in a long trot for the ranch.

Past ten o'clock, he could see the lights of the ranch. They arrived at the low-walled house and the others collected at the hitching rack to greet them. In the starlight, he noticed the two sisters wore divided skirts, blouses, and bandoliers instead of the men's clothing they had on in town. No difference, he had hired them and suspected they could outfit any man alive.

"We ride at dawn. Best everyone get some sleep," he said.

"How far will we go?" Butterfield asked.

"No telling; however far it takes to find them."

"Them?"

"Yes, the ones we're after."

"May I ask—?"

"I'll tell you when the time comes. Good night. Tally, where are we on having everything ready to go?"

"Mules are shod. I have the packs and food, oats, blankets, some bandages, iodine and chloroform, dynamite, caps, fuses. Everyone is equipped with arms like you said, except this last one and I have weapons for her."

"Horseflesh?"

"They said that last gal had a good horse, but the others are on stout horses."

"Good."

"About them two women . . ."

"Yes?" Slocum waited with dread to hear something negative about the sisters.

"They can blast the necks out of bottles at a hundred paces. They took money off the men this afternoon in a shooting match."

"Guess they can fight all right," said Slocum.

"Hell, I won't want to face them. Who's this new one?" Tally asked.

"Don't you recognize Tequila Rosa?"

"Oh, hell, its been a long week and it was dark out there."

"She brought back my stallion, Big Boy."

"Whew. Wasn't she in Colonel Disantos's camp?"

"Yeah. Guess he never got close enough for her to give him that enema she promised him."

"I'd give the son of a bitch one." Tally's face showed his rage.

Slocum clapped him on the shoulder. "You may have that chance. You've done good here, getting all of this ready. We may not have all the gun hands I wanted, but they'll know we've been there after the smoke settles."

"They will," Tally agreed.

14

Before dawn, the women organized the mule packing. Tally and Red each twitched down the mules and they were loaded in minutes. Horses saddled and ready, they swung out of the W Bar 7 with a wave at the owner in the lighted doorway of the main house and they headed south for the border in a long trot.

Slocum sent Indian ahead to scout for them. He felt certain the man had instincts that no white man possessed about things that went on in this land. His own years with Crook's forces, he came to believe that Indians could sense more than a white man could even see if he looked straight at it.

They crossed the border near where Coronado three centuries before brought the first major expedition into this land, watering their animals in the San Pedro. A short break for man and beast and they headed southeast. His goal was to find Cordova first and repay the worthless one for his intervention.

He rode with the women to learn what he could. Curious if they knew anything about Cordova's whereabouts.

"He's up on the Rio Soapia," O'Dell said.

Lou nodded. "Why do you want him?"

"He owes me," Rosa spoke up.

Both women swiveled their heads. "He raped you?"

"No, but he sure made me sore." She used her thumb to

indicate her boobs under the crossed ammunition belts.

Both women chuckled at her. "You are like an old cow who stepped on her tit, huh?" Lou asked.

"Yes." Rosa laughed aloud and shook her head as if they had embarrassed her.

Slocum saw a rider coming hard. It must be Indian. He waved for the them to stay with the mules and loped Boy out to meet him.

"What's happening?" he asked the buck when he rode up.

"There is a company of *federales* camped in the next village."

"How many?"

Indian held up his hand four times.

"Twenty," Slocum said and nodded with a sobering thought. That was almost three to one against his troop. "They doing anything?"

"Laying in camp." The Indian shrugged.

This might be a good test. Conscripts were never very great soldiers. If they could surprise them . . . He thanked Indian and, deep in his own thoughts, he rode back to the women.

"We have twenty soldiers ahead. We need to take them. Their weapons, horses, their uniforms, and let them go back barefooted in their underwear."

"We need a dancer to take off all of her clothes for them," Lou said. "That'll get their attention, horny as those soldiers are."

"I can do that," Rosa said.

"Sure, and if we can't get you out, they'll all gang rape you."

"So? We came to fight."

He looked mildly over at her and nodded. "All right, then it can be arranged, my *companero*."

She nodded and he rode for the front to talk it over with the others. Risk-taking would be part of his plan. He only hoped they could execute this scheme as a well-oiled plan and that all went smoothly.

The sun set in a fiery blaze and they left Butterfield to

watch the mules corralled at an abandoned *rancheria*. The
long ears made too much racket to approach the camp with
them in tow. Closer than a few miles, they were audible in
the open desert country.

"You see some rockets in the sky," Slocum said to the
man, "you bring them up."

"Fair enough," the gambler said and stretched his arms
over his head.

"I'll send you help to drive them as soon as the situation
up there is secure."

Butterfield nodded that he heard him. Slocum turned Boy
back toward his remaining six-person army and followed
them out single file.

Near the village, they dismounted. Slocum and Indian
crept up close. Several fires blazed up and the sounds of
someone strumming a guitar carried on the night wind. He
could see the soldiers scattered about drinking and lounging
about on the ground in the firelight. A queasy sensation roiled
in his stomach. Sending Rosa in there as the bait looked to
him as too dangerous for her safety.

He nodded to Indian he had seen enough and they backed
away.

"What are they doing?" Lou asked.

"What soldiers usually do when they have no fears. Lying
around. Someone was playing a guitar."

"Good," Rosa said and took off the *bandoliers* over her
head and hung them on the saddle horn. "Who has a bottle?"

"I have a bottle of whiskey in my saddlebags," Tally offered.

"Good, get it."

"Wait," Slocum said, having second thoughts over her
welfare. "We can wait until they go to sleep."

"I can distract them. It will work."

Still not satisfied that he had control enough of the situation, he shook his head.

"She'll do fine," Lou assured him.

"Fine, isn't what I want."

Rosa took the whiskey bottle from Tally and began to use

it for perfume. She splashed some under her armpits, on her blouse, and took a small drink, washing her mouth with it, then spitting it out.

"You ready?" she asked, with the slur of someone with a little too much.

"We have to be," he said. He sent Red, Tally, and Indian around to the far side and to be ready when he ordered them to stand up.

He took the other two women. Approaching the jackals, they spread out in the mesquite to work in as close as they dared.

"Whoopee!" Rosa shouted. "Where is the music?"

Her appearance caused a stir and several *federales* got to their feet.

"Who are you?"

"I—am—Isabel and I want to dance. Play the music."

Slocum watched her shove aside a soldier who tried to take her in his arms. His fingers closed on his gun butt.

"I came to dance for you," she said defiantly. "You want to see me dance, don't you?"

"Yes!" went up the roar.

"Then you bring me the music." She circled with the bottle in her hand. "Music! Where is it?"

"Coming, *señorita*," a short fat soldier said, hurrying over with his brass horn.

His lips to the mouthpiece he began to play it. Soon another came and joined him. She swiped a hat from an old man and tossed it on the ground, clapping her hands over her head to the beat. Her footsteps quickened to the music and the catcalls died down as her movements began to hypnotize them.

Where were the officers? He needed them sucked into this, too. They'd be dangerous as any sidewinders. The men they could handle, but the officers had side-arms and could be deadly when confronted.

Lou came on the run. "The captain has a woman in the tent with him."

"Can you contain him? Are there any others?"

"O'Dell has spotted the lieutenant; he's in the shadows watching Rosa." She gave a head toss toward Rosa who he could see was unbuttoning her blouse.

"Can O'Dell handle him?"

Lou nodded affirmative. "When you are ready."

He nodded for Lou to go and handle the office, then waited to let her have time to get back to the tent. If only the others were in their places—he fired a shot in the air.

"Hands in the air! Now, or die!" he shouted in Spanish.

A shot sounded to the left and a woman shrieked in the night. The sounds came from the first tent. Damn! Forced to face down the men with his pistol. He saw Rosa was rebuttoning her shirt.

"Hands higher!" Tally ordered behind them. Red and Indian began to make them kneel with their hands clasped behind their heads.

"It is fine over here," O'Dell said with an officer walking before her, his hands high. "Lou wounded the captain is all."

"He'll live," she said in disgust and shoved him out of the tent with a half-naked girl. "What about her?"

"Let her go," Slocum said. At his words, she tore off into the night like a startled rabbit.

"Is every one of them here?" he asked.

"Looks like we got 'em all," Red said, making the captain kneel on the ground with the others.

"Who are you?" the senior officer demanded.

"Them sons a bitches that got you," Tally said.

"Indian, get some of their pack horses. We need their guns and ammo loaded on them." He looked over the company of men on their knees. "Make one move and you're dead and the man on each side of you as well."

"I'll go help him get the horses," Lou said and left at a trot.

Slocum hardly had time to nod his approval. "Start with that first man down there. One at a time, you undress and put your boots and clothes on the fire."

An audible "Oh, no" came from the soldiers. Red stepped in to grasp the man by his neck like a chicken and held him on his toes. "You heard the man—undress. Now!"

"*Si, señor.*" The *federale* fell all over himself to strip down to his underwear turning the garments inside out to shed them in his haste. The articles that missed the fire Red kicked in. At last the man tossed his boots in the blaze.

"You're next," Red said, shoving the first man back down. The second man jumped up to obey.

From the corner of his eye, Slocum saw a *federale* on the other end jump to his feet and start to run. A pistol shot roared and flashed orange in the night before he could clear leather with his own. Hard hit in the back, the escapee screamed and went facedown. In an instant, O'Dell stood astraddle him and began to take off his clothing as he moaned.

"Anyone else want the same?" Slocum asked. Silence reined over the others.

"Why do you hide behind the skirts of women?" the captain asked.

O'Dell kicked him in the side as she was going past with an armful of uniform and boots she had stripped from the wounded man. " 'Cause you bastards killed all our men. Now you can face the women. We're meaner than our men, no?"

The officer never answered her. She stomped on to the mounting pile and threw the clothing on the growing fire that stunk of burning cloth and leather. Red and Tally were now undressing them two at a time.

"Go find a couple of flare rockets," Slocum said to O'Dell when she returned.

She stepped over to the captain with a large knife in her hand. "Where are the flares you keep? Tell me quick if you don't want to lose this ear."

"In a trunk. In my tent," he said, as she jerked hard on his earlobe.

"Good, I won't have to look for them this way." She laughed all the way to the tent.

In minutes, she returned with the pistol and the flares. Slocum, with his eye on the men all kneeling in their underwear, told O'Dell to fire two of them to signal Butterfield to bring up the pack train.

A loud pop and then the whistle, a bloodlike explosion high above them lighted the entire camp, and a waterfall of crimson fell from the sky. Indian and Lou returned with saddle and packed horses in tow. Rifles, pistols, and ammo were loaded in the panniers. Red took an ax to the spokes on the two wagons. Then Tally tossed a rope over each tent and used his horse to drag them on the smoky fire.

"What do you intend to do to us?" the captain demanded.

"Let all of you walk to Mexico City. Tell them that we are tired of Disantos murdering our people and you can expect more of the same if it continues," Slocum said.

"We will die in the desert," one soldier complained.

"Who will miss you?" Rosa said and Slocum's army laughed.

"Get their horses," he said to her.

"We already have them hitched to their halters by fours," Lou said.

"Fine. You men, get on your feet and start marching south."

"If I live to a hundred I will never stop searching for you," the captain said.

"Good, then I'll save you all those years. Next time we meet, I'll kill you," Slocum said, keeping a hand on his gun butt, just in case.

Grumbling and cursing, they started off in the starlight, walking on tender feet in their socks. He watched them close for any break they might try as the pack and saddle horses were being brought up.

"Tally, you and Lou go help Butterfield with the mules. We need to ride hard tonight. And be miles away from here by sunup."

"Going."

He took the leads to eight horses from Lou and they left the camp on the fly. Slocum, Red, Indian, Rosa, and O'Dell, with a string of horses and enough arms for a company of men. Plus Tally, Lou, and Butterfield rounding out his force.

"Where can we go in the foothills?" he asked Indian.

"Water in Aqua Canyon. We keeping all these horses?"

"No, they make too much dust. We need to cache the weapons, too."

"There is an old *rancheria*, maybe a three-hour ride. We could pull down a building on them."

"Good, that's better than burying them. Save time. Let's ride." He nodded in approval at Indian. The night wind in his face, he felt better about his ragtag army.

15

The *federales'* arms, wrapped in canvas, was secured under the pulled-over, crumbling wall of adobe bricks. Slocum considered it a good cache for sometime when he really needed money in this land or weapons. Indian returned with a report of nothing ahead.

"Let me go ahead to the next village," Lou said, wiping her gritty wet face on a rag. "Rosa, too. We can find if there is any trouble there and save a gunfight."

Slocum nodded. "You two be careful. We'll wait for your report."

Lou nodded and ran for her horse. Rosa joined her and they set out in a lope.

Two hours later, Slocum held up his hand to halt the train when he spotted Lou coming hard on her horse.

"We are in luck," Lou said, reining up her lathered horse. "Cordova is in the village ahead."

"Good. How many men with him?"

"A few." She shook her head under the great sombrero as if they were nothing. "He won't ever be a *generale*."

"If he would go back to Juarez, I'd let him go."

"He can't be a *generale* there, either," Lou said and bounded out of the saddle.

"He can live there." Slocum followed her as she swapped

saddle to the extra mount. "Did Rosa stay there to watch things?"

"*Si*, she is making certain of everything until you can come."

"How many men—I mean soldiers—do I need?"

"Take the big one, Red, and that Indian. Me on this fresh horse and four of us can go take him." Lou's face glowed.

"All right." Slocum agreed. Clearing the would-be *generale* out of this land wouldn't hurt. Besides he owed him for kidnapping Rosa.

With Lou on a fresh horse and the others mounted, they headed for the nearby village. He wondered about Rosa remaining behind, but dismissed it. What if Cordova recognized her? He'd be glad to be there and confront the phoney leader of nobody.

Outside the village, they left their horses in a deep dry wash and followed Lou, who led them through some mesquite thickets by the back way.

"There's Cordova's main man," Slocum said, indicating the *segundo* sitting on the porch with a Winchester across his lap.

"What's he guarding?" Lou asked.

"That casa," Red said as they lined up to view things.

"Indian, go around back and see what you can find out. How many more men does he have?"

"One on the roof over there." Lou pointed to him.

"Damn, it's a trap," Slocum said. "I underestimated the man. See any more?"

"Injun's coming back," Red said.

"They got her."

"Aw, shit," Slocum said.

"They've got Rosa?" Red asked.

"Hell, yes, they recognized her." He closed his eyes and shook his head at Indian. "Wish you had your bow and arrow. We'd take out that guy on the roof."

"I can get him," Indian said.

"Let me have that bastard on the porch. He don't know

me from Adam," Red said, cupping his mouth in his hand as if in deep concentration.

"Be careful, I'm going back to get a rifle, just in case there's more," Slocum said, upset at the turn of events.

"I'll go get her out of there," Lou said, shedding her bandoliers.

"How?"

"I will be Theresa, the cook, looking for work." She removed her sombrero and fluffed her hair. Then pulling the blouse down in front to expose more of her cleavage, she tucked in the tail. "Don't I look like her?"

"Damn, I better go get the Winchester." Slocum set out in a run for the horses. Things were happening fast again. He jerked a Winchester out of the scabbard and started back up the hillside. If Red went in too quickly, or Indian triggered off the sentry on the roof, Lou could be in the cross fire.

He arrived back in time to see the *segundo* stand up and talk to her. He was busy shaking his head and trying to make Lou leave when the Texan rode up.

Slocum could not hear Lou and the *segundo*'s words, but once Red got on the porch he used his gun barrel on the man's head, who went down like a poled steer. When Red swung the rifle around, Indian had the roof sentry under his control. Slocum raced for the casa where Red and Lou were on the porch. The Texan used his boot to crash open the door and Lou was inside in a flash.

No sign of another opposition outside when Slocum reached the porch, but he heard a struggle inside. From the doorway, he could see Red throwing fists and backing Cordova to the wall, with his pants at his knees hobbling him. Getting off the bed, Rosa straightened her clothes. With blood in her eyes, she swept back the short hair from her face to glare at the man.

"Let me have that bastard. I'll make him a gelding!"

"Go see about Indian," he said to Lou and moved to hold back Rosa.

She shrugged his hand off her shoulder. "I want him cut."

"Cordova, there's not room in Sonora for the two of us.

Take your things and go back to Juarez." Slocum used his arm to restrain her.

"I—I—"

"You better leave now. I can't hold her off very long."

"I'm going," he mumbled, pulling up his pants as he struggled to walk. Still seething, she gave him two swift kicks in the seat of the pants. The man held his hands out behind his butt, rushing out the front door.

"He rape you?" Slocum asked.

"No, but my tits are sure sore all over again," she said, holding them up with her hands as if they pained her and making a face at Slocum. "Damn him."

In a short while, Cordova and his unarmed men were on horseback without luggage and headed out of the village. Slocum stood and watched the dejected men ride away. Villagers had begun to gather and they clapped their hands, acting pleased at Cordova's forced exodus.

Lou, with her pistol and ammo belts on again, came back laughing and clapped Slocum on the arm. "Time for a fiesta, boss man."

He agreed with a nod. "Indian, go get the others and the mules."

He turned to study the villagers as they grew braver and came out bringing him and his army some dry wine to drink and bowing to his *campaneras*.

Red, wiping his mouth with his hand, came over. "I think we're going to have us a real time here tonight, boss man." He spun clear around to view a dark-eyed girl going by with a water jug.

Lou pulled on the big man's shirtsleeve to get his attention. "Dummy, there isn't any water in the direction she's going."

"What the hell she going for then?"

"To get you to look at her ass."

Holding his elbow in his hand and the other cupping his mouth, he shook his head. "Hell, darling, you look better than that."

Lou pursed her lips and nodded in approval. "You got

good taste for a gringo." Then playfully she punched him in the gut. "You better take a long siesta today, big hombre; you're going to need it."

"Promises, promises," he said and slapped her hard on the butt.

"You'll see promises," she said, with her rubbing where he smacked her and went for their horses.

"I need a drink," Rosa said, looking around with a scowl.

"Me, too," Slocum agreed. They crossed the street for the cantina.

Inside the dark interior, Slocum ordered a bottle and directed her to a side table. The bartender brought them two cups and a bottle of mescal. Many of the men coming inside tipped their hats to them. He broke the seal and jerked out the cork.

"Enough of this fire water might heal those boobs." Then he held up his cup toward her and grinned as she bristled all over again.

The afternoon turned into night. Music soon carried from the square. For the first time in weeks, the tightness between his shoulders let up. They left the cantina, dined on tamales from a street vendor, and headed for the square and the sounds of instruments.

His plan was going to work: That conniving merchant came next, then Omar Shard needed a lesson. Somhow before these raids were over, it needed to end with uprooting Disantos. As he and Rosa danced under the Chinese lanterns, he about laughed out loud. The damn guns—so busy making war and looking at her boobs, he about forgot them, he still must find a buyer for them.

"What are you thinking?" Rosa asked.

"What do most men think about with a beautiful woman in their arms?"

"Oh, that."

He hugged her tighter and laid his head on top of hers. "No, I am thinking that tomorrow we can even the score with the one who started all this trouble: Omar Shard."

He felt her give a shudder. "He's a mean hombre."

"Yes, but with surprise we can get to him. Did you ever get close to Disantos?" he asked.

She wouldn't look up at him. He swung her around to the music; he knew the answer. No need to ask more. Her role as Tequila Rosa so far had been perhaps tougher than she imagined.

"How close did you get to Disantos?"

She threw her head back and looked up at him with a disappointed head shake. "Not close enough."

"Why did you come back to help me?"

"I heard that you were hiring *pistoleros*."

He looked off in the night. Damn, perhaps the colonel already knew of his plans. "Was it common gossip?"

She shook her head. "I learned it from a friend."

"Anyone else know in the camp?"

"I doubt it. Besides, if I stayed there much longer, I had to choose between sleeping with a pot-bellied sergeant or a lieutenant with consumption."

The musicians stopped to take a break. Slocum led her aside and they stood back in the shadows. The fact she knew about his raising a small army still niggled him. Who else knew?

"Don't move, *señor*." The muzzle of a pistol in his back; cold chills ran down his jawbone. A trap. Where were the others? In camp.

"Back this way, both of you. Be quiet or more will be hurt." Three men under blankets and wearing sombreros. But by the clipped Spanish accent of the man, he knew this was no peon. The other two had guns drawn under their *serapes*.

"This way. We have horses waiting."

In the alley, they tied his hands behind his back. At the side, the one in charge was coughing trying to conceal it, but Slocum heard him, Shoved up in the saddle by the other two, he looked back toward the presidio. The band was playing again.

"Get in the saddle, my Rosa."

"I am, my darling. What took you so long?"

Her words with this man chilled him more. Goose bumps

popped out on the backs of his arms. The officer with consumption that she spoke about as her other choice—she had already chosen him. How could he have been so stupid? The ropes cut into his wrists. They rode down the alley with him wedged between the other two men's horses. No doubt they were the toughest pair in the officer's company. He glanced up at the star-flecked skies. God sure needed to help him this time.

16

His *federale* captors rode hard all night. Two hours after sunup, they let him dismount and untied one hand so he could piss. Both corporals stood, ready to shoot him if he tried anything. The dark-faced one called Montrey held a cap-and-ball pistol on him. Arturo, with the beady eyes of a sidewinder, held the rope that bound to his wrist. Throughout the night, this one had used his quirt to make Slocum's horse go faster.

Slocum's pants rebuttoned, Arturo ordered him on the horse and, once in the saddle, he retied his hands behind his back. The rope cut deep in the skin. Obviously, they had no intention of having to load him again as they had done at the village.

Standing to the side, the lieutenant and his lady talked in soft voices. Tequila Rosa and this officer were no strangers, Slocum decided. Disgusted at the matchup, they reminded him of two lovebirds in a cage. *Coo*ing and *ahh*ing to each other as they walked about in the desert apart from him and his guards, far enough that their actual words were inaudible. Slocum wanted to kick her sweet ass into hell at the moment. At any price, risking even his life, he decided, she was going to get to Disantos. Make that son of a bitch so jealous of his junior officer that Disantos would have to have her. He read her plan; he was simply the sacrificial goat in the deal.

No one could ever for a moment doubt her loyalty to the *federales*—she had turned over the gringo to them. He ground his molars together when the lieutenant, who he heard the men call Mazzarra, give the orders for them to mount up.

"We can't keep *el colonel* waiting."

Waiting—that sumbitch could wait till hell froze over for Slocum's purposes. He twisted in the saddle and looked back. Could his people even figure out where they had taken him? One chance he had—Indian. What had he left behind: a gambler, a big bear of a Texan, two tough *companeros*, and a cowboy. What chance did they stand against the *federales*?

Not much.

By noon, sun time, he could see the white-limed towers of a mission in a grove of cottonwoods. Unfamiliar with the place, it must be abandoned for there were no farms around. Once-cleared fields alongside the road were growing back to mesquite and prickly pear. Humps of dirt and sticks that had once been jackals marked the way. This place like many other northern settlements had to be abandoned because of the earlier Apache scourge over the land.

Then he spotted the shiny cannon and a row of brown tents. Must be Disantos's temporary base, he decided. In a few minutes, he would meet the butcher of Sonora and no doubt shortly after that receive his sentence of death. Only twelve hours before, with the lovely traitor Rosa in his arms, he had been celebrating his second victory of the ten-day war. Day three proved to be a disaster.

The two *federales* jerked him from the horse in front of the church. Mazzarra rode over and smiled. "The rifles? You have them, *señor?*"

Slocum shook his head with the blankest face he could compose. "They were stolen from me."

"Ah, who stole them, *señor?*" He reined up his good bay horse.

Slocum saw the lather at the sides of the horse's mouth where the spade bit fit in them. Sleek coated, this animal was more than an ordinary Mexican army horse. The spirited gelding wanted to dance around.

"I asked you who has them." The officer's stern look grew blacker with impatience.

Bland faced, Slocum finally looked up. "Damned if I know. I came back here to find them. I thought you all had them."

Rage burned in the officer's dark eyes. "I have no time for your insolence. Perhaps when my men are through with you, your memory will improve."

"I don't know how. Those arms were stolen from me. If I had them I damn sure would never have came back here. I'd be counting my money in some border whorehouse."

"You came back for revenge. The rifles, *señor*, where are they?" This time he jerked sharply on the frittering horse to make him be still.

"As well ask that horse as me, brother." Slocum shook his head in disgust. "You're wasting your time, is all I can say. Those guns are gone."

"Take him to the church and get my answers!" Mazzarra said to the pair.

"Where's the boss?" Slocum asked.

"What boss?" Mazzarra checked his horse.

"The butcher of Sonora. You know who I mean."

"In the field, I assume, looking for more traitors to our country." The man's face paled and he began coughing into his leather gloves. To control his horse and cough hard at the same time soon proved debilitating to him.

At last, he managed to say to the pair, "Get the answer from him." And waved them away.

The corporals saluted and took Slocum by the arms to lead him away, but not before he caught the last bland look from Tequila Rosa on her horse. Damn, she was determined at any cost to complete her mission. He would simply have to be a casualty. A mere rock in the stream to step upon for her to cross. He looked up in the bright sunshine at the unfinished tower on the right of the structure. They never completed building a church because, back under the Spanish rule, if it was ever finished, they had to pay taxes on it. A fine thing for him to remember while two thugs strong-armed him on his way to some torture chamber in the bowels of the mission.

If Disantos was out in the field, how long would they punish him? No telling. Nothing he could say or do or promise, either. He tried to think about dancing with the black widow the night before. How he dreamed of her sensuous body in his blankets. Tasting those pear-shaped breasts that Cordova about tore off. His thoughts were miles away when they shoved him in a small room off the main sanctuary portion.

They tore off his rotten shirt and tied his wrists with ropes wrapped around the vegas supporting the roof. Grateful for the low roof, he could stand as the two shouted for him to give them answers. But he was far away, parting her silky legs, poking his dick into her. His hips ached to probe her, and, heady with desire, he began his flight with her to someplace in the fluffy, monsoon clouds that drift over the desert. Even when the loaded quirt struck his back, he never stopped shoving his hard-on into her. The lashes after lashes only made him pump her harder. Her hips rising to meet his thrusts, she arched her back and shoved herself at him. Their pelvis bones rubbed together as they ground out their passion for one another.

Again and again the quirt struck. Blood ran down his back like slips of water easing out of a rock crevice from a small spring. The soldiers roared, they demanded, they cussed him, until at last in the ovenlike confinement of the windowless room, they collapsed on their butts, soaked with sweat.

"He doesn't know" were the last words he heard before he came inside her in one long, debilitating shot and fainted.

He awoke with his shoulder sockets on fire as he hung from the ropes over his head. Darkness had invaded his cell. He could see a square of the starlight beaming down on the sanctuary floor. Somehow he needed to stand up to ease the pressure on his arms. His legs refused to answer him. Teeth gritted, at last he began to rise, but only at the price of more eyelid-squeezing pain.

His back felt like an inferno. How to get away? The ropes around his wrists cut so deep. He threw his head back to try to escape the many fiery stripes in his skin.

Half conscious, he heard men talking either in the sanctuary or outside. No matter how hard he concentrated, only some words were audible. "That stupid Mazzarra . . ."

"Ho, ho, he better screw her a lot . . ."

"Yes, the colonel . . ."

"I know, *el colonel* will have his big dick in her like that . . ."

"I wish it was mine stuck in her tight cunt instead of his . . ."

"You are a stupid private, you only get the ugly ones to screw."

"Yeah, maybe I get fifths after the sergeant and the corporals are all through with a fat, ugly one."

"Even a second with her would be good enough for me."

"This hombre they brought in today—he has an army, no?"

"Some *pistoleros. Banditos*, is all. No army."

"Who told you?"

Slocum tried to stay conscious. The men were gone and he could hear nothing but the night insects sizzle. Soon he fainted and felt his sockets jerked hard when he fell forward and the ropes caught him.

"No use, he's still passed out," someone said and he awoke to see them leaving. He felt too weak to get up. Miles away from the pain, he swung ever so slightly and eased back into the recesses of his mind to escape the pain.

Then a cold bucket of water sloshed on his face and he licked the moisture from his lips trying to quench the thirst that raged through him.

"I grow tired of you," Mazzarra said.

Slocum never answered. First, he felt uncertain his voice would even work, and, second, as long as he could stay in that other world the better his defense would be against the new pain they would try to inflict on him.

"Those rifles, where are they?"

No answer. His blurry vision centered on the silver bar. Mazzarra's face was not in focus, though he could detect the black rage that masked it. He has Rosa, isn't that enough? Why was he in this cell, wasting his time trying to pry answers from Slocum that would never escape his lips? This man needed to be screwing Rosa—*el colonel* would soon return and take her away for him. Why, even his own men said so.

Then Slocum in his daze wanted to laugh out loud. He could see her jamming a pistol up his big hairy ass and hear the butcher Disantos's last screams before the muffled explosions went off inside him. One shot, two, then three, four, five, six, then the hammer clicking again and again on an empty chamber and spent cartridges.

"Where are those rifles?"

"Up . . . Disantos's ass," Slocum managed and his world went black.

He heard the loud blasts. Cannon fire. Explosions. Men shouting in their confusion. The camp was under attack by artillery and a cavalry charge. What in the hell was happening out there? Rifle fire. Winchesters—too rapid for the *federales'* trapdoor rifles. Screams and more explosions. Whoever was out there had artillery, too. Artillery, damn— must be revolutionaries. The whole church shuttered at the next blast.

The bugler was blowing retreat. Must be some force out there. More explosions, more rifle fire—men cussing. Footsteps and someone held a candle lamp up to see.

"Here! I found him!" A woman's voice. The sound of an angel. He felt a smile crease his swollen cracked lips. An angel called Lou. Thank you, God.

"Red, you'll have to carry him. He can't walk."

"That's easy enough, my lady. Cut them ropes, I've got him."

"They've whipped him to death. Be easy! Be easy! We should have got here sooner," Lou scolded as Red ducked the low lintel and carried him into the sanctuary.

Thank God. Like a feather, he felt himself being transported in the big Texan's arms. He couldn't hold his head up and knew it bobbed like it was loose. At the side door, he heard another voice. "Is he alive?"

"Barely," Lou said. "We need him in the saddle, I can hold him till we get out of—" Another explosion nearby flashed on the tall stuccoed side of the church and the shock wave shook everything.

Slocum felt strong hands putting him on a horse. Soon she was behind, her arms were around him and she reined the horse away. Her lovely breasts stuck hard in his sore back, she hugged him to them and they left in a trot. Stars were out and, though he felt helplessly drunk, a small smile cracked his sore lips at the thought of being delivered from the teeth of his enemies by an angel. Then another explosion behind them shattered his thinking.

"Go tell that gawdamn Indian to save the rest of that dynamite. Hell fire, he's like a little kid with a new toy," Lou told Red sharply and he rode off. "Easy, big man, we'll find you a doctor. Till then, O'Dell ain't half bad at fixing up folks."

He passed in and out of consciousness as they rode away. Sometime when he woke up to half awareness, he saw the stars and realized his army was there—with him. Riding in the night, her strong arms were around him. He closed his eyes, satisfied he was safe at last.

17

Birds sang in the trees. Wind rustled the cottonwoods and the fractured sunlight filtered down on the blanket where he laid facedown.

"You going to make it?" Tally asked, squatted on his boot heels close by Slocum's face.

Lying on his belly, Slocum tried to focus on him. He could see the cowboy's knees and his boots and spurs.

"I think so. Just hide, is all."

"It damn sure ain't pretty, but Butterfield and them women's been squeezing Spanish dagger for the juice. Say it'll heal you."

Trying to raise, Slocum shook his head. "We ain't got time for that—" He collapsed on his face.

"You tell us what comes next."

"Next . . ." Slocum blinked at him. What would he do if he were well? The trouble was, he was uncertain what he would do—could do—next. Finally he managed, "I'll figure it out."

"We can do it for you, boss."

"God, I believe you can. Who figured out the dynamite?"

"Indian said he could drive them out of camp with it fired among them on arrows. Took us half a day just to figure out the length of the fuse we needed, was all."

"Did good. You see Rosa during the raid?"

146

"No. Too much dust and confusion. We hustled them out. Butterfield scattered their horses good; O'Dell and I fired our Winchesters into the middle of them. We had all the rifles loaded so the firing never stopped."

"I heard it, thought there must be an army out there."

"I never saw her. She with them? They holding her prisoner?"

He shook his head. "No. Guess I sure missed my judgment on her. She delivered me right to them at the dance."

"Why?"

"She wants to kill Disantos so bad . . ." He bit his lip, the whole episode knifed him in the guts. Rosa, wherever you are, I hope you get your wish.

"Who else do we need to scare the hell out of?" Lou asked.

"That double-crosser Shard. He's got a store south of St. Michael's—"

"I know him," Lou interrupted in their conversation. "His fat ass is already blowed off. You ride a stretcher?"

"I guess."

"Good. Red and I have one made. Everyone get ready to move out," Lou shouted. "We've got another war to fight to earn our money."

Two long poles lashed to the stirrups of two side-by-side horses formed a stretcher between them. Red gingerly laid Slocum on the blanket that swung between the rails. In a braying of mules, they left camp at midday.

The strong cactus juice she made him drink each time they halted to let their horses breathe numbed him enough so that he neither minded the heat, the dust, the shaky ride, nor his wounds.

"We can get there by mid-morning." she said, riding in close to him.

"Do we look suspect?" Slocum asked.

"We look like a ragtag army." A smile beamed on her dirt-streaked face looking down at him.

"Find a place to camp and take them at night."

"Better idea," she agreed.

• • •

So when the coyote howled at the rising moon, Slocum sat on his butt in a small stream and O'Dell poured tin canfuls of cooling water over his fiery back.

"You feel any better?" she asked, with her skirt hiked up to keep the hem dry and exposing her bare legs in the starlight.

"Some—what's that? Someone's coming."

"I've got it," Butterfield said and headed out with a rifle in the direction of the approaching rider.

"Halt!"

"Don't shoot! Don't shoot!"

"Who is it?" O'Dell asked him.

Slocum recognized the voice and shook his head in disgust. "Diego."

"Let the sumbitch in," he shouted to Butterfield.

"Say's he's Diego."

"If he's a little ratlike critter, it's him all right."

Leading a horse that was winded, Diego hurried over to the stream bank.

"Oh, Slocum, am I glad I found you." He wadded his hat in both hands. "I have a real buyer for those guns. I've been everywhere looking for you."

"Who told you I was here?"

"I followed your tracks."

"Who wants my guns now?"

"A man with the money."

Seated on his butt on the sand bottom, Slocum felt ready to rise up and kick the ass off the man—even with his bare feet. "Tell me his name!"

"All right, all right, don't get mad. His name is . . ."—Diego lowered his voice—"*Señor* Valdez."

"Never heard of him."

"Oh, he is very legitimate. He has the gold to pay you."

"When?"

"Two days he can meet you."

"Make it three."

"Where?"

"At the village of Tres Madras."

"He will be there, Slocum, I promise."

"If this is another trick, your hide will be nailed to the front door of the church. You hear me?"

"Yeah, what—what happened to you?"

"Some *federales* had quirt practice on my back."

"Oh, no—"

"Diego, your life ain't worth a plug nickel—" Slocum threatened the man.

"I know, I know. I'm going for him." The small man mounted his horse and lashed him with the reins to make the poor animal hurry. Slocum dropped his gaze to the dark surface of the stream. He better not be lying this time.

"Let's get up on the bank, I've got more aloe vera juice to smear on your back," O'Dell said.

He agreed and rose stiffly. Those two corporals would pay for his beating; sometime, someplace, he would exact his revenge for every lash. He used the towel she handed him to dry off while she unfurled a blanket for him to sit upon.

"You don't act like you trusted him?"

Slocum laughed. "Trusting Diego is like taking your life in your own hands—risky."

They both laughed. Tally came over and joined them. He squatted on his boot heels.

"Tally, if anything happens, you meet that little bandit and his buyer at Tres Madras. Just know it might be a trap."

"I savvy that. You got plans for us for tomorrow?"

Slocum glanced up and the others had come over to hear them, too.

"We scouted Shard's fortress," Tally said. We can give them a few rounds of our artillery shells over the wall and we'll scare the popop out of everyone. Then when all his guards run off, we charge the place and give him what for."

"You think the guards will run off?" Lou asked.

"I would. I thought those were real shells coming in," Slocum said.

"What then?" Tally asked.

"Shard wrecked my gun deal. His plan was to have some

half-assed bandits steal the guns, then he could buy them cheap. He needs a real lesson taught to him."

"We plan to hit his compound about sunup?" Tally asked.

"Yes. We need to be there and ready to go at sunup."

"Good. We'll be sure he won't forget this lesson." Tally stood up.

They told him good night and went to their blankets. It would be an early morning's rising to ever get setup by then. The smear she had put on his back helped some, still he laid on his belly. Shard would get his next.

Still too weak to ride, he let them help him into the stretcher and his army headed out with the morning star high in the northeast sky. Next to the last party for his crew, the demise of Disantos would be the last one. He had not forgotten his two men's deaths.

Slocum was seated on a rooftop with a rifle and plenty of ammunition to observe the operation. Shirtless, the morning breeze swept his bare skin and he felt it must be healing for his scars itched until he wanted to claw them. Across the wash, he could see over the wall of Shard's compound and observe the people inside the yard busy loading a pack train with blankets and other goods Shard had traded for. No doubt on their way to Mexico City.

Then a sparkling streak came arching in and struck the stucco side of the store building. It fell to the ground and someone screamed before the explosion sent up a mushroom cloud of dust into the air. Burros went crazy and left the open gate of the compound, bucking and farting their way. Blankets were scattered all over and some of the men on lead ropes were being dragged away in the stampede. Screaming women fled out all the gates.

Explosion two went through a second-story window and blew out all the glass in the upstairs rooms. He spotted a naked women with a sheet wrapped around her. He watched her in his telescope as she tied the sheet to the balcony. Once secure, she made no hesitation in her birthday clothing and down the sheet she went. Once on the ground she pulled on it twice to see if it would give, then deciding naked and alive was better than staying—she fled the yard. Stones obviously were hurting her bare soles for she winched at every step.

Slocum clenched his molars at the third and forth round of explosions. The overexcited cattle being held for slaughter that day leveled the pens and then headed for the street amid the dust and confusion.

Four armed men rushed into the courtyard. Shouting and cursing the artillery, they argued aloud about which way the bomber was. When the telltale sparkling trail of the fifth round came arching in, Slocum knew the argument was going to be cut short. All four threw away their arms and raced for the gate—late enough. Three of them were hurled into the street from the blast.

The resistance was over. Slocum closed his telescope and rose with some stiffness. His moment of triumph was at hand, he'd go meet Shard. Once off the ladder, he walked with a limp for the grounds. Muscles hurt that had never hurt him before.

O'Dell charged up with a saddle horse. "They act surprised."

"Yes, but be careful. I'll walk." He eased himself down the path into the dry wash and up the other side through the mesquite. Then with his rifle in both hands, he entered a one-man gate, searched around, and then stepped in the courtyard. O'Dell came on foot right on his heels, her Colt in hand, equally looking about for any resistance.

Someone cursing and coughing, sounding angry as a wounded bear, came out of the smoky store. A black-bearded face and only wearing his red underwear, Shard staggered out of the main entrance.

"Who did this?" he roared.

"Who's asking?"

Shard squeezed his eyes to see in the haze that hung between them. "I'll rip you from limb to limb."

"I doubt that," Slocum said and used the rifle for a cane to lean on.

"Who the hell are you?" Shard said, and glared.

"I'm the one you planned to steal the rifles from."

"Slocum . . ." He searched around as the army began to converge on him, each member on horseback edging closer and closer. "What—what the hell you—going to do?"

Lou twisted in the saddle and looked to Slocum for an answer.

"Tie him up," Slocum said. "We're about even. Looks of things here, he's lost about enough to learn a lesson."

"Do it," she said to the men.

"Get enough ammo to replace what we've spent on him and some more dynamite," Slocum said.

"We will—you need a horse?" Lou asked.

"O'Dell's gone for one."

"You able to ride?"

"I think so."

"No falling out on us." She dismounted and going by the grumbling merchant gave him a kick in the butt where he sat tied up on the ground. "You're lucky. You'd double-crossed me, I'd have staked you out on an anthill and poured honey on your balls."

Slocum smiled as he steadied the horse to mount him. At last in the saddle, he reined him over to where Shard sat.

"Next time get a better plan."

"You ain't heard the last of this."

"I damn sure better not hear much more or I'll come back and level this sumbitch. It'll be dust and ashes the next time I come, not no hit and run."

"Curse you! May you roast in hell!!"

Coming out the doorway with her arms full of ammunition, Lou stopped and glared at him. "You needing kicked some more?"

Shard swallowed his tongue and sulked.

"That's better," she said, loading the two cloth sacks over her horn. "I hate hearing all them threats by a man I can still castrate."

His arms full of two cases of dynamite, Red laughed aloud at her words. "He's going to keep on till he gets himself in deep trouble."

"Yeah," Butterfield agreed, carrying an armful of whiskey bottles.

"We was going to offer you some of these canned oysters," Tally said. "Shame you won't make the party."

"Let's get out of here," Slocum said. "The smell's getting bad."

"I want a sack of them canned tomatoes," Red said and in a bearlike gait ran back inside. He soon reappeared with a sack slung over his shoulder. Slocum nodded for Indian to come down from his sentry post. Time to ride, they had rifles to sell.

18

The midday sun blazed down hot on Tres Madras. A dry wind rustled the cottonwoods' coinlike leaves. Persistent flies buzzed about his head. A dozen buzzards roosted in the treetops as if waiting for a meal of fresh guts to arrive on wagonwheels for them. Except for sidestepping on a limb to move over and pick a short fight with a fellow bird of carrion, the buzzards did little but half flap their wings occasionally to allow the wind to reach their feathered breasts. Slocum had them on his mind.

Did they know more than he did about the future? It would be nice to have a good premonition of what lay ahead. Earlier, Tally assured him that the "rifle graves" were undisturbed. They locked their horse and mule stock in the rear courtyard of the mission. That way, no one could sneak up and run them off in case of an attack. Slocum hired two local women to bring the animals hay. With little opportunity for any employment in the area around this abandoned mission, the women and their children hurried off to cut down fodder for him.

Tally, Red, and Butterfield were working with the local blacksmith to reset shoes on some of the animals. The young man brought his meager tools and made a fire in an old oven with his charcoal. Brutus proved himself a craftsman and the men liked him. The bantering going on was loud and laughter filled the air around the old church buildings.

Indian was somewhere out beyond the heat waves that distorted the far-away saw-edged mountains that Slocum could see from the front gate of their stopover. Not a bad fort, the twelve-foot-high wall surrounded the cemetery, the enclosed courtyard in back, and the front section that once held a flower garden and a fountain when the stone-paved ditch ran water through it. Slocum wondered about the source of all the water that at one time fed this site and the once-cleared farmland around it now regrowing in patches of pancake cactus and mesquite bushes.

Perhaps the great earthquakes that shook the border region a decade before had sealed off the source. Many well-watered places preceding those shocks were, overnight, as if God had turned off the faucet and water no longer was available.

The hand-dug well in the garden was their last effort to restore life to this once Garden of Eden. Water drawn by the pail from it was sweet, but not enough to fill the ditches. No, the mission failed when the water quit flowing down the ditches and, except for a handful of resolved individuals like Brutus, they left their jackals and hard-packed fields to go elsewhere to scratch a living from the ground.

"What will you do when this war is over?" O'Dell asked Slocum, sitting cross-legged on the ground, busy mending a shirt for one of the other men.

"Go look for another way to exist. This gunrunning is getting too tough. No one wants to be fair. It's all in double-crossing you." Slocum lowered himself to his knees and then sat across from her on the ground.

"So many people want to live off the work of others?"

"I think so. In a land without law, and what law it has is so severe it takes the young men and destroys them, there is little room for anything but death."

"Will you try to destroy Disantos?"

"No." He shook his head, the decision weighing heavy. So far they'd been lucky, but he lacked the force it would require to take Disantos. "I've changed my mind about that. It's too dangerous for all of us. I can't risk it. After we make the gun trade, the war as we know it will be over for us. The people need to rise up and destroy Disantos. You can't fight other people's battles for them. Besides, they would only send in another Disantos to replace him. But if the people rise up and throw off the yoke, then they will listen."

She nodded thoughtfully, shifted around the brown shirt in her hands and started back to sewing. "What about Tequila Rosa?"

"If she lives long enough, she might become a *generale*."

"You don't hate her for turning you in to them?"

He shook his head. "She's fighting her own war. And nothing must stand in her way. She has forsaken her church and place in the community. By this time, any virtues she had are gone. If she could turn her back on God, it was not hard to turn her back on me."

O'Dell laughed aloud at his words and then sucked on her finger.

"I better watch myself. I almost sewed my finger to this damn shirt. You are too generous." Bent back over her work, she acted intense about the repairs.

"Only one thing, I won't let her have another chance to betray me."

"Good." She held the garment up to examine her work; satisfied, she dropped it in her lap and adjusted the bandoliers on each shoulder. "Will these men come to buy the guns, or try to take them?"

"In days gone by I would have trusted them as being honest." He shook his head. "Now, I am suspicious of everyone."

"My sister and I won't betray you."

He winked at her. "In you two, I still have faith."

She stood up and stretched her arms over her head. "I am beginning to enjoy this way of life too much. Ride with good men, have good horses, fine food. I could learn to love this."

"There are good things about it. I better get ready to pay my hay hands," he said, as the women were returning with tall stacks of fodder piled on their donkeys. They came single file through the gate into the courtyard.

"Perhaps we should slip away at siesta time," O'Dell said, behind her hand.

He nodded thoughtfully, agreeable to the notion. Only his obligations kept him from saying yes. "Perhaps."

A wink and she swept up the shirt and was gone. Slocum nodded in approval at the burro train bearing the freshly cut grass with the smell of newly mowed hay. Where they found it he was uncertain, but they knew this land.

"You like?" the older woman asked, spreading out her arms.

"I like." The horses and mules out back would like it even better. He put his arms around the woman's shoulders and hugged her. "You have worked hard. I will give a bonus to all of you."

"Oh, *si*. You should come here more often, *señor*."

"Nice here," he said, as if looking around for the first time. "Birds sing and it is quiet. Do the buzzards always roost here?"

"Since the spring went dry."

"Must have been a sight. I mean, when the water ran through here."

"Ah, it was . . ." She glanced up at him as he herded her to the gate. "It was a Garden of Eden, *señor*."

"Did they try to dig out that spring?"

"Oh, *si*, and they went far inside the mountain, but there was no water."

"Feed my animals," he said to her. "Then I will pay all of you." He made a sweeping wave at the other two women and the half-dozen cheering children.

She bowed her head in thanks and began to direct her helpers. The horses and mules came over to smell it and soon had to be elbowed aside so they could unload the fodder. Slocum waited at the gate to let them out.

He paid each women two pesos and all the children got coins from him. They nodded and smiled, pleased at the money in their hands.

With more shouting thanks, they led their burros away. Slocum rubbed his bristled upper lip. How far away were his buyers? Another day they should be there. If that banty-legged Diego even so much as tried a trick this time, he was going to ring his scrawny neck.

Soon he decided to sprawl himself out in a hammock for a siesta. This was the way Mexico was supposed to be: long-tailed mockingbirds imitating others in the treetops, an after-noon breeze keeping the hot air stirred, and no dangers at hand. Satisfied, he put the hat over his face and soon was asleep.

Later, he awoke, threw his legs over the side, and mopped his sweaty face and neck on his kerchief. To let the dry air evaporate his perspiration and cool him, he held out the shirt. How long had he slept? No telling. His army lay asleep all over the courtyard in hammocks and on bedrolls.

He slapped on the sombrero, then raised his arms up and stretched. His back still felt tight. Hitching the holster on his right hip, he headed for the gate. Perhaps he should go look at the source of the once-powerful water source. It couldn't be far; besides, he was getting stiff from all the inactivity of loitering around. He followed the white skeletons of dead cottonwood trees. They led him to the foot of a small hill. There, the once-surging spring basin swirled out and filled the ditch and watered the crops. Long dry, only the faded scale of the watermarks was left. The shells of mussels and crustaceans littered the long-dried mud and the efforts of their mining in the hillside was exposed in tailings.

He lowered himself into the bowl, imagining how once, in the same spot, the cold water would have taken his breath away. Perhaps if some severe charges were drilled deep into the igneous strata with rock drills, the explosion might loosen the source. He wondered if they had tried such a test or even had the money to try one. Might be all a waste, but he couldn't help believing that water was going somewhere else and needed to be diverted back.

He climbed out and went to the mission. In the shade, he found the men and Brutus busy shooing horses again.

"Did anyone try any deep-rock drilling and blasting at the Spring?" he asked the younger man.

"No, we tried to mine for it."

"Too much work. How long a rock drill can you make here?"

"Six feet?"

"You make some drills. You get the men to make holes that deep or deeper in the bottom of that bowl up there."

"Then what?"

"I'll send or bring back enough dynamite to blow them."

"But we have no money to pay you, *señor*."

"No problem. You drill the holes and one of my soldiers will bring back the stuff if I can't come."

"Why would you do that for us, *señor*?"

"I like this place. If it had water I could come stay here longer."

"You could stay here forever."

He reached out and clapped the blacksmith on the shoulders. "Maybe not that long."

"The holes will be drilled."

Slocum nodded that he heard the man. The sun was about to set. Orange, purple, and red streaked the sky. Another pretty sunset. He stood with his itching back to the gate's frame and rolled a cigarette. A match struck on the stucco and he lighted it. Slow like, sipping on the hot smoke that settled him as the nicotine reached his bloodstream and relaxed him.

Earlier in the day, Lou had butchered a large barren ewe. The rich fragrance of sheep fat sizzling on mesquite coals carried on the gentle wind.

First good day in a hundred sorry ones. He let the tension slip from his tight shoulder and those muscles up the backs of his legs to his butt. Nice not to have to be looking ten ways for one's own safety. The scars on his back were about healed, thanks to their doctoring. Where was that treacherous Rosa?

Soon a horse approached and he could see the hatless Indian. He reined up in the gate before him.

"See them?" Slocum gave a head toss to the south.

"Yes. They are coming. Perhaps a half dozen. Mostly peons. They have a pack train. Maybe three men are *pistoleros*."

"Good work. Put your horse in the pen behind the church. There's hay. The food is about ready." Perhaps this buyer was honest—he could hope so, anyway.

"I have smelled it for a long ways." A smile crossed the brown face in the fiery light.

"So have I," Slocum said and followed him inside the courtyard.

He drew in another heady breath of cooking mutton and the desert's creosote fragrance. Maybe if he found them water he could live in this place forever.

19

No sign of Diego. Slocum frowned, but went ahead to do business with the man in charge of the pack train, who brought out his gold. Twenty-peso coins in newly minted gold. Slocum bit on one and decided they were real enough.

"Now, where are your rifles?" the man said. A Spaniard, his temples were gray, he was clean shaven, and had the erect posture of someone of class and station. He even rode up like that.

"We have to unearth them, sir," Slocum said and the digging with picks and shovels began. "Have a seat here on the hammock. O'Dell will bring you a cup of mescal. They may be some time getting down to them."

"Why bury them, *señor*?"

"Safer that way. There are scoundrels in this land that would sell their own mothers as whores. No honesty. They tried to rob me, instead of pay my price for the weapons. Hired bandits to try me."

"I understand," he said and toasted O'Dell, when she arrived with his cup of liquor. "And in *Norte America*, what do you do?"

"Same as down here: try to make a living."

"Ah, it is never easy."

"Never." Slocum watched the men toss aside shovel after shovel of rocks and debris. The clanging of shovels and picks filled the air. The women took them water, even poured some over their bare heads to cool them. Then a shout and Tally jumped in the hole.

"We've got the first box." Soon it appeared from the grave, was taken over to the buyer, and pried open. He inspected each weapon in the first case, nodding in approval at them.

"Good rifles," he said to Slocum.

"I only sell good ones. By the way, where is Diego?"

The man shook his head. "Who?"

"A little banty of a gun seller. Looks like a rat."

"I never saw him. A man named McDougal sent me here."

"Indian!" Slocum shouted. He searched around knowing the hole-digging business was not Indian's kind of work. Slocum hurried for the church.

"Something wrong?" the buyer asked, calling out to him.

"Not yet," he said and found Indian in the sanctuary braiding horse hair for a new bridle.

" 'I think we've been double-crossed. You better saddle up and go look see. They're probably coming on his trail."

"How you know this?"

"Diego, that stinking little gun seller, never talked to this man out here. I'm concerned it's a double cross again."

Bridle in hand, Indian nodded and rushed out for his mount. In a minute, he returned with his horse. Slocum brought out his rifle and saddle to speed the process.

"Be careful. We'll have this gun deal over in an hour. You won't be able to hook up with us, so meet me at the border. I'll pay you there."

"No worry. You damn good man. I ride for you again someday."

Indian was in the saddle, lashing across both sides of his horse. He left the courtyard at a wild pace.

Slocum sighed and headed back. O'Dell was coming to meet him.

"Trouble?" she whispered, shoving a cup of mescal in his hands.

"Maybe. Diego never talked to this man. Something wrong here. I sent Indian to keep an eye out.

"Lou and I will saddle all the horses, meanwhile, just in case."

Slocum agreed with a nod. Just in case.

"Problems?" his guest asked when he rejoined him.

"No, but you can't be too careful." He looked over at their activity, pleased that they were into the second grave and making good progress. Nothing was ever slower than digging a hole to go after anything—guns, gold, or contraband.

In minutes, the crates began to appear. The buyer's men were loading them on their animals. Things were going smoothly. Slocum went after a drink at the well, then took a walk to the gate. Nothing but azure skies—no column of dust in the south, that was good news.

Maybe, just maybe, they could get saddled up and be gone.

"Where're them women?" Red asked, climbing out of the hole. "Let a man die of thirst—" Then he saw Slocum's frown of disapproval for him and he went off to the well mumbling to himself.

Slocum poured the buyer more mescal and some for himself. "We're about to the last crates."

"Good. I would like to be many miles away from here by tonight."

"Yes." He had the same plan only in a different direction. The border called him. What had Indian learned? No telling.

The money was paid and Slocum slung the heavy saddlebags over his shoulder and shook hands. "Be careful. This man I spoke of, Diego, may have sold us both out."

"To whom?"

"Maybe Disantos, maybe another bandit lord. No telling. Be careful, and good luck."

"*Gracias, señor.*"

"Our horses are already saddled. I need someone to go out and get the Indian. We're two hard days' ride from the border from here. I don't intend to let much grass grow under our feet."

"I'll go get Indian," Tally said.

"Everyone else, gather up our stuff. We don't need those

shovels and picks anymore, put them in the church. Someone
will need to be buried here."

"Bet it was pretty when it had water in them ditches," Red
said, going by.

"All hell lacks is cold water," Slocum said, taking his reins
from O'Dell.

His army mounted. Tally tore out to get Indian, and Slocum rode in the lead headed north. Still a few hours of daylight, then they could be in the hills. He looked back at the
pale cottonwoods. Maybe there was a real aquifer under
them—somehow he needed to return and find it for the local
people. Live there forever . . .

By sundown, they were in the foothills. Indian and Tally
had joined them with no sighting of the army or bandits.
Slocum looked back south. It didn't make sense, but little
had made any sense since he had started on this fated gun
run. Dust storms and bandits, double-crossers; why, he could
hardly name all the bad deals. Two good men dead, too.
Ernest and Gilberto. And where was the traitor Tequila Rosa?
Thoughts of her sensuous body made him short of breath as
he rode.

They followed a trail of white powder cut in the rocks,
through sage and cactus, over the steep ridges and down
again into the shadows of the hills. Indian knew of a small
water hole ahead. Slocum hoped there would be enough there
to quench their thirst. The women had brought along the rest
of the cooked mutton, so their lips would be greasy anyway.

At last, in a spur-ringing dismount, they tied their horses
to mesquite limbs and single file went up the narrow cut to
a small spring in the chaparral. Quail were *whit-woo*ing in
the greasewood brush.

Slocum looked around at the towering hillside of malipia
boulders. An entire army could hide up there and no one
would see them. Bronco Apaches had no doubt done the
same thing in the old days. Tough place, but for their purposes secure enough. He soon bellied down and slurped the
cool sweet liquid. His thirst quenched at last, he soaked his
kerchief in the overflow, so he could wipe off his horse's

muzzle and cool him a little. His saddle canteen filled, too, he decided there was not near enough water here for all the horses and mules. They'd make it another day all right.

On his feet, he started back down the canyon path as twilight settled in the gorge. Had his money at last and it had hardly settled on him—pay the army what he owed them, sell the mules, pay for the rifles, repay Dossie and he'd be lucky to have forty bucks left. Life dealt him some weird hands. This had been one of those such hands.

Why couldn't he feel at ease? Some little bird, some little warning kept him on edge. When he reached the horses, the women were handing out food.

"Listen, after we eat, I want to ride some more. No sign of the army or Diego has me wondering. They might be at the border waiting for us, but I'd like to take our chances and get there. Anyone wants paid—"

"Hell, we came in as one, we're riding out as one," Red said and the others agreed.

Slocum took the meaty rib that O'Dell handed him. "They ain't quitting you for nothing," she said with a grin.

He laughed after her.

Everyone on their horses. Indian took the lead. The steep up-and-down trail rocked Slocum from side to side in his saddle. Against a sky full of stars, they descended into the desert again. The pale ground spread for miles until the peaks of the mountains in Arizona became a backdrop against the sky.

It was the screams of men and rifle shots that laid down an orange fire line. An ambush. Slocum's heart caught in his throat. Horses and mules, stung by ricocheting bullets and hot lead, screamed, reared, and bucked away into the darkness. Slocum was off his horse, the money-filled saddlebags on his arm. He let the reins slip through his hands as the panicked animal whipped his head from side to side to escape his hold. The night became full of rifle fire like mad hornets.

"Get down!" he shouted, not certain if he was the only one alive.

What did they lack making the border? A couple of miles

and they would have been free. The shooting let up some. Then orders were given and more shots were fired.

"What's happening?" Slocum asked in a big hiss.

"They've got Butterfield," Red answered. "Women're fine. Tally says he's all right. Injun's gone or dead."

"Naw," Tally said. "He went for his bow."

Keeping low with his rifle and saddlebags, Slocum hurried over to join them. They were behind enough of a mound to serve as a defense.

"They got greedy. Shot too soon or they'd have had us all dead," Red said, lying on his back, reloading his rifle chamber.

"Save your ammo and pray for that Indian's return."

"Pray for what?" Red asked.

"He gets that mule with his dynamite and bow on it . . ." Slocum looked at the sky remembering how he almost thought about leaving the dynamite behind at the mission; then he decided they might need some more; besides, if he left it, those peons might blow themselves up.

A fresh wave of shots went zinging off the top of the mound. Good place to lie and wait, Slocum decided. Maybe till hell froze over.

The sugarloaf mountains in the east began to turn flannel. Then a whooshing sound went over their heads. Slocum ducked. He watched the trailing fuse dropping sparks in its wake fly toward the shooters. Everyone buried his face. The explosion drew the screams of horses and soon they thundered off into the predawn, but not before another missile exploded and set the army to cursing.

After round six, Indian came on the fly.

Everyone clapped him on the shoulder—but then informed him that Butterfield was dead. Indian shook his head. "Bad deal, never expect them here."

"Neither did any of us," Slocum agreed. He crawled up in time to see the army fleeing to the west on foot. "It's over. Get the horses. We can make the border in a run from here."

"What about Butterfield's body?" Red asked.

"Toss it on a horse, he deserves a burial in the U.S.A."

"I think so, too." The big man set out to complete the task. One mule got away. Slocum waved their concern away and climbed in the saddle. "Let's go for the border."

Two hours later, they watered men, women, mules, and horses in the large tank at Peralta Springs. Both women hung their bandoliers on their saddle horns and bailed off in the pool. They threw handfuls in their sunburned faces. Soon their blouses were soaked and their nipples showed through the material. Then men decided to do the same thing, shed boots, guns, and some clothing to join them.

Water flew and laughter rang. Slocum sat on the bank in the shade and shook his head at the commotion. Drunk on relief, he decided, since there wasn't a drop of liquor left in anyone's saddlebags or pack.

He listened to the Mexican mockingbird overhead in the rustling cottonwood leaves and smiled. He had the gun money and was on home ground. What an army.

One dead and one traitor. Where was the treacherous lady? He felt the sun's heat expire from his face. Whew, some trip. All to sell a handful of weapons. He began to count out their money.

The next day he reached Dunavan's Warehouse and he paid everyone his or her pay. Red and Lou were headed for Texas with their money. He knew of a neat spread for sale; they could use it for a down payment. Indian was going to the San Carlos Reservation and find him a new squaw with his riches.

Tally and O'Dell were going to Utah and chase wild horses. She even asked Slocum if he minded her going off with the short cowboy. He smiled and told her no—he had no place, no roots. For her to be happy. She kissed him and thanked him.

It was all over. After he repaid Dossie, he had Boy, two mules, and enough dynamite to blow up a mountain. Over a few drinks in a border town bar, he decided, those folks at Tres Madras needed his explosives. So after dark, he saddled up and headed south. Boy leading, the two long ears came easy. He crossed into the Sierra Madras foothills and spent the next day in a canyon watered by a trickle.

Nightfall, he was on the move again. He used the telescope a lot, but saw no pursuit. Resting in the heat of the day, riding hard all night, he reached the village on the third day.

Brutus looked up and blinked his eyes at the sight of him. "You are back so soon?"

"We need to stash this dynamite up at the spring. Then hide my stock in the mountains."

The blacksmith agreed and they stored the crates of explosives in the cave. After they finished, they rode back and Brutus's wife, Nana, took charge of the animals.

"I know of a canyon with grass and water where we can hide your horse and mules," she said and, with her children, went off with them.

Slocum and Brutus began making the star drills. A slow process of drawing the tension out of the steel rods, hammering the crosslike point, then putting the hardness back in so it would be like diamonds.

In three days they had the drills. Armed with hammers, the new drills, Slocum, Brutus, a man named Ree, and an older one named Padre, all trekked to the cave.

Their work went slow. One man held the bit, the other hammered. After each blow, the holder rotated the drill clockwise a small turn. Hour after hour, slowly the shaft was swallowed by the unforgiving rock. Days passed and the foursome kept drilling. One hole completed, another was started a few feet away.

"You are still drilling?" Nana asked when they dragged in long after dark. Coated in rock dust, weary to the bone, they barely ate their food and fell on pallets to sleep like dead men.

Days became weeks and at last the dynamite was gently slid in the holes, loads were set. Slocum measured the burn rate of the fuses. At last, they unwound them and went outside.

"Everyone get back from the mountain. Rocks may fall down, get blown out." He waved them aside. When they **went over the first rise out of sight, he lit the fuse and ran** to catch up. He hurried over the crest and joined the others in the sandy draw.

"How much longer?"

"Not long."

The explosion shook the ground hard. Dust blew out of the mine entrance like a great giant's cough. The resounding crash of the mountain falling in shook the earth underneath them. They crawled to the crest and dared look. Nothing. No water came from the entrance. Tons of rock clogged the cave's entrance and, crestfallen, they shook their heads in defeat.

"We tried," Brutus said and the other two agreed, numb and tired.

"The aqua has left us," Ree said. "It will never return."

"God's still mad at the people here," Padre said and started shuffling in his sandals for his adobe. "He has never forgiven us."

"Maybe like the people in the village said, we were fools thinking different," Brutus said.

Too tired to argue, Slocum nodded in agreement. He and Brutus went to his place. His wife came running to meet them.

"Is there water? I heard and felt the explosion."

Brutus shook his head. "Nothing but more dust. Find that bottle, Slocum and I need much whiskey to wash away our losses."

"Nothing." She looked to the north in disbelief.

"More dust," he said and hugged her shoulders.

"I'm sorry," she said.

"It was a good plan."

Slocum nodded. But no water came out of the ground.

Like men made of stone, the two drank all of Brutus's whiskey. Then Slocum thanked them and said he would not stay for supper. He had a hammock in the mission yard. He was going there to sleep for two days—let no one come wake him for that long anyway.

"I can go get your horses and mule when you are ready. We hate to see you leave."

He held up his hand that he heard and trudged off to his swing. There was more liquor in his saddlebags. He intended to pass out from it and never wake again.

He fell asleep drinking and dreamed that Rosa came to him. She removed his clothes and tried twice to arouse him. Her hand jacking hard on his dead root, he would only pass out again.

"It is time to get up," a woman said in his ear. "Your irrigation water is in the ditch. You better set the gates."

"Sure," he said and sat up on the edge of the hammock. He rubbed his numb face and closed his eyes to the spear of golden sunshine coming over the wall. The woman had run to the church. She looked familiar from the backside—who was she?

Damn, some dreams were real. He could smell water. Water eating up the dust. He rose and went over to see the ditch brimming with water and darkening the ground as it spilled over the sides.

"Here," she said, handing him a shovel. "Open the rows. We can replant the vines the padres had here."

He took the spade and began to chip at the hard ground. Stupid dream. There would never be any water here. God had forsaken them, the old man said.

Then he watched the liquid spill down the depression, snaking its way forward. Oh, if this was only not a dream. Damn, he looked over and recognized her famous boobs.

"Can you forgive me?"

"Sure," he said. "This is only a damn dream."

Then she stood up from her digging and shook her head, gazing hard at him. "No, this is for real."

"I know a dream when I'm in one."

She shook her head ever so slightly. "I came in last night. You were so asleep I could not wake you. Then I began to hear water trickling in. I figured you had water coming to irrigate this place and make it a garden again."

He blinked at her. No, it was real. How much water? Then he straightened and looked at her. "I took a helluva beating because of you."

"Sorry. There was nothing else I could do. When Mazzarra found me at the dance that night, it was lie or die."

"Did you get him—Disantos?"

"I got very close—no, he still lives and orders good people shot." Her shoulders slumped. "I guess I was a fool to come here looking for you."

"Why me?" He blinked at her, still numb from his hangover.

"I need your help."

"What this time?"

"I want you to get me in a whorehouse in Fronterous that he uses when he comes there."

"How in the hell would I do that?"

"Take me in as your prisoner and sell me to the woman who runs it."

"Why not ride up and apply?"

"They say she buys all her girls."

"They don't have slaves in Mexico."

She shook her head that he was wrong "Oh, yes, from here to the federal district, girls and young women are sold as slaves every day."

"Won't he know you?"

"I will dye my hair."

"I don't like it. They could drug you. Hell only knows what they might do." Disantos had no scruples. No matter how badly he hated the butcher, he could not ease that by sacrificing her.

"Get me there. It may be my last chance to get him."

"Why?"

"There are rumors he may be made a *generale*."

"Damn, then he could shoot more people. First, we better go tell Brutus about this water and then we can talk about this deal."

He looked at her hard again. What a set of tits. They made his heart flutter even to think about fondling them—but she also was the same snake that bit him.

He pulled on his boots and strapped on his gun. Sell her to some whorehouse. The whole plan sounded shaky to him.

There might be a trap set for him up there, too.

"Come quick!" he shouted, to the blacksmith standing in his yard. "We've got some water. Get Nana and come on."

"What? Are you still drunk?"

"No sober as a judge. There's water going down the old rows of the vineyard. Hurry, I thought I was dreaming, too."

They raced back and when Brutus saw the ditch full, he jumped in and Nana joined him. They splashed and danced in it.

"Oh, Slocum where did this water come from?"

"That mountain we blew up, I guess. Don't know how much or how long it will last, but its running right now."

"Mother of God, this is a blessing," Brutus shouted and threw handfuls in the air.

"Plenty to get baptized in, anyway," Slocum said with Rosa on his arm, and gave a head toss to the wet pair. "I want to hike up to the source and see how much we have."

"Coming," Brutus said and climbed out giving his wife a pull, they fell in behind them in a run.

"God has not forgotten this place," Brutus kept telling his wife.

No, He sure hasn't, Slocum reminded himself as they hurried. They topped the crest and they could see the water spilling out over the fresh-split gray rocks in a good stream and entering the aquifer.

"Good as years ago," Brutus said. "Before the earthquakes."

"Now the work will begin. Water will have to be rationed out to each farm. There will be fights for more—this will not be easy to manage."

Brutus nodded. "You can stay and help us."

"No, that was a dream. I have no real dreams. Not ones I can live with. No, you and your neighbors must do this water project."

"You scare me," Nana said, looking taken aback.

Slocum shook his head. "Your husband is a strong man. He'll handle the matter well."

"Come by again, amigo. We owe you much. Where will you go from here?"

"Perhaps Fronterous. I have business there." He glanced over at Rosa beside him and she nodded her head.

20

"They will never believe I've kidnapped you," Slocum said as he stared into the glowing coals of their fire. "The word will be out and then your life won't be worth much more than a plugged nickel. No, we need to have a very wild kidnapping take place."

"Someone could get killed."

"Well, if it doesn't look real . . ."—he shook his head, deep in thought as to how to do this so it looked real—"then you might get more than you bargained for. No telling what might happen."

"I am not afraid to die doing this."

He shook his head and lighted a roll-your-own with a blazing stick from the fire. He dragged on it, then handed it to her to smoke. She drew a deep pull on it. The tip glowed red and she handed it back to him with an exhale.

"What now?"

"Get in the hammock. Sometimes I do my best thinking making love."

"Oh," she said, and took the blouse off over her head. He closed his eyes at the sight of them. They made his stomach flop over—and all she wanted to do was shoot some damn colonel in the ass. Whew. But how?

He climbed in and kissed her, gently feeling her right tit. When she moved away from his hand, he decided she was

174

too sore to bother and proceeded to bring her up to speed. His hand slid between her silky legs, which parted, and soon his fingers' action began to stimulate her.

In minutes, she was on fire and he listened to her moans of pleasure with a smile. But by then her arousal began to affect him and he climbed on her in a perilous move that threatened to throw both of them out of the hammock. Her hands gripping both sides, the swing settled down, and he began to probe her wet gates. Swollen tight, they offered a great sleeve for his aching rod.

Her moans grew louder and he fought to reach a peak with her. Then she clutched him with both hands and clenched her teeth for the final moment. A loud "Oh" from her and she bucked her hard belly at him. He drove home and came in a depleting fountain, to collapse on top of her.

Out of wind and his heart running away, his mouth found her mouth and began to smother her. Her brown eyes looked glazed and at last, she moved her mouth aside to gulp for air. "What did you think?"

"I thought it was damn foolish to let him have you even for a minute."

"Oh, come on, you must help me, Slocum."

"I will," he said, at last on his back, looking at the twinkling stars. But he couldn't think of much more than he wanted her for himself. Whew.

"Can we try it my way first?"

"How is that?" Slocum asked.

"We know he likes to screw whores."

"Good-looking ones."

"Right. So they must have some there. We let him get inside and in the room with one of them, then we take him."

"I can't see how that will work." He shook his head.

"I know more about whores than you do. Number one, they are greedy. Number two, some of them don't like his ass. Others, he killed their relatives, right?"

"Ordered them shot anyway."

"That's what I mean—we need to find out about this place

and learn as much as we can. Then spring the trap. Who can we trust up there?" she asked.

"I'm not certain, but I think there's a way. We can ride to Fronterous and find out."

"What if they arrest you?" she asked.

"Hell, I've got away before."

"But then you had an army."

"Yeah, all eight of us."

"I heard that he shot those two men of yours."

"Yes, Ernest and Gilberto. Probably why he's still on my most-hated list."

"Am I on that list?" She raised up and looked at him.

"No, not today."

"Good. Should we ride for there today?"

"I guess," he said, not anxious to get out of the hammock with such a prize in it.

"Or do you wish to stay here and play some more?"

He gazed at the pear-shaped breast in his face and closed his eyes. "We better get started."

"You're certain?"

"Hell, no, but you're sore and I'm horny. We better get up."

"Still? After this?" She hooded her brows in disbelief at him.

"Yes."

She shook her head and then half raised up to kiss him on the mouth. "I'm glad that you have accepted me. I cried after I heard what they did to you—but I couldn't escape him."

"I understand."

"No . . ." She began to cry. "No one understands. They shot my Estevan and tore my life apart."

"Hey, I'm getting up."

"You have a plan?" She snuffed her nose and big tears ran down her brown cheeks. With the side of her hand she tried to dam them. At last, she slipped from the hammock and went to her clothing for a towel.

"I'm working on one," he said. "Working hard."

•   •   •   •

After reaching Fonterous, in twelve hours, they had learned lots about the colonel's ways. Disantos was expected back any day. Rosa had talked to some of the girls in the house while Slocum had sought information about the colonel's movements. They met in the night to exchange information, squatted in the shadows behind a wall.

"He likes a girl who works up there named Baby Doll." She tossed her head toward the major whorehouse in town.

"That's his usual?" They both spoke in low voices.

"Most times, but they say he likes little girls, too."

"How little?"

She shook her head and pinched her lips. "Like ten or so."

"They got them there?"

Rosa nodded. "I told you they bought slaves."

"But so young?"

"Yes, they want to please *el colonel*."

"He's supposed to be coming back here. Did you hear exactly when he'll be back?"

"I couldn't learn."

"Then we must wait, close by, and not arouse any suspicion."

"Every day that you stay here . . ." She shook her head in disapproval and shifted her weight to the other leg.

"That's one more day we don't have to wait for him."

"Oh, he stays in a suite in the Hotel Seville."

"Good, we will go rent it and learn all about it. Can you borrow some fancy clothing. We can go there as a rich couple and look over the setup."

She nodded. "Tomorrow I will find some. Where will we meet again?"

"Down by the river bridge." He searched around in the night—saw nothing. "We must be careful."

"Yes," she agreed, and straightened. "Tomorrow." And she left him in a rustle of her many-layered skirt.

He straightened his blanket poncho and set the palm hat back on his head. Back to the cantinas and listen for more news about the colonel. Little girls—yuck, the man was mad anyway.

In a smoky cantina, he sipped on a ten-cent beer. His hat brim pulled down and acting half passed out on a bench in the rear of the den. His ears listened to the border Spanish being thrown about.

"There is a new whore at Maria's Cat House."

"What is her name?"

"I'm not sure, but they say she is in heat all the time."

"*Carumba*, she must be crazy. All the whores in that place lie on their backs like corpses. I swear it would be better to screw a dead woman than one of them."

"Ah, amigo, it would be much cheaper." Then they both laughed.

He learned about a sick goat, a funeral for a baby the next day, a man who wanted to catch his wife's lover, but could never surprise them together.

"What will you do to him?"

"Make him pay."

"How much?"

"Two pesos, like they charge me over there. Why should he get it free? I don't get it free when I go to a *puta*. He only comes to her because it is free."

"You mean he don't love her?"

The man shook his head. "Free is why he uses her."

"That is bad."

"Yes, there is no telling how many pesos he owes me now."

Slocum eased out of the place. He waited in the alley until he saw the troubled man in search of his wife's lover go weaving down the street. At a distance, he trailed him until he saw him disappear in a jackal. Good, he knew where she lived now.

For the rest of the night, he slept on the ground under the bridge. The river in low summer flow rushed over a rock outcropping close by and made a hushing sound. An owl came in the night, hooted, and woke him. His fingers closed on the six-gun he slept with.

Mid-morning, he went to the man's house and knocked on the door. A short woman in her twenties came with two young children clinging to her legs. Attractive enough.

"*Señor*?"

"Could I buy some food? I have money to pay you."

She went past him, stuck her head out, and searched both ways. When she looked at him again, she acted satisfied. "Of course. Come in my poor casa."

"My name's Joe."

"Come sit at my table, Joe," she said, herding the babies ahead of her. "It is time for their nap."

"Oh, did I come at a bad time?"

Her smile was broad and she shook her head to dismiss his concern. "No, I like company. My husband, he works all the time."

The babies in a crib bed, she scolded them to go to sleep. When she turned, she pulled down on her blouse to expose her small cleavage and shook her head as if to clear her thoughts. "My name is Alicia."

"So glad to meet you." He smiled at her and nodded.

"Frijoles all right?"

He studied her shapely butt as she swished over to the fireplace and began to put some in a bowl. Such a shame that her man worked all the time, or was he in the cantina the rest of the time?

"Hush," she said to the whimpering baby and carried the bowl to Slocum.

"Here," she said and made him uncross his leg. She raised herself up and sat on him. Then she began to feed him with a spoon.

"First, a man needs food to have strength, no?"

"Yes," he said with his arms around her.

"You real hungry?"

"Yes." He accepted the second spoon of beans.

"Maybe you need something to hold?" She took his hand and slid it under her blouse. When his finger reached her small breast, she nodded with approval and readied another spoonful for him.

"They are very nice."

"That feels good. You are very gentle."

He glanced out the open door and saw them coming. With their red sashes, palm sombreros, and tan uniforms, they came riding up the road from the river bridge.

"Oh, the *federales* are back," she said, looking past him and arched her back to shove the boob at his thumb, teasing the small button-size nipple. Then she turned back to feed him some more beans.

"We cannot go to the hammock out under the shade." She shook her head in disappointment. "The nosey neighbors would tell him. But I can bend over that barrel or I can sit on you in this chair."

"The chair is fine."

She undid his belt and he rose as she fought down his pants, then unbuttoned his underwear and caught his half-stiff shaft in her stubby fingers. He could read the instant fascination she had for his dick. Like a child at Christmas opening her favorite gift.

"Oh, I wish . . ." she cried.

"What . . . ?"

But by then, she was on her knees and her tongue was coming up the seam underneath the shaft.

He could hear the clang of their swords passing by. No way they could see back in the dark room, but he thought how funny it was. He pleasured himself with her while the *federales* rode by in formation, not ten yards away.

She finally rolled out an Indian rug on the dirt floor and pulled him down with her. He closed his eyes and savored the moment. Stupid husband should have to pay for her, too—he had more there than he could ever care for. Why did he frequent lifeless *putas*? Dumb, he told himself as she arched her back for more. Oh, he liked this.

Under the bridge, Slocum sat huddled. Darkness shrouded the night and only the night insects and the water's rush kept him company.

"You asleep?" Rosa asked, coming quietly.

"No."

"The colonel returned today."

"I saw him ride in."

"I found some clothes I can wear, but—"

"He's already in that hotel suite."

"Yes. What can we do?" She frowned at him.

"Check in the hotel."

"But he will know you."

"Not clean shaven, in nice clothes."

"Where will you get all this?"

"I'll be ready, right after noon. I will meet you at the stables at one o'clock."

"Fine," she said, sounding less than thrilled by his plan.

"You sleep under here?" she asked as a wagon and team went rumbling overhead on the thick planks.

"My casa."

She shook her head in disapproval, then spoke in a serious tone. "If we get him, I want you to promise to leave him to me." Her brown eyes were slits waiting for his answer.

"All right. But be careful and meet me tomorrow."

Clean shaven, new clothes, he met her in the sour-smelling stables. She looked peeved to have to walk in her finery through the bedding and manure to where he stood.

"You look nice."

"You, too, sir, but I am going to smell like a horse if we stay in here very long."

"Oh, yes, we will. Like we traveled a long ways to get here."

She stopped, then nodded in approval at his plan.

"Time that we went and found our hotel room, my dear." He offered her his arm.

An hour later with their hotel door ajar enough so they could watch for the colonel's coming and going, they learned his boot heels made a distinctive sound on the pine floor.

"He's not been back in a while," she said.

"He may have gone to the whorehouse."

Then from the hallway, they heard two voices. One man's and the other a young girl's.

"You be nice to him," the man's deep voice said. "He is a very important man."

"Yes."

"Don't cry. Whatever happens, you are a big girl and don't cry."

"I won't."

"I'll unlock the door. Then you take off all your clothes, climb in bed, and wait for him."

"Yes."

"You know the rest?"

"Last time—"

"Yes, you pleased him last time. He likes you and gave you much money."

Slocum looked at Rosa and made a disapproving face.

"No wonder, I couldn't get in his bed," she said, in a stage whisper. "I saw her for a moment going by. She can't be over ten years old."

"He'll get his."

"Damn right, and it won't be long either."

The man left and Slocum felt the room key in his pocket. Same key opened all the doors—he hoped.

The sounds of the boot heels on the steps made him hold his finger to his mouth and she nodded. Soon the swaggering figure went by and they listened to the door being unlocked and opened.

"Ah, my dear—" they heard, then silence when the door closed.

"How long should we wait?"

"Ten minutes. I figure by then, he won't hear us unlocking his door."

She gave a shudder of revulsion. Then with the short-barreled Colt in her hand, she patted her palm with the barrel. "I've been waiting for this."

He wanted to tell her revenge was never as sweet as the anticipation promised her, but she'd never listen. Closure would not come like she expected, but with the colonel gone she'd at least know that he couldn't ever molest another little girl.

They went down the hall on the balls of their feet. Each creak under their footfall sounded louder than thunder. He inserted the key hoping that Disantos had not done the same inside. The key fit. He drew his Colt, with his left hand twisted the key, and the soft click told him enough. He nodded to her and then wrenched open the door.

"Stay right there," Slocum said to the man's bare back. He was sprawled over the child. "Don't move an inch. Get her out of there."

"Who the hell—?"

"Judge and jury are here, Colonel Disantos." Slocum pressed the muzzle of his gun to the back of his head as Rosa lifted the small naked girl off the bed, talking softly to reassure her—it was all right.

Slocum slipped a rope over the man's right wrist, then another over his left. When she finished dressing the sobbing girl and got her outside the room, she could tie his hands to the iron headboard.

"You will never get away with this. My men will have you in seconds. They are posted as guards all around the building."

"Sorry, but they just left a few minutes ago."

"What for?"

"Oh, you forgot already. Your big treat. You're treating them at that big whorehouse on the hill. A phantom just came by, got them, and soon they will be in heaven—at your expense, of course."

"Of course. What are you doing to me?"

"Me? Nothing, but keeping you here until she has that little girl taken care of."

"Who in the hell are you?"

"Guess we never met. My name's Slocum."

"The gunrunner—revolutionary."

"Sorry, gun salesman. I try to stay out of your war down here."

"In a different life we might have been friends," Disantos said, and laughed.

"I doubt it," said Slocum, and then looked at Rosa, who had returned.

Rosa held her late husband's Colt. "Don't move, colonel," she said. "It's got a hair trigger."

He reached up and secured both ropes to the iron headboard. Then he tied Disantos's feet spread apart to each corner post. Testing his work, he glanced at her; she gave a silent nod of approval.

"Now what?" Disantos asked, trying to see them.

"This lady here has some questions I'm certain she wants answered. I'm going to get our horses ready." He looked at her to be certain the reality of the situation had set in, and to see if she'd changed her mind.

"How long do I have?" she asked Slocum with resolve.

"Ten minutes or so."

She nodded numbly. "I can handle it from here."

"You don't want me to stay?"

"No." Her back stiff as a ramrod, she pointed the Colt at the ceiling.

"Meet me out front. We'll need to ride."

"You'll never get away with this," Disantos said in the angry voice of a commander.

"Yes, we will, you murdering bastard," she said through her teeth. With a handful of his hair in her left hand, she poked the gun's muzzle in his face. "My name is Tequila Rosa. I want you to remember that, too, when you get to hell. You can tell the devil I sent you to see him."

Slocum was out the door when the colonel moaned aloud for the first time. Down the stairs, two at a time, he heard more pained noises from the upper room. In minutes, out of breath, he reached the stables and, as planned, their horses were standing saddled and hipshot in the alleyway.

He paid the man, swung in the saddle and started up the street, leading hers. Did he hear a muffled gunshot? Uncertain of the sound, he made the horses lope, scattering chickens and stray burros. Making children draw back and look at him with dark eyes.

It will be a better world for them to grow up in. He looked

off to where Alicia's jackal sat on the barren hillside, recalling how tight she clutched the ten-dollar gold piece in her fingers and wildly kissed him good-bye. Then he saw Rosa standing on the porch of the hotel searching for him. He arrived in a cloud of dust.

"He won't kill any more husbands," she said, taking the reins to her gray horse. "Nor rape any more children."

"Good. Let's ride." He bent over and helped lift her in the saddle. Satisfied she was in place, he nodded and they left in a hard run.

Four days later, he waited on the Southern Pacific platform, Bowie Station, Arizona Territory. Beside him, Isabel— Rosa—stood with her carpetbag and small purse.

"This cousin in Las Cruces . . . ?" he asked.

"I will be fine there. Where will you go?"

He looked off at the Chiricahuas and the Dos Cabezas Mountains and nodded. "I'm not certain, but I'll be fine there, too."

"When I get to hell, I'll be sure to look you up," she said.

"I'd like that. Be sure to wear something low cut."

She looked at him in disbelief. "The past nights. . ."—her voice to a whisper—"you've surely played with them enough."

He shook his head and smiled at her. "Never enough."

At the sight of two riders passing by the station on the dusty street, he turned his back. One rode a blanket-ass Appaloosa. Then he heard the train coming. He bent over and kissed her on the mouth, gathering her up in his arms as the engine swished past them.

"Got to leave, girl. Be careful."

"I will, but why—?"

No time for words. He hurried around the station to the left side, unhitched his horse, swung up, satisfied the pair had gone on toward the businesses in Bowie. For the first hundred yards in a long trot, his back itched expecting a hot bullet. Then the train roared by on the high roadbed over him, and when it clacked past him he saw her at the open **car window and waved to her. Then he dared look back. No** sign of the Kansas bounty hunters, the Abbott brothers. He sent Boy under the trestle that crossed the dry wash and headed him toward Mount Graham in a high lope.

He knew an Apache woman—two or three days' ride north of there. Feeling better about his close encounter with those two bounty hunters in Bowie, he galloped Boy through the mesquite patches and stirrup-high tall grass.

Tequila Rosa would slip through history's pages known as the mysterious woman who so cruelly killed the *federale* Colonel Disantos in revenge for her husband's death and his other black deeds. Slocum nodded and licked his dry lips—a lot more miles to ride.

Watch for

SLOCUM AND THE BONE ROBBERS

299th novel in the exciting SLOCUM series
from Jove

Coming in January!

JAKE LOGAN
TODAY'S HOTTEST ACTION WESTERN!